Change in the British Flora 1987 – 2004

Allium ursinum, Ramsons Bob Ellis

Botanical Society of the British Isles

D1609825

Botanical Society of the British Isles
London
2006

Change in the British Flora 1987 – 2004

(A report on the BSBI Local Change survey)

M. E. BRAITHWAITE

Botanical Society of the British Isles

R. W. ELLIS

Botanical Society of the British Isles

C. D. PRESTON

Centre for Ecology and Hydrology

Assisted by

The Vice-county Recorders of the
Botanical Society of the British Isles

P. Rothery

Centre for Ecology and Hydrology

Financially supported by

The Heritage Lottery Fund

Botanical
Society of the
British
Isles

Botanical Society of the British Isles
London
2006

Published by the Botanical Society of the British Isles
c/o Natural History Museum
Cromwell Road, London SW7 5BD

ISBN 0 901158 34 8

Designed by Paul Westley
Printed by The Saxon Print Group

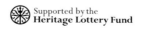

Contents

Foreword

The BSBI Local Change project is a highly successful initiative which has quantified changes in the British flora which have taken place over the last 20 years. It builds on the previous excellent work of the Botanical Society of the British Isles (BSBI) and the Biological Records Centre (BRC) which measured changes in the distribution of plants since the 1930s as a part of the *New Atlas* project.

The study considers changes in individual species, but this report also contains analyses of plant changes grouped by Broad Habitat, and an investigation of the possible causes of change. These analyses will be vital in helping to determine future conservation policy for both species and habitats. This report comes at an important time in the development of conservation policy, with the UK Biodiversity Action Plan currently under review. By identifying the causes of change, and the habitats most affected by these, it will be possible to target conservation work effectively.

Over 70% of the terrestrial area of the UK is managed for agriculture, horticulture and forestry. A goal of the Global Strategy for Plant Conservation is that management policy for this large area needs to be consistent with the conservation of plant diversity. Agri-environment schemes have a particular role to play in achieving this goal, and will need to take note of the reasons of change identified in this study. Increased nutrient levels are considered an important cause of change, and will need to be addressed through a range of measures.

The important new findings on the impact of climate change on the British flora will need to be considered carefully in order to produce a policy response that best protects British ecosystems. It is disturbing to note that the composition of the alien flora is apparently being influenced by climate change, with some species whose range in Britain is already expanding appearing to have been favoured by recent higher temperatures. Policies formulated with respect to non-native species will need to take this into account.

As part of the BSBI Local Change project, the collaboration between BSBI and BRC has undergone further development, with BSBI handling all of the data collection and BRC scientists (based in the Centre for Ecology and Hydrology, Monks Wood) assisting in the analysis and interpretation of the data. BRC is co-funded by the Joint Nature Conservation Committee (JNCC) and the Natural Environment Research Council, and JNCC is delighted that this new collaborative approach has resulted in such a valuable and relevant report. JNCC hopes that it will serve as a model for future collaboration between BSBI and BRC.

Adrian Darby
Chairman, JNCC

Malcolm Vincent
Director of Science, JNCC

Executive Summary

BSBI Local Change has been part of a joint three-year project with Plantlife, *Making it Count for People and Plants*, funded by the Heritage Lottery Fund.

The key objective of BSBI Local Change has been to measure distributional changes since 1987 in the individual species of the British Flora at tetrad scale (2 km x 2 km). This has been achieved by a repeat survey during 2003-04 of a sample of 811 tetrads in a regular grid across Britain previously surveyed in 1987-88. 761 tetrads (94%) were visited by BSBI members and of these 635 (78%) yielded data sufficiently comparable to the 1987-88 survey to be suitable for analysis. This coverage represents just over 1% of the land area of Britain.

In assembling the data for the re-survey, BSBI developed a decentralised computer recording capacity that eliminated the need for central data entry. The analysis of the results was facilitated using a statistical model based on the concept of the probability of a species being recorded where it is present.

Local Change has met its key objective by generating useful statistics on change for 860 species found in 15 or more of the sample tetrads, comprising 726 native species and long-established introductions (archaeophytes) and 134 species introduced in recent centuries (neophytes). More limited statistics have been generated for 38 very widespread species and many rarer species.

Native and archaeophyte species are analysed in groups related to Broad Habitat. The most important findings are the following.

- There has been a loss of species of infertile habitats, particularly Calcareous grassland and Dwarf shrub heath. Habitat fragmentation may have been the main underlying cause but much of the fragmentation occurred some time ago and isolated fragments suffer species loss for many reasons, including eutrophication and both over and under grazing.

- Climate change has led to an increase in some species, particularly ruderal species found in urban habitats and the transport network. Southerly species have also fared better than northerly species in Neutral and Calcareous grassland. It is much more difficult to point to cases where climate change has led to losses but this may reflect the extraordinary persistence of many upland plants rather than any suggestion that they will remain unaffected indefinitely.

- There is scope for further work on the ecology, habitat and dispersal of ruderal species, as Local Change has demonstrated a high level of increase in such plants, with a link to climate change.

- Eutrophication may be the main driving force affecting change in wetland species. Many species of wetland habitats show an increase or decline though no overall change has been detected in the group as a whole.

- One of the most striking changes in the British flora in the 20ᵗʰ century was the great decline of the weed species of arable fields. The Local Change survey indicates that such species are no longer declining as a class and indeed there is some evidence of modest recovery, though some of the more specialised species do continue to decline and the Local Change results do not provide information on the scarcest species. Agri-environment policies including set-aside are thought have contributed to this reversal of fortune, but increases are also occurring in other, ruderal, habitats.

- The results for species of coastal, aquatic and montane habitats are disappointingly inconclusive. Further consideration needs to be given to the way in which change in these species is monitored.

For neophytes, the main conclusions are as follows.

- Those neophytes that have been widespread since the first Atlas survey in the 1950s continue to spread and they are being joined by further introductions. However, they still represent only about 16% of the species analysed, demonstrating that the majority of neophytes have very local distributions.

- Southern England is being colonised by aliens to a greater extent than other areas and climate change may be a factor here.

The survey has provided information on the tetrad frequency of species within their British range as established by the *New Atlas*. These tetrad frequencies, and the tetrad estimates that can be derived from them, are a major step towards establishing the relative abundance of species, though they would need to be combined with studies at yet finer scale before the ideal of measuring the abundance of a species across Britain could be fully realised.

Local Change has demonstrated its value and should be repeated with very similar methodology after a further period. The survey is filling a key niche between infrequent, comprehensive surveys at the 10-km square scale and the Countryside Survey which, because it is based on small plots, provides accurate data for the relatively few most widespread species but cannot monitor change in the many less common species that occur too infrequently in the small samples.

1. Introduction

In 1987-88 members of the BSBI recorded the vascular plants in a series of 'tetrads' (2 x 2 km squares) throughout Britain and Ireland. The British tetrads were re-surveyed in 2003-4. In this book we compare the results of the two surveys, analysing them critically for the light they throw on changes in the British flora in the intervening years.

The original survey, the 'BSBI Monitoring Scheme', was led with great enthusiasm by Dr T.C.G. Rich, ably assisted by Mrs Rosemary Woodruff. There were two elements to this survey. The first was to record one in nine 10-km squares, so that the results could be compared with those obtained when the squares were first surveyed for the *Atlas of the British Flora* in the 1950s. The second task was to survey three tetrads within each of these 10-km squares, to provide a baseline for further studies of change. The formal reports of the results of the survey and the subsequent scientific papers concentrated on the comparison of the 10-km square survey with the *Atlas* survey (Rich & Woodruff 1990, 1996, Palmer & Bratton 1995) and on various methodological aspects of recording (Rich & Woodruff 1992). The results of the tetrad surveys were not explored to any great extent at the time, with the exception of a paper by Le Duc *et al.* (1992), but they were used in some subsequent research projects (e.g. Firbank *et al.* 1998, Roy *et al.* 1999). The Monitoring Scheme tetrads have now been resurveyed in the 'BSBI Local Change' project, a name we have also used to cover the entire operation of survey and resurvey. This resurvey allows us to concentrate for the first time on the analysis of change in Britain at the tetrad scale, a much finer scale than that of the 10-km square.

In this report we have taken two main approaches to the analysis. The first is the study of individual species. The survey was species-orientated, in that recorders were asked to compile species lists from the tetrads they surveyed (Chapter 2). The basic result of the survey is a comparison, species by species, of the distribution recorded in 1987-88 with that recorded in 2003-04. The ways in which we have analysed the species' results are explained in Chapter 3. Each species constitutes a unique story, differing in detail from that of all the other species. We have tried to tell many of these stories by maps and accompanying text for the individual species. However, we are also interested in general trends, as these should allow us to highlight the most important factors currently influencing plant distribution in Britain. To investigate the overall trends, species have to be treated in groups and their individual details subsumed into a generalised picture. We have grouped native species and long-established aliens (archaeophytes) on the basis of their habitat preferences, and for each Broad Habitat we have used statistical analysis to suggest the possible driving factors of change. This analysis and the accompanying individual species accounts form the core of the book (Chapter 4). Recently introduced species (neophytes) and species which have to be excluded from the analysis for a variety of reasons are treated in separate sections (Chapters 5, 6). We then examine in detail the accounts of recorders in several different areas of Britain to investigate the extent to which their individual field experience explains, supports or casts doubt on the conclusions reached by the analysis of the general patterns (Chapter 7).

A survey like that of the BSBI Monitoring Scheme cannot be repeated after an interval of 16 years with the same precision as a laboratory experiment or a field trial. Taxonomic knowledge and approaches to field recording develop during such a period, and a different set of volunteers is available, so that areas are often resurveyed by a different team with differing recording skills and efficiency. Inevitably, these changes influence the results. In such circumstances statistics make a good servant but a bad master. In interpreting the results, we have therefore interpreted the statistical results in the light of our own judgement of those recording factors which could have influenced them.

Two major projects which have been published between the two BSBI tetrad surveys provide essential background against which we have assessed our results. The first and most directly relevant is the *New Atlas of the British and Irish Flora* (Preston *et al.* 2002a). This provides an updated account of the distribution of British and Irish vascular plants at the 10-km square scale, based on a survey between 1987 and 1999. It was based on the original Monitoring Scheme survey of 1 in 9 squares, extended in the subsequent years to the remaining 8 in 9. The *New Atlas* and associated publications (Preston *et al.* 2002b, Preston *et al.* 2003b) analyse changes at 10-km square scale between 1930-69, the period which included the comparable survey for the original *Atlas of the British Flora* (Perring & Walters 1962), and 1987-99.
The second major project is the CEH Countryside Survey, summarised by Haines-Young *et al.* (2000) and in other publications (e.g. Smart *et al.* 2003, 2005). This describes changes in physical features of the countryside, such as hedges and walls, and in the commoner Broad Habitats. The results are based on the repeat recording of vegetation in a stratified random sample of 1-km squares, within which there is detailed recording of the species in small plots. The small plots have been assigned

to the same Broad Habitats we have used in our analysis. In addition to the relevance of its results, the techniques of data analysis pioneered by the Countryside Survey (Bunce *et al.* 1999, Firbank *et al.* 2000), in particular the use of plant attributes to characterise the prevailing directions of change, have helped us develop our interpretations of the atlas and Local Change surveys.

The BSBI Local Change survey therefore takes a place between the extensive 10-km square atlas surveys and the intensive surveys of smaller plots that characterise the Countryside Survey. The results of any one of these surveys inform the interpretation of the others, and can be related to more specific surveys of rare and scarce species. We hope that they are gradually leading us to a deeper understanding of the ever-changing British flora.

2. Scope and Methodology of the Survey

Scope and organisation

Objectives

BSBI Local Change has been a re-survey of 811 pre-selected sample tetrads (2 × 2 km national grid squares) in a regular grid across Britain completed in the two field seasons 2003 and 2004.

The sample tetrads have been those that were surveyed during the BSBI Monitoring Scheme 1987-88 (see Appendix 4 p.372). Local Change has thus been a second survey of these tetrads. The aim has been to record as many as possible of the taxa - species, subspecies and hybrids – that were present in the tetrad. It was understood that one could not expect to find all the taxa present in a reasonable amount of recording time but that one could expect to record a truly representative list. As Local Change has been a repeat survey there was an emphasis on re-finding those taxa recorded in the 1987-88 survey.

The prime objective of Local Change has been to observe change in the British flora. It has been hoped that the design of the survey would enable change to be measured in many species for which other studies had been unable to measure change, primarily because of the different spatial scales at which they were surveyed. A further objective has been to study the relationship between the distribution of a species at tetrad scale with that at hectad scale as a step, if taken forward with other studies, towards assessing the abundance of the British flora as well as its distribution.

Funding

BSBI Local Change has been part of a joint three-year project with Plantlife, *Making it Count for People and Plants*, funded by the Heritage Lottery Fund.

Project Organisation

BSBI appointed Pete Selby as BSBI Volunteers Officer to carry through Local Change. Following Pete Selby's untimely death in 2003, Bob Ellis has filled the post.

The Volunteers Officers set up a network so that the records made in the survey could be entered on computers locally using the computer programme 'MapMate' and centralised electronically using its distinctive 'synchronisation' facility.

At local level, recording was generally organised by the BSBI Vice-county Recorder or designate. In some areas there have been nationally organised field meetings.

To encourage those relatively new to recording, BSBI has endeavoured to pair up less experienced recorders with those with more experience. These opportunities for learning have been very much a key part of the project and have done much to carry the tradition of field recording to a new generation.

Access

The survey of pre-selected survey squares is dependent on the cooperation of landowners and land managers. We record our deep gratitude to the very many people who have granted our members permission to record plants on their land. It is a great privilege indeed to enjoy the benefits of this tradition of cooperation.

Survey methodology

Appendix 4 reproduces the instruction booklet for BSBI Local Change. A summary is presented here.

Geographical Scope

The survey has covered England, Scotland and Wales.

Taxonomic Scope

As for the *New Atlas* the standard flora used for the project has been the *New Flora of the British Isles* by C.A. Stace (second edition, 1997).

Recording Alien Species

Fashions in the recording of alien species continue to change. The Monitoring Scheme instructions requested that plants obviously cultivated or planted should be excluded. The instructions for the *New Atlas* reflected the concept introduced by Stace of recording everything that occurs in a 'wild' situation. In particular planted trees in the countryside were recorded, as they may be a major feature in the landscape with an influence on the wildlife found there. The recording for the *New Atlas* also sought to classify records of aliens as to whether they were established/naturalised, surviving, casual or planted.

Local Change has introduced a revised concept of recording all plants that occur in the 'wild' whether they are planted or not. Under this concept any plant outside a garden may be recorded including planted trees and field-crops. Field-crops are included as there are usually few species involved and their presence or absence indicates something of the nature of the countryside and contributes to defining the weed flora present in the fields in which they are cultivated.

There can be no hard and fast definition of where gardens end and the 'wild' begins. Public parks and the parks and woodlands of larger houses are often important refugia for our native plants. They usually also contain a great variety of planted species. A sense of perspective must be sought when recording in such places. It is helpful to record a representative selection of the major plantings, particularly if they are of native species, but it is unrealistic to expect to record a complete inventory of all the species covered by Stace (1997). In applying this concept there was no intention that the survey should involve a complete inventory of street trees. Within gardens it remained permissible to record true weeds but not deliberately introduced plants that happen to have self-seeded or spread vegetatively. Further it was accepted that it was wholly impracticable to seek to record gardens systematically for their weeds.

Recorders have generally separated planted species from natives and established aliens. Similarly casuals, together with more or less isolated individuals of self-seeded woody plants that may survive longer than a few years, were generally recorded as casual.

In practice it has not proved practical to computerise data on planted and casual status consistently, let alone analyse such data, so to establish the native, archaeophyte or alien status of a species reliance has been placed on the national status as given in *PLANTATT* (Hill *et al.* 2004) or, for species not included there, the *New Atlas*.

The different approach to recording aliens in the Monitoring Scheme and Local Change has meant that no meaningful comparisons have been possible between the two surveys for species that are frequently found planted. Sadly this has meant that no measures of change are available for any tree species or for many shrub species.

Difficult Taxa

It has been considered crucial that only taxa that have been certainly identified were recorded. In the event of identification problems recorders have been asked to seek such help as was available locally and leave out what they have been unable to identify.

In the limited time available in any tetrad, it has been considered far more important to aim to cover the area as methodically as possible than to spend excess time on difficult taxa.

K. Pryce

Use of 1:25,000 Maps

In many areas the Monitoring Scheme recording in 1987-88 included marking maps with the route taken or making notes of the detailed localities visited. This practice was standardised as far as possible in Local Change using 1:25,000 OS maps.

It has not proved practical to assess whether the availability of routes from Monitoring Scheme increased the chance of re-finding species.

Time Targets for Recording Tetrads

For typical lowland tetrads the target total time for field recording has been ten hours, typically divided into three or four visits at different times of the year of two or three hours each. This target has not been considered practicable or, indeed, necessary in many upland tetrads where one comprehensive visit at a suitable time in the summer has been felt to be all that was appropriate.

Notable Species

Local Change has emphasised the recording of 6 or 8 figure grid references for notable species found. Many recorders used a GPS to record such localities. These localities are available as a baseline for future studies.

Using a GPS Bob Ellis

3. Assessing the Results of the Survey

Assessing the Results of the Survey

This section reports on the coverage achieved by the survey and the approach adopted to measuring change.

Coverage

The basis on which tetrads were selected for analysis is explained.

Overview

The pattern of tetrads selected for both surveys, the A, J &W tetrads in every ninth hectad in Britain, provides a possible 811 tetrads with at least some land area. 800 of these tetrads were visited in 1987-88 and 761 in 2003-04. 755 were visited in both surveys.

As it was clear that not all the tetrads visited had been adequately surveyed, it has been necessary to devise a basis for selecting those where the coverage was such that the results were sufficiently comparable for analysis. Two possible approaches were considered: one based on recording time and one based on the number of species recorded. While ten hours survey time had been given as a guideline, the time and number of visits needed for an adequate survey varies enormously from tetrad to tetrad, from a low for a tetrad of monotonous upland acid grassland to a high for a lowland semi-urban tetrad with a wide variety of fragmented habitats. The relative expertise of recorders also affects the time needed for an adequate survey. Consequently survey time was discarded as a possible basis for the selection of tetrads and a basis related to the species recorded has been used.

Selection of tetrads by the number of species recorded

A subset of species was selected specifically for the purpose of comparing the coverage of tetrads. Taxa thought to be significantly affected by differences in recording practice between the surveys or by differences in botanical skills between recorders were eliminated, i.e. neophytes, trees, commonly planted shrubs, crops, subspecies, microspecies and other segregates, hybrids and other critical taxa. This left a subset of 797 species. The distribution across tetrads of the coverage of these individual species was examined using the ratios LC (Local Change) / MS (Monitoring Scheme) −1 where MS exceeded LC and 1 - MS / LC where LC exceeded MS. This distribution is shown in figure 3.1.

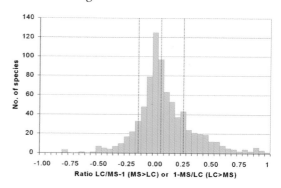

Figure 3.1 Distribution of apparent change of individual species in the subset used for selecting comparable tetrads. Mean ratio = 0.09, median ratio = 0.05

This subset was further refined by excluding the 'tails' of the distribution i.e. those species subject to most apparent change. Species with ratios outside the range -0.15 to +0.25 (i.e. me dian ± 0.2) were excluded.

Using this refined subset of 547 species, the distribution across tetrads of the ratios of number of species recorded in each tetrad was examined. This distribution is shown in figure 3.2.

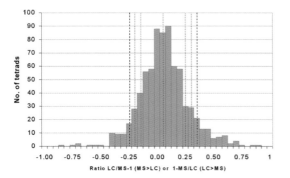

Figure 3.2 Comparability of tetrads by numbers of species recorded. Mean ratio = 0.06, median ratio = 0.06

To determine an appropriate cut-off point, the Change Factor was calculated for 'narrow', 'middle' and 'broad' ranges. The 'middle' range was found to be biased while the 'broad' range was comparable to the 'narrow' range and was preferred as it enabled more data to be analysed. The range chosen has ratios from -0.24 to +0.36 (i.e. median ± 0.3).

Comparison of tetrad species lists
In a few tetrads there were alarming systematic differences between the lists of species recorded in the two surveys, perhaps reflecting errors in locating the survey area. Such anomalies were eliminated by comparing the re-find rates. Comparisons were made between MS and LC and between LC and MS and the lower of the two was tested. This distribution is illustrated in figure 3.3.

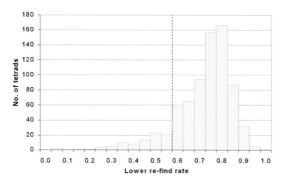

Figure 3.3 Distribution of lower re-find rates.

Tetrads with a lower re-find rate of less than 57.5% were excluded from the analysis.

A final check was made by examining tetrads with particularly low species totals. All these could be explained by the terrain, either as small areas of coast or homogeneous areas of upland moor or coniferous forest, and no tetrads were excluded as a result of this test.

Tetrads selected for analysis
The process described above resulted in the selection of 635 tetrads for analysis. These are mapped in figure 3.4

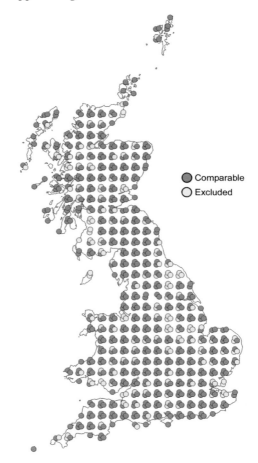

● Comparable
○ Excluded

Figure 3.4
The 635 comparable tetrads selected for analysis.

Regional Bias

As the survey analysis shows change related to climate change we have tested for any regional recording differences that might have biased the results. We have prepared three regional groupings using mean January temperatures for the tetrads supplied by CEH.

The analysis for comparability of tetrads by numbers of species recorded was applied separately for 3 ranges of January temperatures, -2.04 to 2.77°C, 2.78 to 3.55°C and 3.56 to 7.78°C. The resulting distributions are illustrated in figure 3.6. The tetrad recording ratios are also shown as a scattergram in Figure 3.7. No significant bias is evident.

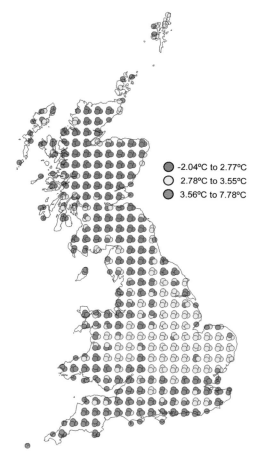

Figure 3.5 Map of tetrads showing mean January temperature ranges.

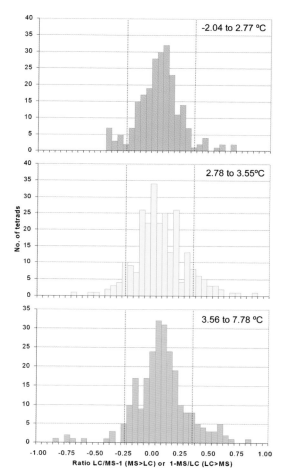

Figure 3.6 Comparability of tetrads by numbers of species recorded for 3 ranges of mean January temperature.

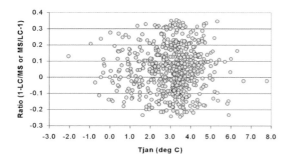

Figure 3.7 Scattergram of tetrad recording ratios against mean January temperature.

Summary of Methods for Measuring Change

Appendix 2 sets out in detail the methods used for measuring change from the results of BSBI Monitoring Scheme and BSBI Local Change. A summary is presented here.

Selection of recording units (tetrads) for analysis

As described above an empirical review of the LC data has led to the selection of 635 tetrads for analysis out of the 811 tetrads in the stratified sample.

Adjustment for over-recording

The raw survey data for LC shows a significant increase in recorded range over MS for most species, typically around 8%. This largely relates to over-recording in LC relative to MS, so an adjustment is required. No useful set of species is known which can be considered to have undergone no real change; in order to be useful such a set would have to include both scarce and widespread species. In these circumstances change can only be measured relative to a baseline of the average of a representative set of species. A selection of the best-recorded native species has been chosen as the baseline.

Relative net change in proportion to range, or 'Relative Change', is measured as the residual from a linear regression line of net change divided by range plotted against range. For gains, range is the recorded range in LC and for losses it is the recorded range in MS.

Estimating, for each survey, real range and the average probability of finding a species in a recording unit (tetrad) in which it is present

Three independent equations relating to five unknowns are derived by applying probability theory to the process of repeat recording. One unknown is eliminated by assuming that there are no real gains for species with net losses and no real losses for species with net gains. This assumption is thought to be approximately true for many species but not all. A second unknown can then be calculated from the adjustment for over-recording. This allows estimates of real range and recording probability to be derived for each species in each of the two surveys.

We have not been able to carry through this probability concept quite as we would have liked as it is relevant to the adjustment that is made for over-recording in the second survey relative to the first. This is because a circular argument arises where the calculation of the probability of finding a species is dependent on knowing the relative recording effectiveness of the two surveys and vice versa.

Change Factor

A weighted relative measure of change, the 'Change Factor' (CF), is derived from the estimate of Relative Change by an exponential weighting based on the estimate of real range. The use of real range involves an additional weighting relating to the extent to which a species is under-recorded.

Subject to important caveats, CF can be thought of as a measure of relative change in the tetrads where it is scarce at the edge of a species' distribution.

Measures of change

The analysis thus provides the following three measures of change:

Recorded Change – the net change shown by the raw survey data, shown in the tables with the maps as Mapped Change. Only the raw survey data is available for individual species distribution maps, as presence/absence data cannot be adjusted for over-recording at the tetrad level.

Relative Change – the net change adjusted for over-recording in LC relative to MS

Change Factor (CF) – a weighted measure of change suitable for work on groups of species, not available for species recorded in less than 15 tetrads in total in MS and LC or in more than 534 tetrads in total in MS and LC.

The measures of change developed here cannot be expected to be equally appropriate to each individual species, as there are some species for which the survey data is more defective than average.

Confidence limits

The recorded proportion of refinds, gains and losses enables a binomial distribution to be defined from which crude confidence limits are calculated to be applied to Relative Change and CF. These confidence limits do not take account of all the uncertainties in the data, in particular any regional- or habitat-related variation in recording efficiency. They are expressed as 90% confidence limits.

An example may help to clarify the methods adopted. In the LC dataset *Campanula rotundifolia* has 39 gains, 213 refinds and 51 losses against MS. These are what are shown in the distribution map. There are 12 more losses than gains so the 'Recorded Change' is 12/264 or 5%: this is the 'Mapped Change' in the table. *Campanula rotundifolia* is not a mobile species and it is reasonable to believe that there have been few or no real gains so that almost all the recorded gains and many of the losses are due to the plant being 'missed' in one or other survey in tetrads in which it is present. In other words the chance of finding the species during a given survey in a tetrad in which it is present is less than 1 (certainty) and has an average value that is characteristic of the species and has some degree of stability, even though it is a function of many variables and will vary from tetrad to tetrad and from survey to survey.

Example application

Campanula rotundifolia
Harebell

Mapped Change	- 5%	
Relative Change	-11%	± 7%
Weighted CF	-21%	±12%
Tetrad Frequency	67%	

Key to maps   ● Loss   ● Gain   ○ Re-find
       New Atlas distribution

Continuing with *Campanula rotundifolia*, the recorded range in MS is 264 tetrads and the adjusted net loss 30 tetrads, a decline from 264 to 234 tetrads. The recorded range in MS is the number of tetrads in which a species was recorded in MS and is the sum of the refinds and losses. The adjusted net loss of 30 tetrads is more than the unadjusted net loss of 12 tetrads as over-recording has been allowed for. This loss can be expressed as a factor measuring decline, 'Relative Change', by taking -30/264 = -0.11, an 11% decline. The value of this Relative Change must fall between -1 and 1 as, where there are net losses, the denominator is the MS range including losses, and, where there are gains, the denominator is the LC range including gains. Thus a Relative Change of 0.50 for a species is a very large gain and would mean that 50% of the tetrads in which it was recorded in LC were tetrads where the species was not also recorded in MS. This is equivalent to an increase of 100% on the MS refinds, but is not expressed in this way as it is desirable that doubling and halving the range give a factor of equal size, 0.50 and -0.50.

The probability model estimates the real range as declining from 312 tetrads to 277, a loss of 35 tetrads giving a factor of -35/312 = -0.11 or -11%, just about the same result. Again the factor falls between -1 and 1 as the denominator is the range at the time of MS for losses and the range at the time of LC for gains. *Campanula rotundifolia* is a well recorded species with a probability of being recorded where it is present in LC (P_2) of 0.91 or 91%. For less well recorded species P_2 is lower and the probability model estimates the true range to be more strikingly greater than the recorded range.

For *Campanula rotundifolia* the weighted 'Change Factor' (CF) is -0.21. This may be interpreted roughly as meaning that, for those tetrads at the edge of the range of *Campanula rotundifolia* where it is very scarce, especially in the south-east of England, 21% of the tetrads may have lost the species in the period between the MS survey in 1987/88 and the LC survey in 2003/04. There is no suggestion that this is true for the tetrads in the core part of the range of *Campanula rotundifolia* where it remains frequent: this reflects the absence of evidence as to whether or not there are losses at population level in the core area where all that is known is that the species is still present at tetrad scale.

For *Campanula rotundifolia* the 90% confidence limits are ± 0.12 against a weighted factor of -0.21 so that, while it is almost certain that *Campanula rotundifolia* has decreased sharply, there is a not inconsiderable degree of uncertainty as to the exact extent of the change.

The last statistic in the table is the tetrad frequency. This concept is taken up elsewhere in the report. *Campanula rotundifolia* has a tetrad frequency of 0.67 or 67%. This means that on average across its hectad distribution it is present in 2 of the 3 LC sample tetrads in a LC sample hectad in which it is present. For *Campanula rotundifolia* one can pick out one area of the map by eye where it is present in about 2.5 of each group of three sample tetrads, a tetrad frequency of 0.83 or 83%, and another area where it is present in about one of each group of three sample tetrads, a tetrad frequency of 0.33 or 33%.

4. Native and archaeophyte species in Broad Habitats

Bob Ellis

Introduction

The plants of Britain can be divided into four groups on the basis of their history and persistence:

natives are believed to have colonised Britain naturally,

archaeophytes are believed to have been introduced by human agency before AD 1500,

neophytes are more recent introductions which form established populations, and

casuals are introductions which do not form persistent populations.

In analysing the results of the Local Change surveys, we have separated the natives and archaeophytes from the neophytes and casuals. Doubtfully native species (described as 'native or alien' in the *New Atlas*) and neophytes are not included in the analysis, as recording conventions for some alien species were different in the repeat survey and many were recorded more comprehensively. However, any such species recorded in more than 15 tetrads in the combined surveys are listed under the Broad Habitats in which they occur, to provide a slightly more comprehensive picture of overall change.

This analysis of change excludes both the extremely widespread species for which reliable Change Factors are not available and the rarer species for which there are too little data (see Appendix 3).

Natives and archaeophytes included in the analysis have been divided into groups of species which are characteristic of particular habitats, using the Broad Habitat classification developed for the UK Biodiversity Action Plan (Jackson 2000). This recognises 21 Broad Habitats that support vascular plants (there are some additional purely marine habitats which lack them). The preferential Broad Habitats of the plants included in the Local Change survey are listed in '*PLANTATT*' (Hill *et al*. 2004), with a few additions and corrections indicated in the electronic version downloadable from the Biological Records Centre website. Some species occur in a single Broad Habitat but most are found in more than one; the *PLANTATT* list allows a maximum of four.

From the perspective of the current surveys, the Broad Habitats differ greatly in 'width'. Most are, as their name suggests, broad, incorporating a range of different but related habitat types. We have subdivided these using a classification based on the distribution of the component species, explained below. The Montane Broad Habitat (BH15) is a relatively small group, as many montane plants are too rare for inclusion in this analysis. As it is also fairly homogeneous we have not subdivided it. A few Broad Habitats include too few species to be much use to us, both because they are rather species-poor and because most of their characteristic species are either too common or too rare to be included in the analysis. We give these Broad Habitats, Coniferous woodland (BH2), Improved grassland (BH5) and Bracken (BH9), an abbreviated treatment. This leaves Broad Habitats which we have dealt with rather differently, either because they are very heterogeneous (Boundary and linear features, BH3) or because there is a very wide overlap in their preferential species (the three wetland habitats, BH11, 13 & 14 and the coastal habitats, BH18, 19 & 21). The special treatment accorded to these Broad Habitats is dealt with in the individual accounts.

The relationship of Broad Habitats, BAP priority habitats and National Vegetation Classification communities is summarised in Table 4.1.

The full accounts follow a common format. They start with a brief description of the Broad Habitat and a mention of any special problems in recording the species of that habitat for the two surveys. The subsequent sections are outlined below.

Changes in the Broad Habitat, 1950-2004

This brief summary is intended as a background against which the results of the Local Change surveys can be assessed. It outlines the main factors which have affected the habitat since 1950. It is split into two,

Number	Broad Habitat	NVC communities	BAP Priority Habitats
BH1	Broadleaved, mixed and yew woodland	W1-17,19	Upland oakwood
			Lowland beech and yew woodland
			Wet woodland
			Upland birchwoods
			Lowland mixed deciduous woodland
			Upland mixed ashwoods
BH2	Coniferous woodland	W18	Native pinewoods
BH3	Boundary and linear features	B21-23,24*; OV18*,19*, 21*,22*,24*,25*,27	Ancient and/or species rich hedgerows
BH4	Arable and horticultural	OV1-11,13,14-17, 18*19*21*22*36	Cereal field margins
BH5	Improved grassland	MG6*,7; OV12,23*,25*	Upland hay meadow
BH6	Neutral grassland	W24; MC9-12; MG1-5, 6*,8-13; OV28*	Lowland meadows
BH7	Calcareous grassland	CG1-14	Upland calcareous grassland
			Lowland calcareous grassland
BH8	Acid grassland	U1-6,19	Lowland dry acid grassland
BH9	Bracken	U20; W25	
BH10	Dwarf shrub heath	H1-10,12,16,18,21; M15*,16; OV34	Lowland heathland
			Upland heathland
(BH11)	Fen, marsh and swamp	M4-14,22-24,25*, 26-38; S1-19,20*,22-28; OV26,28*,29-33,35	Reedbeds
			Purple moor-grass and rush pasture
			Fens
BH12	Bog	M1-3,15*,17-21,25*	Blanket bog
			Lowland raised bog
(BH13)	Standing water and canals	A1-7,8*,9*,10,(11-16)*, 19*,20*,21-24	Mesotrophic lakes
			Eutrophic standing waters
			Aquifer fed naturally fluctuating water bodies
(BH14)	Rivers and streams	A8*,9*,(11-16)*, 17,18,19*,20*	Chalk rivers
BH15	Montane habitats	H13-15,17,19,20,22; U7-15,18; W20	
BH16	Inland rock	U16,17,21; OV37-40,41*	Limestone pavements
BH17	Built-up areas and gardens	OV20,23*,24*,41*,42	
(BH18)	Supralittoral rock	MC1-8	Maritime cliff and slope
(BH19)	Supralittoral sediment	H11; SD1-19	Coastal vegetated shingle
			Machair
			Coastal sand dunes
(BH21)	Littoral sediment	S20*,21; SM1-28	Seagrass beds
			Mudflats
			Coastal saltmarsh

Table 4.1. The BAP Broad Habitats discussed in this report, and their relationships to National Vegetation Classification (Rodwell 1991-2000) and BAP Priority Habitats. Broad Habitats in brackets in the first column have not been treated individually in this report (see text). Asterisked NVC communities are assigned to more than one Broad Habitat. Sources: Hill *et al.* (2004) for NVC communities and the NBN Habitats Dictionary (www.nbn.org.uk) for the Priority Habitats.

dealing with the period before the BSBI Monitoring Scheme (1950-1986) and that covered by the two surveys (1987-2004). Amongst the published sources on which we have drawn for these introductory sections are the BAP Habitat Statements (www.ukbap.org.uk) and two English Nature booklets (Brown *et al.* 2001, Townshend *et al.* 2004) as well as the more specialised books and articles cited specifically. The results of the Countryside Survey (Haines-Young *et al.* 2000) are a particularly useful source of information for the later period.

A number of factors affecting the Broad Habitats are generic, and apply to most if not all of them. These include conservation activities, which have led to voluntary and statutory protection of important sites since 1950, and recent climate change. To avoid constant repetition, these are covered once at the start of the Broad Habitat accounts.

Earlier studies of changes to the species of the Broad Habitat

This section briefly reviews earlier studies which, like ours, analyse changes by habitat and by ecological attribute. A range of studies are cited, at scales ranging from that of the county or vice-county to those based on permanent plots, and over time periods extending from a brief span of recent years to several centuries. There are not many such studies, as species' attribute data have only recently become available and the habitats recognised by earlier authors are sometimes difficult to equate to the current Broad Habitats. There is also a serious regional bias in that most published studies concentrate on S.E. England, where the historical records of plant distribution are most numerous and the changes in range are most apparent. We emphasise that this section is not intended as a comprehensive review of earlier studies, it simply cites a sample of earlier work in an attempt to answer the question 'What did we know, or think we knew, about changes to these species before the current survey?'

The BSBI Local Change surveys

The Broad Habitat considered as a whole

The results of our analysis are summarised here. The Change Factor described earlier (Chapter 3) is used to generate a mean value for the Broad Habitat as a whole, given in a summary at the head of each account. The statistical significance of the value is also stated, with probabilities of less than 5% being treated as statistically significant and probabilities of less than 10% as being marginally significant.

We then go on to analyse the Change Factors in relation to certain attributes of the ecology or distribution of the species. These attributes have been selected for their potential importance in governing the responses of species to some of the factors which have affected the Broad Habitat in recent decades. The main attributes we have analysed are listed below:

History in Britain

Most Broad Habitats are dominated by native species, but where there is a substantial proportion of archaeophytes we have looked for differences between the two groups.

Perennation

Have annuals, biennials and perennials shown a similar change? The analysis uses the primary type of perennation (P1) given by Hill *et al.* (2004).

Wider distribution

Have northern and southern species shown a similar change? The species we analyse have been divided into four categories, obtained by simplifying the phytogeographical classification set out at length by Preston & Hill (1997) and summarised by Preston *et al.* (2002a) and Hill *et al.* (2004).

> *Northern* species include those with an Arctic-montane, Boreo-arctic Montane, Boreal, Boreo-temperate or Wide-boreal distributions in the northern hemisphere (i.e. E1=1-5 in *PLANTATT*). Boreo-

temperate species occur in both the Boreal and Temperate major biomes and Wide-boreal species in the Arctic, Boreal and Temperate biomes.

Widespread species are those with a Wide-temperate distribution (E1=6). These occur in the Boreal, Temperate and Southern major biomes. This is always a very small category as there are few Wide-temperate species in Britain and they tend to be the commonest species, so most are too widespread to be included in the analysis.

Temperate species are restricted to the Temperate (or broadleaved woodland) major biome (E1=7). These are therefore intermediate in distribution between the Northern and Southern species.

Southern species are those with a Southern-temperate or Mediterranean distribution (E1=8-9).

pH requirements

These have been assessed using Ellenberg R values, adapted for the British flora by Hill *et al.* (1999) and also given in *PLANTATT*. Plants with R=1 are indicators of extremely acid conditions, and the scale rises to R=9 for those of very basic substrates.

Fertility requirements

Ellenberg N values provide an estimate of the extent to which the species grows in fertile soils. Plants with N=1 are indicators of extremely infertile sites, and the scale rises to N=9 for those of extremely nutrient-rich situations.

Light requirements

Ellenberg L values provide an estimate of the shade-tolerance of the species, ranging from L=1 for plants of deep shade to L=9 for those normally occurring in full sunlight.

Statistical analysis of the Broad Habitat species groups

Statistical analysis has been carried out on the Change Factor estimated for each species assigned to a Broad Habitat using ecological and other attributes of the plants. The history of the plant in Britain (whether a native, archaeophyte or neophyte), its wider distribution (whether northern, temperate, widespread or southern) and its perennation (whether annual, biennial or perennial) are variables with a limited number of choices. They are analysed as individual categories. Other ecological attributes, notably the Ellenberg scores, have a wider range of possible values and these are analysed to see if they show a trend rather than as individual categories. Further analysis examines the correlation of these several variables.

Statistical analysis of the single variables

For the categorical variables (History in Britain, Perennation, Wider distribution), one-way analysis of variance is used to test for differences in the Change Factor across categories (Sokal & Rohlf 1981). The results are presented as an F-value (the ratio of between- to within-category variation) and its p-value (the chance of observing a value as or more extreme on the null hypothesis of no difference) to measure the statistical significance of the result. Thus for Calcareous grassland the results of tests for differences in levels of perennation are $F_{2,99} = 3.12$, $p = 0.049$, where 2 and 99 are the degrees of freedom for perennation (number of levels minus one) and residual (number of observations minus number of levels of perennation). In this case the difference is said to be statistically significant at the 5% level. Following Cox & Snell (1981), we use the p-value as a measure of evidence against the null hypothesis and regard results significant at the 5% level ($p < 0.05$) as moderate evidence, and at the 1% level ($p < 0.01$) as strong evidence

In contrast, for the Ellenberg scores the Pearson correlation r is used to test for a trend. Thus for Ellenberg N values for the Calcareous grassland species, $r = 0.28$, $p=0.007$, indicating strong evidence for an increase of the Change Factor with N. Negative values of r indicate a decreasing trend. Note that a statistically significant correlation does not imply causality.

Modelling the effect of combinations of variables

Many of the ecological attributes listed above are correlated. Very acidic habitats, for example, are usually very nutrient-poor so there is a correlation between Ellenberg R and N values. These environmental values are also correlated with climatic variables in Britain, as infertile, acidic habitats are much more frequent in the colder and wetter north and west than in the warmer and drier south and east. For each Broad Habitat the effect of the different attributes has been modelled to establish which attributes will account for the variation in Change Factor and which are redundant. Because of the current interest in climate change, we have been particularly concerned to establish whether the observed changes might be the result of the non-climatic ecological attributes such as Ellenberg N, or whether climatic factors are needed to account for them. In this analysis we have used three additional attributes, the mean January and July temperatures and mean annual precipitation (subsequently called rainfall) of the 10-km squares in which the species are mapped in the *New Atlas* (see Hill *et al.* 2004). This analysis has not only enabled us to investigate whether or not climatic variables may be implicated in the change, but has also allowed us to suggest potentially important climatic variable(s).

The relative contributions and importance of the non-climatic and climatic variables in accounting for variation in the Change Factor were examined using multiple regression analysis (Sokal & Rohlf 1981). The analysis aims to separate the effects of the non-climatic and climatic variables which are themselves inter-correlated, and in particular to test for effects of climatic variables after allowing for possible effects of non-climatic variables. For each Broad Habitat, a range of models involving selected combinations of variables were fitted and compared in terms of the percentage variation accounted for R^2, and the statistical significance of the variables in the models. Choice of non-climatic variables for inclusion in the analysis was based on ecological considerations. Note that, as in tests for correlation with single variables, the multiple regression analysis cannot establish causality. However, the method extends the single variable analysis by attempting to allow for possible confounding effects of other variables, and identifying variables which show consistent effects over range of models. In this sense the evidence for an effect a particular variable may be strengthened.

Species groups within the Broad Habitats

The groups of species in the Habitat Group that have been subdivided were created by a TWINSPAN analysis of the British distributions mapped in the *New Atlas* for the 1987-99 dateclass. The choice of end groups was pragmatic – we selected end groups which were as homogeneous as possible but ideally presented a large enough sample size for analysis. For each Broad Habitat, the TWINSPAN analysis is illustrated by a tree diagram showing a coincidence map at each level. The maps show the number of species in each 10-km square, with squares with 20 or more species shown in the deepest shade. The number of species in the group is shown in the top left-hand corner of the map and the mean Change Factor in the top right-hand corner. If the mean Change Factor is significantly different from the mean for all native and archaeophyte species (or marginally so), then a thickened and coloured border illustrates this. Significance here is based on a t-test on the means. If $p \leq 0.05$, this is considered significant and if $0.05 < p \leq 0.10$, this is considered marginally significant. A significant decrease is shown with a red border; a marginally significant decrease with an orange border; a significant increase with a deep blue border and marginally significant one with a pale blue border. The same convention is used in a summary bar for each Broad Habitat and each end group. In addition, the summary bar shows the average number of tetrads for the species in the group, providing an indication of how widespread that group is.

For ease of reference, each end group was assigned the name of one of the species within it. Each 10-km square was assigned a score, S, according to the number of species belonging to the group occurring within it in the 1987-99 date class in the *New Atlas*. This is effectively the equivalent of the depth of colour on the coincidence map. Each species was then ranked according to the formula $\Sigma Ss/(\Sigma Hg\sqrt{\Sigma Hs})$ where ΣSs is the sum of these scores for the species, ΣHg is the total number of hectads for the group and ΣHs is the total number of hectads for the species. The highest-ranking species attributed solely to this Broad Habitat was selected, provided that there was such a species in the top 25% of species listed. Otherwise, the highest-ranking two-habitat species was chosen. The chosen species should therefore be typical of the habitat and of the geographical range of the group.

The mean Change Factor and its significance are presented for each species group in the same format as that of the Broad Habitat as a whole. The text comments on the overall change, and on the possible reasons for the increase or decrease of particular species within the group. We have tried to point out any species for which the Change Factor has been unduly influenced by aspects of recording practice rather than genuine change.

The results for each species are then listed in a table under the following headings. An explanation of all the column headings is provided in the Glossary p.329.

Species
Broad Habitats
Native Status
WD, Wider Distribution (see above, p.16)
EN, Ellenberg N values (see above, p.17)
G, Gains
L, Losses
R, Re-finds
Total, total of gains, re-finds and losses
TF, Tetrad frequency
RC, Relative Change
CF, Change Factor
90% Conf. Limits, 90% confidence limits for the Change Factor

Case studies of individual species

For most species groups, we have included at least one case study to show the results for a particular species. The analysed tetrads are mapped, with gains in blue, losses in red and refinds in yellow. The statistics provided for each species are defined in the Glossary. The results for the species in question are discussed in a brief text. As the Local Change surveys have been species-orientated rather than habitat-orientated, the species accounts present the core results of the survey.

The species accounts follow the following pattern. Marked variations in tetrad frequency within the range of a species are indicated, as is likely recording bias. Notable correlation or divergence from trends for the species shown by the *New Atlas* follows. We sometimes comment on the geographical patterns shown in the spread and retreat of species, a subject on which there is scope for a more detailed study of the results of the project. Finally, suggestions are made wherever possible as to how the observed trends might relate to major driving forces of change in the British countryside in the period between the two surveys, with particular reference to increased soil fertility levels (eutrophication), agricultural policies (especially agri-environment policies), conservation management (such as pond creation), drainage, coniferisation, urban development and climate change. Changes thought to relate to climate change do not imply that similar change can be expected in the future, indeed there is evidence in relation to ocean currents to suggest that some recent trends may be reversed.

The mathematics on which the confidence limits quoted in the species accounts are based is such that they only give a rough guide to the significance of the change shown for an individual species. Some are rather too broad and some rather too narrow. Where we have reservations, these are made clear.

As authors we have taken part in both surveys and have been engaged in botanical recording in the intervening years (in particular in relation to the *New Atlas*). We have drawn on our own field experience as well as the published accounts of others, including the autecological accounts provided by Grime *et al.* (1988), in seeking to explain the observed changes as best we can. While the relationship of observed changes to driving forces is inevitably tentative and subjective, we have been reassured by the seemingly consistent patterns of change borne out by the statistics cited. We expect that future botanists will, with the benefit of hindsight, be able to point to factors which we have overlooked and to gain a deeper understanding of the fortunes of individual species.

Doubtfully native species and neophytes in the Broad Habitat

The doubtfully native species and neophytes listed for the relevant Broad Habitat by Hill *et al.* (2004) and recorded in more than 15 tetrads in the combined surveys are listed.

Two factors potentially affecting most Broad Habitats

The factors affecting the Broad Habitats in the period since 1950 are summarised at the start of the individual accounts. However, both nature conservation and climate change have potentially affected all Broad Habitats and so to avoid repetition they are dealt with here.

Conservation

A remarkable feature of the last 50 years has been the increasing concern for nature conservation. This has led to the statutory protection of species and habitats, through mechanisms such as the SSSI network, the Biodiversity Action Plans and the provisions for specific species in the Wildlife and Countryside Act. It has also led to much voluntary effort, including the establishment of numerous nature reserves through the Wildlife Trusts and the protection of large areas of wider countryside though bodies such as the National Trusts. This report is not the place to present a detailed history of conservation in this period. However, the effect of conservation action needs to be added to the more specific factors influencing the distribution of species in Broad Habitats. Some Broad Habitats are particularly charismatic and have attracted much attention from both statutory and voluntary conservation bodies (e.g.

Broadleaved woodland, Calcareous grassland); others have received much less attention.

Climate change

The period between the two BSBI surveys has been one in which the British climate has become appreciably warmer. This is illustrated by the mean monthly temperatures for the years before the two survey periods and for the survey years themselves (Table 4.2). The temperatures of the preceding year are included as this could have a marked effect on vegetation in the following season. The differences in temperature between the two periods typify recent changes in the British climate: between 1900 and 1987 fewer than one year in six had a mean temperature above 10°, but nine of the 11 years between 1994 and 2004 exceeded this threshold.

The figures for mean monthly precipitation are given in Table 4.3. The main feature to note is that 2003 was exceptionally dry – it was the driest year since 1975 and only six other years since 1900 have been drier. Unlike the temperature figures, this does not reflect a long-term trend but is an individual feature of this particular year. This drought may well have influenced the results of the project, both by affecting the appearance of vegetation (and thus the ease with which species can be detected) and the actual species composition. This must be borne in mind when interpreting the results of the survey.

Year	Jan	Feb	Mar	Apr	May	Jun	Jul	Aug	Sep	Oct	Nov	Dec	Total
1986	3.5	-1.1	4.9	5.8	11.1	14.8	15.9	13.7	11.3	11.0	7.8	6.2	8.74
1987	0.8	3.6	4.1	10.3	10.1	12.8	15.9	15.6	13.6	9.7	6.5	5.6	9.05
1988	5.3	4.9	6.4	8.2	11.9	14.4	14.7	15.2	13.2	10.4	5.2	7.5	9.77
2002	5.5	7.0	7.6	9.3	11.8	14.4	16.0	17.0	14.4	10.1	8.5	5.7	10.60
2003	4.5	3.9	7.5	9.6	12.1	16.1	17.6	18.3	14.3	9.2	8.1	4.8	10.50
2004	5.2	5.4	6.5	9.4	12.1	15.3	15.8	17.6	14.9	10.5	7.7	5.4	10.51

Table 4.2 Mean monthly temperatures in 1986-88 and 2002-04, taken from the Central England Temperature series (www.met-office.gov.uk/research/hadleycentre/obsdata). The lowest values for each month are in **blue** and the highest in red.

Year	Jan	Feb	Mar	Apr	May	Jun	Jul	Aug	Sep	Oct	Nov	Dec	Total
1986	128	20	83	87	88	45	55	118	29	98	121	142	1013
1987	34	60	93	69	49	109	73	69	66	180	82	60	994
1988	169	65	107	45	66	40	139	89	72	94	50	46	981
2002	87	115	53	48	81	57	93	76	41	144	176	148	1118
2003	91	39	37	43	71	76	65	21	35	68	117	100	761
2004	123	50	50	91	48	59	75	157	50	155	53	64	974

Table 4.3 Mean monthly precipitation in 1986-88 and 2002-04, taken from the England and Wales total precipitation series (source as Table 4.2). The lowest values for each month are in orange and the highest in green.

Coppiced woodland in Norfolk Paul Westley

Broadleaved, mixed and yew woodland (BH1)

Species	116	Average tetrads	207	Mean CF	- 2	Significance	0.06
				Decrease marginally significant			

This Broad Habitat includes all woodland composed of broadleaved trees, and mixed woodlands where broadleaved trees form at least 20% of the total area of tree canopy. Yew woodland, Juniper woodland and large stands of scrub are also included. It therefore encompasses many different woodland types, and a wide range of both generalist and specialist species are associated with it. In particular, many woodland herbs are also found in hedgerows and unimproved grassland.

Woodland is much more likely to be affected by the deliberate introduction of native or alien species than other semi-natural habitats. Whereas the management of woodland nature reserves is usually fairly orthodox, private woodlands can be managed for various commercial reasons (including forestry and pheasant-rearing), as landscape features or sometimes, it appears, simply as an extension of the owner's garden. They often provide the visitor with minor (if not big) surprises. Trees and shrubs are often planted in existing woodland, and also (of course) elsewhere to create new woods, shelter belts and hedgerows. Planted trees and shrubs were inconsistently recorded in the two BSBI Local Change surveys. All trees and most shrubs are therefore excluded from this analysis, the only shrubs

included being those that are rarely planted.

Changes in the Broadleaved, mixed and yew woodland habitat, 1950-2004

1950-1986

The main changes in British woodlands in this period included:

- the loss of broadleaved woodland to agriculture, roads and urban development, or conversion to conifers;

- increasing density and shade within woodland as sites recovered from the clear-felling or the extraction of timber, particularly in the two world wars, and as traditional management practises such as coppicing became less frequent;

- the loss of woodland grassland in glades and rides as these areas have become overgrown or more heavily shaded by the surrounding trees;

- increasing nutrient levels, especially at edges adjoining intensively farmed land;

- death of elms;

• increasing numbers of deer, including native species and the introduced Muntjac, which have shown a particularly dramatic rise in numbers in southern England;

• the impact, especially in southern England, of exceptionally severe droughts in 1975-6.

Although British woods are still very profoundly influenced by past and present human activity, the general effect of decreased management in recent decades has perhaps been an approach in many woods to a rather more natural state, with an increase in shading and in the amount of standing and fallen dead wood. For further details of recent changes in woodland, see Kirby *et al.* (2005) and Rackham (2003).

1987-2004

In recent years the loss of ancient, broadleaved woodland has slowed down as the value of this habitat has become generally recognised. However, established woods have continued to be affected by increasing numbers of deer in southern England and sheep in the uplands, and hence by increased browsing and grazing. Grey squirrels have also had an increasing impact in some woods. Woodland soils, especially non-calcareous soils, have become less acidic, apparently as a result of decreasing SO_2 pollution ('acid rain'). Nutrient levels have continued to increase. However, the changes which may be expected as a result of eutrophication may be retarded in some woods by increasing shade. The great storms of 1987 and 1990 affected many woods in S.E. England, often reversing the general trend for woodlands to become shadier and thus temporarily increasing the diversity of the ground flora.

It has become clear that the conifers planted in some woodlands (especially on heavy soils) in lowland England have failed to thrive, and some woods have been deliberately 'deconiferised'.

Much new broadleaved woodland has been planted in recent years, as have many new hedges. The CEH Countryside Survey estimated a net increase of 5% in the area of Broadleaved woodland between 1990 and 1998 (Haines-Young *et al.* 2000). This resulted from a 7% loss of existing woodland, more than balanced by a 12% gain from the Coniferous woodland, Arable and horticultural and Grassland Broad Habitats. As newly planted woodlands are initially too open to support a characteristic woodland flora, and woodland biodiversity increases only slowly, the authors of the Countryside Survey report regard this high rate of turnover as a cause for concern.

Earlier studies of changes in the species of Broadleaved, mixed and yew woodland

Despite the considerable changes in British woodlands in the 20th century, woodland species are usually thought to have shown less dramatic changes in range than those of many other habitats. Dony (1977) commented that the woodland flora of Bedfordshire "remained remarkably constant" between 1798 and 1976, and in several other southern English vice-counties the proportion of woodland species which have become extinct is less than that in most other habitats (Preston 2000, Walker & Preston in press). Comparison of the two Atlas surveys also showed that, at the 10-km square scale, woodland species had been relatively successful in most British regions between 1930-69 and 1987-99.

In the Netherlands, woodland species also did well in the 20th century, showing a net increase, although species of nutrient-poor woodlands have shown marked decreases since 1975 whereas plants of nutrient-rich woodlands have tended to increase (Tamis *et al.* 2005).

The BSBI Local change surveys

Overall, with a group mean CF of -2, the species associated with woodland show a marginally significant decrease.

If the woodland species are pooled, the tendency for species with northern ranges to have decreased compared to those of more southerly distribution is apparent ($F_{3,112} = 13.74$, $p = 0.013$).

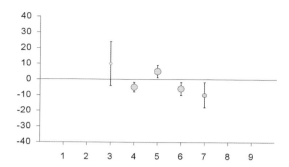

Wider Distribution	No. species	Mean CF	Standard error
Northern	32	-11	4
Temperate	68	0	2
Widespread	1	+15	-
Southern	15	+8	6

Inspection of the mean Change Factors suggests that there might be a tendency for species of more acidic soils to have fared less well than those of more base-rich substrates, but this difference is not statistically significant ($r = 0.16$, $p = 0.090$).

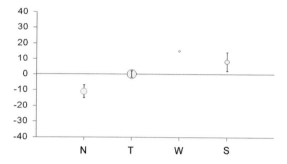

Ellenberg R	No. species	Mean CF	Standard error
2 (very acid)	1	-28	-
3	6	-16	10
4	11	-2	4
5	22	-3	4
6	28	-2	4
7	45	-3	7
8 (basic)	3	+22	16

Although woodlands have been more shady in recent decades, there is no statistically significant relationship between the Ellenberg L values and Change Factor L ($r = -0.11$, $p = 0.25$)

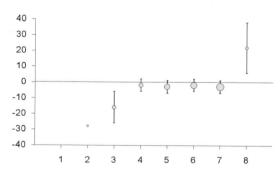

Ellenberg L	No. species	Mean CF	Standard error
3 (shade)	4	+10	14
4	34	-5	3
5	36	+5	4
6	31	-6	4
7 (well-lit)	11	-10	8

However, there is a marked tendency for plants of more nutrient-poor soils to have fared less well than these of more nutrient-rich soils ($r = 0.24$, $p = 0.008$).

Ellenberg N	No. species	Mean CF	Standard error
2 (very infertile)	3	-38	18
3	12	-12	5
4	19	-5	3
5	37	+3	4
6	31	0	4
7	13	0	4
8 (very fertile)	1	+7	-

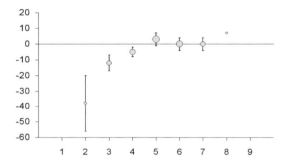

The evidence from the BSBI Local Change surveys does not suggest that there have been dramatic changes in the woodland flora. Most species' groups show no overall change, although there is considerable variation between species in the widespread and southern groups. The evidence for the relatively greater decrease of species with northern ranges identifies a trend which has not hitherto been commented on; these losses might (of course) reflect the loss of non-woodland populations. The relative decrease in species of nutrient-poor soils parallels the Dutch experience.

A comparison of our results with the long-term studies of woodland plots published recently by Kirby *et al.* (2005) follows the discussion of the species groups.

What environmental variables are driving the changes in Broad-leaved, mixed and yew woodland?

The multiple regression analysis using non-climatic variables shows a consistent effect of Ellenberg N ($R^2 = 6.0\%$, p=0.008 with N as the single variable) but little evidence of an effect of the other non-climatic variables. Adding the Wider Distribution terms gives a significant improvement ($R^2 = 13.5\%$, with both variables statistically significant). However, the effect of Wider Distribution disappears when climatic variables are added to the model. Presumably both sets of terms provide a measure of the climatic niche of the species, but the direct measurements have more explanatory power. Similarly, the inclusion of January or July temperatures (which are highly correlated with each other, and correlated with N) also reduce the effect of Ellenberg N. An effect of January temperature, but not of July temperature, is apparent when both are included in the model.

We therefore suggest that the changes in woodland may have been driven by increasing temperatures, with warmer January temperatures the most likely factor.

Species groups

Distributional analysis reveals five main groups of woodland species.

Broadleaved, mixed and yew woodland (BH1): classification of species

Viola reichenbachiana group (1.1.1)

Species	21	Average tetrads	62	Mean CF	+ 3	Significance	0.84
		Moderately local		No change			

This group comprises species with a southerly distribution. It includes many calcicoles, and the areas with the greatest concentration of these species show the familiar pattern of calcareous rocks in southern England.

Ranunculus auricomus and *Tamus communis* are the only species showing a significant trend that is not affected by special factors. Both have declined.

The species showing greatest loss, *Polygonatum multiflorum*, was previously over-recorded because of confusion with *P.* × *hybridum*, a garden escape. Both *Euphorbia amygdaloides* and *Lamiastrum galeobdolon* have cultivated subspecies and these records have been excluded.

Two of the species that show most increase, *Iris foetidissima* and *Convallaria majalis*, have been augmented in the past by garden escapes. The *Iris* may now be spreading naturally, but changes in recording practice may explain some of the apparent increase in these two species. *Carex strigosa* and *Lathraea squamaria* show an apparent marked increase, but both are based on small samples so the gain may not be real.

Euphorbia amygdaloides, Wood Spurge Bob Ellis

Ranunculus auricomus, Goldilocks Buttercup Gillian Beckett

Species	Broad Habitats	Native Status	WD	EN	G	L	R	Total	TF	RC	CF	90% Conf. Limits
Polygonatum multiflorum	1	N	t	6	9	13	9	31	38	-27	-28	38
Euphorbia amygdaloides	1	N	t	6	7	16	38	61	43	-25	-27	14
Ranunculus auricomus	1	N	n	5	24	33	42	99	42	-20	-24	21
Lamiastrum galeobdolon	1	N	t	6	18	27	76	121	27	-17	-20	14
Viburnum lantana	1, 3	N	t	5	16	17	48	81	52	-10	-11	19
Tamus communis	1, 3	N	s	6	23	20	211	254	85	-6	-9	8
Rhamnus cathartica	1, 3	N	t	6	27	24	44	95	60	-4	-5	22
Stellaria neglecta	1, 3	N	t	7	20	18	20	58	49	-3	-4	30
Luzula forsteri	1	N	s	2	7	6	13	26	48	-4	-4	36
Agrimonia procera	1, 3, 6	N	t	5	9	8	3	20	20	0	0	53
Campanula trachelium	1	N	t	6	12	10	10	32	30	+1	+1	42
Ruscus aculeatus	1, 3	N	s	4	15	11	16	42	30	+4	+5	34
Rosa stylosa	1, 3	N	t	4	11	9	4	24	51	+5	+5	52
Viola reichenbachiana	1	N	t	5	35	25	42	102	48	+5	+6	24
Epilobium roseum	1, 3, 14, 17	N	t	7	20	16	6	42	38	+7	+8	42
Lithospermum officinale	1, 3, 7	N	t	5	7	5	5	17	19	+8	+8	54
Daphne laureola	1	N	s	5	15	8	18	41	24	+13	+14	30
Convallaria majalis	1, 7	N	n	5	12	5	6	23	25	+30	+32	41
Carex strigosa	1, 14	N	t	6	9	3	6	18	25	+31	+32	42
Lathraea squamaria	1, 3	N	t	6	9	3	5	17	19	+34	+35	44
Iris foetidissima	1	N	s	5	57	9	30	96	51	+47	+54	17

WD: Wider Distribution   EN: Ellenberg N   G: Gains   L: Losses   R: Re-finds   TF: Tetrad Frequency   RC: Relative Change   CF: Change Factor (weighted)

Iris foetidissima, Stinking Iris Bob Ellis

Ranunculus auricomus
Goldilocks Buttercup

Mapped Change	-12%	
Relative Change	-20%	±21%
Weighted CF	-24%	±21%
Tetrad Frequency	42%	

Iris foetidissima
Stinking Iris

Mapped Change	+55%	
Relative Change	+47%	±15%
Weighted CF	+54%	±17%
Tetrad Frequency	51%	

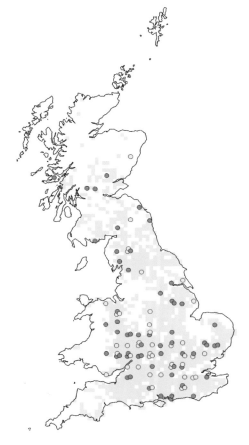

Ranunculus auricomus is a plant of woodland on somewhat calcareous soils and is only moderately frequent except in a limited core area centred in the Wye valley. It also occurs in hedges and grassland, especially churchyard grassland, and in woodland it tends to be found in glades and on the edges of rides. It is in marked decline across much of its range.

Iris foetidissima is frequent at tetrad scale within its limited southern distribution. It has increased across its range and this may be due not only to garden escapes but also to its ability to thrive in drought-prone scrub. It could thus have been favoured by climate change.

Key to maps ● Loss ● Gain ○ Re-find
░ *New Atlas* distribution

Circaea lutetiana group (1.1.2)

Species	34	Average tetrads	145	Mean CF	+ 3	Significance	0.85
		Moderately widespread		**No change**			

This is the second group of species with predominantly southern distributions, although these species have a much wider British range and are much less closely associated with calcareous soils. Like the *Viola reichenbachiana* group, there is no evidence that the mean change factor for these species differs from the overall value.

Campanula latifolia, the species with the most negative change value, is discussed below. *Orchis mascula* occurs in woodland and in more open habitats. In woodland it may have suffered from the reduction in open habitats which has characterised our woodlands in recent decades, and from increased deer numbers, and grassland populations may have been lost because of agricultural improvement.

Three of the species that appear to be increasing most markedly are often found as well-naturalised garden escapes, namely *Carex pendula*, *Myosotis sylvatica* and *Hypericum androsaemum*. *Carex pendula* may also have been favoured by its relative unpalatability to deer. At Monks Wood, Huntingdonshire, where it occurs as a native species, dense stands have developed in areas where coppice regrowth failed because of heavy browsing by Muntjac (Cooke & Farrell 2001). Several other species show significant increases. *Carex sylvatica* is discussed in the species account. *Polystichum setiferum* (like other woodland ferns) may have benefited from milder winters or the increased shading in woodlands in recent decades or both. *Dryopteris carthusiana*, which shows an apparent increase, is more a moorland than a woodland species; in woodland in often grows in acidic sites which have been colonised by trees after drainage. *Rumex sanguineus* is found in a wide variety of habitats. The trends in these two species need not necessarily be related to woodland.

Campanula latifolia, Giant Bellflower Michael Braithwaite

Species	Broad Habitats	Native Status	WD	EN	G	L	R	Total	TF	RC	CF	90% Conf. Limits
Campanula latifolia	1	N	t	6	6	18	15	39	25	-45	-47	23
Orchis mascula	1, 7, 16	N	t	4	27	37	36	100	32	-22	-27	23
Moehringia trinervia	1	N	t	6	52	70	159	281	72	-15	-26	16
Listera ovata	1, 11	N	n	5	24	31	25	80	27	-21	-25	26
Polystichum aculeatum	1, 16	N	t	5	27	33	43	103	38	-16	-19	22
Osmunda regalis	1, 11	N	s	4	7	9	12	28	23	-18	-19	35
Festuca gigantea	1	N	t	7	52	60	130	242	65	-11	-19	17
Poa nemoralis	1	N	n	5	56	61	80	197	57	-11	-17	21
Bromopsis ramosa	1	N	t	7	48	46	152	246	67	-6	-10	16
Melica uniflora	1	N	t	5	24	22	85	131	46	-6	-8	15
Adoxa moschatellina	1	N	n	5	39	36	76	151	48	-5	-7	19
Carex paniculata	1, 11	N	t	6	20	18	36	74	30	-5	-5	24
Mycelis muralis	1, 16	N	t	5	28	23	62	113	46	-2	-3	19
Arum maculatum	1	N	t	7	33	16	266	315	82	-1	-2	10
Milium effusum	1	N	n	5	23	18	45	86	35	-1	-1	21
Cardamine amara	1, 14	N	t	6	27	22	38	87	46	-1	-1	24
Platanthera chlorantha	1, 6	N	t	4	5	4	7	16	11	0	0	47
Circaea lutetiana	1	N	t	6	54	37	196	287	68	0	0	15
Hypericum maculatum	1, 3, 16	N	n	5	26	19	45	90	48	+2	+2	23
Epipactis helleborine	1, 7	N	t	4	21	17	18	56	30	+2	+2	33
Veronica montana	1	N	t	6	55	38	104	197	55	+3	+5	19
Elymus caninus	1, 3	N	n	8	50	37	50	137	49	+5	+7	24
Carex laevigata	1, 16	N	t	4	20	13	15	48	31	+12	+13	33
Sedum telephium	1, 3, 16	N	t	5	31	20	23	74	42	+12	+14	28
Dryopteris carthusiana	1	N	n	4	47	28	47	122	47	+12	+16	22
Polystichum setiferum	1	N	s	6	36	13	74	123	51	+13	+16	15
Scirpus sylvaticus	1, 11	N	t	6	10	4	10	24	21	+21	+22	36
Veronica hederifolia	1, 3, 4, 17	AR	s	6	94	42	207	343	88	+11	+23	17
Carex sylvatica	1	N	t	5	70	25	115	210	57	+17	+25	15
Ceratocapnos claviculata	1, 9	N	t	5	27	8	30	65	33	+25	+28	21
Rumex sanguineus	1	N	t	7	90	27	240	357	84	+13	+28	13
Hypericum androsaemum	1, 3	N	s	5	62	16	66	144	54	+28	+36	15
Myosotis sylvatica	1	N	t	5	107	35	75	217	68	+32	+49	17
Carex pendula	1, 14	N	s	6	82	8	72	162	56	+41	+51	11

WD: Wider Distribution EN: Ellenberg N G: Gains L: Losses R: Re-finds TF: Tetrad Frequency RC: Relative Change CF: Change Factor (weighted)

Campanula latifolia
Giant Bellflower

Mapped Change	-36%	
Relative Change	-45%	±25%
Weighted CF	-47%	±23%
Tetrad Frequency	25%	

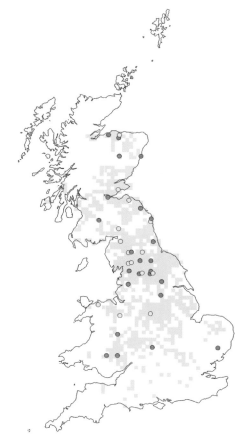

Carex sylvatica
Wood-sedge

Mapped Change	+24%	
Relative Change	+17%	±10%
Weighted CF	+25%	±15%
Tetrad Frequency	57%	

Campanula latifolia is notably sparse at tetrad scale except in a modest core area in northern England where it is more frequent. There is strong evidence of decline throughout its range. While it may recover after forestry disturbance in woodland it is more vulnerable in hedgerows where it may be out-competed following eutrophication.

Carex sylvatica is very frequent in the south and much scarcer in the northern half of its range. It may, like *Carex pendula*, be less palatable to deer than other herbs and therefore have benefited from the increase in deer in British woodland in recent decades. It is also capable of colonising secondary woodland and plantations, often along rides, and this may account for its apparent spread.

Key to maps ● Loss ● Gain ○ Re-find
▨ *New Atlas* distribution

Hyacinthoides non-scripta
Bluebell

Mapped Change	+1%	
Relative Change	- 5%	± 6%
Weighted CF	-13%	±16%
Tetrad Frequency	83%	

The distribution of *Hyacinthoides non-scripta* is notably stable. This is such an abundant and well-recorded species where it occurs that the over-recording adjustment that leads to a negative Relative Change is probably partly unwarranted. The apparent losses in the east of its range are likely to relate to records for the garden hybrid in the first survey being replaced by correct records in the second survey.

Key to maps ● Loss ● Gain ○ Re-find
▨ *New Atlas* distribution

Bob Ellis

Lonicera periclymenum group (1.2.1)

Species	32	Average tetrads	406	Mean CF	- 3	Significance	0.12
		Widespread		No change			

This is the most wide-ranging of the woodland groups, frequent throughout Britain except for some of the least wooded terrain in Scotland and the Fenland of East Anglia. Not surprisingly for such a frequent group, many of the species occur in a range of habitats.

Whereas most of the woodland and hedgerow specialists appear to be stable, there are a few exceptions: *Sanicula europaea*, *Rubus idaeus* and *Mercurialis perennis* show a decline while *Cardamine flexuosa*, *Carex remota*, *Allium ursinum* and *Geum urbanum* show an increase.

Phyllitis scolopendrium shows a marked increase and, while this is a multi-habitat species, the trend is in line with that of *Polystichum setiferum* (see *Circaea lutetiana* group 1.1.2) and may relate to the increasing canopy densities in unmanaged woodland, to climate change or a combination of both factors.

Allium ursinum, Ramsons Bob Ellis

Species	Broad Habitats	Native Status	WD	EN	G	L	R	Total	TF	RC	CF	90% Conf. Limits
Sanicula europaea	1	N	t	5	35	51	97	183	50	-18	-26	16
Hedera helix	1, 3	N	s	6	24	28	450	502	92	-6	-26	7
Viola riviniana	1, 7, 16	N	t	4	59	54	417	530	88	-4	-24	26
Conopodium majus	1, 6	N	t	5	59	66	293	418	79	-8	-23	17
Pteridium aquilinum	1, 9	N	t	3	28	30	419	477	83	-6	-21	10
Rubus idaeus	1	N	n	5	54	61	272	387	79	-8	-21	15
Anemone nemorosa	1, 16	N	t	4	50	58	193	301	64	-10	-19	15
Rubus fruticosus agg.	1, 3	N	s	6	18	12	490	520	94	-4	-19	11
Potentilla sterilis	1	N	t	5	42	46	225	313	72	-8	-16	13
Fragaria vesca	1, 7	N	t	4	59	61	200	320	69	-8	-15	17
Mercurialis perennis	1	N	t	7	28	30	283	341	74	-7	-15	9
Hyacinthoides non-scripta	1, 9	N	t	6	52	47	324	423	83	-5	-13	16
Dryopteris filix-mas	1, 2	N	t	5	59	46	415	520	94	-2	-13	25
Salix caprea	1	N	n	7	72	59	330	461	92	-2	-9	22
Stellaria holostea	1	N	t	6	45	37	296	378	78	-4	-9	13
Ajuga reptans	1	N	t	5	63	50	260	373	75	-2	-6	17
Ranunculus ficaria	1, 3	N	s	6	81	62	358	501	91	-1	-6	29
Blechnum spicant	1, 2, 10, 16	N	t	3	45	32	258	335	78	-2	-5	13
Glechoma hederacea	1, 3	N	n	7	40	23	348	411	87	-1	-4	12
Silene dioica	1	N	n	7	56	38	332	426	81	-1	-4	16
Dryopteris dilatata	1, 2	N	t	5	59	36	429	524	91	0	-2	26
Scrophularia nodosa	1, 3	N	t	6	73	52	233	358	75	0	+1	19
Holcus mollis	1, 3, 9	N	t	3	84	55	330	469	89	+1	+6	25
Brachypodium sylvaticum	1	N	t	5	56	25	260	341	72	+3	+7	13
Lonicera periclymenum	1	N	s	5	63	28	366	457	82	+3	+9	17
Geum urbanum	1	N	t	7	49	11	371	431	87	+3	+11	11
Primula vulgaris	1, 16	N	t	4	77	40	306	423	76	+4	+12	18
Geranium robertianum	1, 16	N	t	6	55	18	453	526	96	+2	+13	20
Allium ursinum	1	N	t	7	62	24	122	208	52	+13	+20	14
Carex remota	1, 14	N	t	6	65	20	134	219	59	+15	+23	13
Cardamine flexuosa	1	N	t	6	95	40	355	490	90	+7	+29	22
Salix cinerea	1, 11	N	n	5	94	34	371	499	91	+8	+33	21
Phyllitis scolopendrium	1, 16	N	t	5	84	16	163	263	62	+21	+33	11

WD: Wider Distribution   EN: Ellenberg N   G: Gains   L: Losses   R: Re-finds   TF: Tetrad Frequency   RC: Relative Change   CF: Change Factor (weighted)

Sanicula europaea
Sanicle

Mapped Change	-11%	
Relative Change	-18%	±13%
Weighted CF	-26%	±16%
Tetrad Frequency	50%	

Sanicula europaea is often a scarce component of the woodland flora and exploits habitats with a sparse ground flora. Rank vegetation is on the increase in many woods and it is not unexpected that this species and its habitat appear to be in decline.

Allium ursinum
Ramsons

Mapped Change	+21%	
Relative Change	+13%	±10%
Weighted CF	+20%	±14%
Tetrad Frequency	52%	

Allium ursinum is widespread and frequent in the lowlands but largely confined to sites with a continuous history of woodland or scrub so its apparent increase is unexpected. This may relate largely to better coverage especially in sites such as hedgerows and riversides away from woodland where individual colonies may be small and even impermanent. Such small colonies may only be evident for a short period in spring.

Key to maps   ● Loss   ● Gain   ○ Re-find
▨ *New Atlas* distribution

Lysimachia nemorum group (1.2.2)

Species	15	Average tetrads	259	Mean CF	- 4	Significance	0.16
		Widespread		No change			

This is a group of very widespread northern and western species, a counterpart in many ways of the *Circaea lutetiana* group of southern species. Like that group, the majority of species occur in a range of Broad Habitats.

The great majority of the species in this group have a negative change factor, although the change is rarely sufficiently marked to be statistically significant at the level of the individual species.

The very marked exception to the tendency of this group to show a decline is *Dryopteris affinis*, a member of the *D. filix-mas* complex which has become increasingly familiar to botanists in recent decades. It seems likely that this was under-recorded in the first survey, although it may also have shown a modest increase like other ferns. If this species is excluded, the mean change factor for the group (-7) becomes significantly different from that for all species. Only two other members of the group have positive change factors, and that of *Luzula sylvatica* is only marginally significant.

Species	Broad Habitats	Native Status	WD	EN	G	L	R	Total	TF	RC	CF	90% Conf. Limits
Melampyrum pratense	1, 2	N	n	3	23	36	51	110	43	-23	-28	19
Galium odoratum	1	N	t	6	33	36	60	129	41	-11	-14	20
Salix aurita	1, 16	N	n	3	41	42	158	241	64	-8	-12	14
Teucrium scorodonia	1, 9, 16	N	s	3	33	32	237	302	64	-6	-12	11
Luzula pilosa	1, 2	N	n	3	49	49	122	220	57	-7	-12	17
Oxalis acetosella	1, 2, 16	N	n	4	38	33	306	377	77	-5	-11	11
Carex pallescens	1	N	n	4	31	31	50	112	46	-8	-10	22
Lysimachia nemorum	1	N	t	5	49	45	199	293	67	-5	-10	14
Geum rivale	1, 16	N	n	4	31	28	110	169	55	-6	-8	15
Athyrium filix-femina	1, 16	N	n	6	52	38	317	407	78	-2	-6	15
Blechnum spicant	1, 2, 10, 16	N	t	3	45	32	258	335	78	-2	-5	13
Chrysosplenium oppositifolium	1, 14	N	t	5	42	26	213	281	68	-1	-1	12
Luzula sylvatica	1, 16	N	t	4	52	23	159	234	58	+7	+10	13
Polypodium vulgare sens. lat.	1	N	w	3	76	35	238	349	69	+7	+15	15
Dryopteris affinis	1, 16	N	t	5	114	29	190	333	71	+22	+42	13

WD: Wider Distribution   EN: Ellenberg N   G: Gains   L: Losses   R: Re-finds   TF: Tetrad Frequency   RC: Relative Change   CF: Change Factor (weighted)

Melampyrum pratense
Common Cow-wheat

Mapped Change	-15%	
Relative Change	-23%	±18%
Weighted CF	-28%	±19%
Tetrad Frequency	43%	

Galium odoratum
Woodruff

Mapped Change	- 3%	
Relative Change	-11%	±19%
Weighted CF	-14%	±20%
Tetrad Frequency	41%	

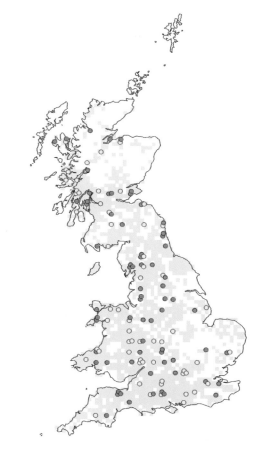

Melampyrum pratense is a very widespread plant in the central Highlands but elsewhere it is infrequent at tetrad scale and more dependent on acid woodland habitat. While some losses may be associated with coniferisation, this species is an annual and populations may have reacted more quickly than those of perennial species to increased shade and soil fertility in woodlands.

Galium odoratum is relatively infrequent within its range as it is largely restricted to ancient woodland on at least slightly calcareous soils. There is a faint suggestion of decline, possibly related to eutrophication and habitat disturbance by forestry operations.

Key to maps ● Loss ● Gain ○ Re-find
　　　　　　▨ *New Atlas* distribution

Oreopteris limbosperma group (2)

Species	14	Average tetrads	61	Mean CF	-17	Significance	0.01
		Local		**Significant decrease**			

This is a markedly northern and western group, its distribution complementary to that of the *Viola reichenbachiana* group. The species are mainly plants of woodland and rocky gorges.

Dryopteris expansa, *Vicia sylvatica*, *Platanthera bifolia* and *Melica nutans* have shown the most marked declines, though these results are based on small samples. *D. expansa* is a critical species and the result must be considered unreliable, but the other species are well-known and easily recognised. They might be vulnerable to heavy grazing pressure.

Only *Symphytum tuberosum* appears to have increased significantly. We have included this species in the analysis as it is traditionally treated as a native, but we believe it is more likely to be a neophyte (see the individual species account below).

Species	Broad Habitats	Native Status	WD	EN	G	L	R	Total	TF	RC	CF	90% Conf. Limits
Dryopteris expansa	1, 15, 16	N	n	2	5	14	4	23	62	-59	-61	39
Vicia sylvatica	1, 3, 16	N	n	5	4	9	3	16	23	-50	-52	48
Platanthera bifolia	1, 10	N	n	2	4	10	5	19	25	-49	-50	40
Melica nutans	1, 7, 16	N	n	3	4	9	5	18	35	-44	-46	42
Hymenophyllum wilsonii	1, 16	N	n	3	12	14	15	41	52	-15	-17	33
Gymnocarpium dryopteris	1, 16	N	n	4	19	21	39	79	55	-12	-13	22
Rubus saxatilis	1, 7, 16	N	n	4	12	13	16	41	36	-12	-13	33
Oreopteris limbosperma	1, 16	N	t	3	37	31	130	198	72	-4	-6	14
Stellaria nemorum	1, 14	N	n	7	7	6	9	22	31	-2	-2	42
Circaea x intermedia	1	NH	t	6	11	9	17	37	44	-1	-1	32
Trientalis europaea	1, 2, 10	N	n	3	14	10	38	62	77	-1	-1	21
Phegopteris connectilis	1, 16	N	n	4	19	10	78	107	63	+1	+2	15
Equisetum sylvaticum	1, 16	N	n	5	45	32	74	151	59	+3	+4	20
Symphytum tuberosum	1, 3	N	t	6	15	6	20	41	41	+17	+18	27

WD: Wider Distribution   EN: Ellenberg N   G: Gains   L: Losses   R: Re-finds   TF: Tetrad Frequency   RC: Relative Change   CF: Change Factor (weighted)

Gymnocarpium dryopteris
Oak Fern

Mapped Change	- 3%	
Relative Change	-12%	±23%
Weighted CF	-13%	±22%
Tetrad Frequency	55%	

Symphytum tuberosum
Tuberous Comfrey

Mapped Change	+26%	
Relative Change	+17%	±27%
Weighted CF	+18%	±27%
Tetrad Frequency	41%	

Gymnocarpium dryopteris is seen to be notably scarce away from the Scottish Highlands where it remains frequent. The evidence of decline is very weak and there is insufficient data from the southern part of its range to confirm the evidence in the *New Atlas* that this is where the losses are concentrated.

The tetrad distribution emphasises to what a large extent *Symphytum tuberosum* is a plant of the east of Scotland from Inverness to Berwick upon Tweed. Here it is traditionally regarded as native but is much more likely to be a neophyte which is very frequent and possibly still consolidating its range after arrival only a century or two ago. In addition to growing in woodland it also occurs by rivers. Elsewhere it is infrequent and remains more obviously an introduction. There is little evidence of spread beyond its core areas.

Key to maps ● Loss ● Gain ○ Re-find
▨ *New Atlas* distribution

Doubtfully native species and neophytes in Broadleaved, mixed and yew woodland

Two doubtfully native species are attributed to woodland and recorded from at least 15 tetrads, and a larger suite of neophytes may occur in woodland.

Species	Broad Habitats	Native Status	WD	EN	G	L	R	Total	TF	RC	CF	90% Conf. Limits
Doubtful Status												
Aconitum napellus sens. lat.	1, 3, 14, 17	NA	t	6	12	4	7	23	17	+34	+35	38
Berberis vulgaris	1, 3	NA	t	3	9	7	1	17	16	+11	+13	62
Ribes rubrum	1	NA	t	6	86	47	95	228	63	+14	+23	20
Neophytes												
Allium paradoxum	1, 3	AN		7	10	3	2	15	26	+50	+51	46
Campanula persicifolia	1, 3	AN	t	6	16	1	2	19	30	+75	+76	33
Claytonia sibirica	1, 3	AN		6	31	17	37	85	40	+12	+14	23
Crocosmia x crocosmiiflora	1, 3, 17	AN		4	86	7	42	135	48	+54	+64	12
Doronicum pardalianches	1, 3	AN		5	6	9	13	28	21	-22	-23	32
Eranthis hyemalis	1, 3, 17	AN		6	21	7	5	33	34	+45	+49	34
Galanthus nivalis	1, 3, 17	AN	s	7	123	36	71	230	65	+38	+58	17
Hyacinthoides hispanica	1, 3, 17	AN		6	65	27	18	110	65	+38	+50	24
Impatiens parviflora	1	AN		8	8	6	6	20	29	+6	+6	51
Juncus tenuis	1, 3, 13	AN		4	33	15	43	91	51	+16	+18	21
Lysimachia punctata	1, 3, 17	AN		5	48	9	27	84	38	+44	+50	18
Ornithogalum angustifolium	1, 3, 7, 8	AN	s	4	42	22	10	74	42	+30	+38	30
Pentaglottis sempervirens	1, 3, 17	AN		7	99	17	77	193	56	+39	+53	13
Petasites albus	1, 3	AN		7	5	2	8	15	32	+14	+15	41
Pulmonaria officinalis	1, 3, 17	AN	t	6	18	8	7	33	34	+31	+34	36
Rhododendron ponticum	1, 10, 16	AN		3	55	28	111	194	49	+9	+13	16
Ribes nigrum	1, 3, 14	AN	n	6	51	44	38	133	44	0	0	26
Ribes uva-crispa	1, 3	AN	t	6	77	58	142	277	66	+2	+3	21
Tellima grandiflora	1, 3, 17	AN		4	22	4	1	27	48	+70	+77	29
Vinca major	1, 3, 17	AN		6	93	12	42	147	56	+52	+64	14

WD: Wider Distribution   EN: Ellenberg N   G: Gains   L: Losses   R: Re-finds   TF: Tetrad Frequency   RC: Relative Change   CF: Change Factor (weighted)

Comparison of BSBI Local Change surveys and studies of woodland plots

Evidence for change in the British woodland flora between 1971 and 2000-3 at a much finer scale than that of the BSBI surveys, woodland sites and 200 m² woodland plots, has recently been published (Kirby *et al.* 2005). Unlike other surveys, one can be certain that these changes have taken place in woodland. This survey concluded that there were no dramatic changes in the composition and structure of the woods, but it did detect evidence for the decline in woodland specialists. The differences in scale, habitat and time period mean that one would not necessarily expect a close agreement between the results of Kirby *et al.* (2005)'s survey and BSBI's, but it is interesting to compare them (Table 4.4). Most of the species which have decreased in both woodland sites and woodland plots have negative change factors. The two species with large positive change factors, *Viola odorata* and *Hypericum androsaemum*, are frequently found as garden escapes outside woodland. There is a further group which have decreased in plots but not necessarily in sites. It is surprising to find that *Iris foetidissima* and *Carex sylvatica* are in this group, in view of the evidence that these have increased at the tetrad scale. Only a small group of species have increased in the woodland plots and most of these have positive change factors. In general, the woodland survey suggests a greater decline in woodland specialists than the BSBI survey, but it is considering a longer time scale and much smaller plots of land.

Table 4.4. Comparison of results from the BSBI Local change surveys and Kirby *et al.*'s survey of woodland sites and plots between 1971 and 2000-03

Decreased in both woodland plots and woodland sites between 1971-2001 (Kirby et al.)

Species	BSBI CF
Moehringia trinervia	-26
Sanicula europaea	-26
Vicia sepium	-25
Solidago virgaurea	-20
Polystichum aculeatum	-19
Festuca gigantea	-19
Potentilla sterilis	-16
Fragaria vesca	-15
Mercurialis perennis	-15
Luzula pilosa	-12
Oxalis acetosella	-11
Vaccinium myrtillus	-11
Bromopsis ramosa	-10
Stellaria holostea	-9
Tamus communis	-9
Geum rivale	-8
Athyrium filix-femina	-6
Silene dioica	-4
Ribes nigrum	0
Epipactis helleborine	+2
Veronica montana	+5
Primula vulgaris	+12
Polypodium vulgare sens. lat.	+15
Viola odorata	+20
Hypericum androsaemum	+36
Mean change factor	-7

Decreased in woodland plots but showing no change in woodland sites, or present in too few sites to assess change, 1971-2001 (Kirby et al.)

Species	BSBI CF
Campanula latifolia	-47
Melampyrum pratense	-28
Listera ovata	-25
Conopodium majus	-23
Lamiastrum galeobdolon	-20
Stachys officinalis	-19
Geranium sylvaticum	-17
Viola palustris	-16
Stachys sylvatica	-15
Galium odoratum	-14
Gymnocarpium dryopteris	-13
Rubus saxatilis	-13
Lathyrus linifolius	-12
Lysimachia nemorum	-10
Melica uniflora	-8
Valeriana officinalis	-7
Blechnum spicant	-5
Hypericum pulchrum	-2
Campanula trachelium	+1
Scrophularia nodosa	+1
Equisetum sylvaticum	+4
Brachypodium sylvaticum	+7
Lonicera periclymenum	+9
Luzula sylvatica	+10
Geranium robertianum	+13
Carex sylvatica	+25
Convallaria majalis	+32
Iris foetidissima	+54
Mean change factor	**-5**

Showing no change in woodland plots, and no change in woodland sites, or present in too few sites to assess change, 1971-2001 (Kirby et al.)

Species	BSBI CF
Euphorbia amygdaloides	-27
Carex pallescens	-10
Hypericum hirsutum	-5
Chrysosplenium oppositifolium	-1
Polygonatum multiflorum	-28
Adoxa moschatellina	-7
Hypericum tetrapterum	+20
Mean change factor	**-8**

*Increased in woodland plots; increased in woodland sites (*Polystichum setiferum*) or showing no change in woodland sites (all other species) between 1971-2001 (Kirby et al.)*

Species	BSBI CF
Anemone nemorosa	-19
Hyacinthoides non-scripta	-13
Milium effusum	-1
Allium ursinum	+20
Carex remota	+23
Phyllitis scolopendrium	+33
Carex pendula	+51
Polystichum setiferum	+16
Mean change factor	**14**

Coniferous woodland (BH2)

Species	10	Average tetrads	247	Mean CF	- 1	Significance	0.63
				No Change			

This Broad Habitat includes all coniferous stands where broadleaved trees make up less than 20% cover, with the exception of yew woodlands. It therefore includes both the remaining stands of native *Pinus sylvestris* woodland in Scotland and the large areas of conifer plantations established on the less agriculturally productive land in the twentieth century. The native pinewoods have a small but distinctive set of vascular plants, outliers of the Boreal forest flora (e.g. *Goodyera repens*, *Linnaea borealis*). They are much too rare to be represented in the species analysed here. Conifer plantations tend to have a rather poor flora and an even poorer reputation amongst field botanists. The species listed below as occurring in Coniferous woodland form too small a sample to be analysed the way we have treated the more speciose Broad Habitats. We therefore simply tabulate the results.

Two species show a distinct trend, *Melampyrum pratense* and *Listera cordata*. A species account for *Melampyrum pratense* is provided under Broadleaved woodland. Although conifer plantations have destroyed large areas of semi-natural habitat, they have also played a part in assisting the spread of a few native species. This is under-estimated by the treatment here, as most of these are primarily non-woodland plants. Lycopods, and *Lycopodium clavatum* in particular, are frequent colonists of forestry tracks, as are some annual weeds (see the species accounts of *Spergularia rubra* and *Veronica arvensis*, for example).

Species	Broad Habitats	Native Status	WD	EN	G	L	R	Total	TF	RC	CF	90% Conf. Limits
Melampyrum pratense	1, 2	N	n	3	23	36	51	110	43	-23	-28	19
Dryopteris filix-mas	1, 2	N	t	5	59	46	415	520	94	-2	-13	25
Luzula pilosa	1, 2	N	n	3	49	49	122	220	57	-7	-12	17
Oxalis acetosella	1, 2, 16	N	n	4	38	33	306	377	77	-5	-11	11
Blechnum spicant	1, 2, 10, 16	N	t	3	45	32	258	335	78	-2	-5	13
Dryopteris dilatata	1, 2	N	t	5	59	36	429	524	91	0	-2	26
Trientalis europaea	1, 2, 10	N	n	3	14	10	38	62	77	-1	-1	21
Vaccinium vitis-idaea	2, 10, 15	N	n	2	20	9	72	101	63	+4	+5	15
Senecio sylvaticus	2, 8, 9	N	t	6	58	40	53	151	47	+8	+12	24
Listera cordata	2, 10, 12	N	n	2	38	11	17	66	65	+41	+46	24

WD: Wider Distribution   EN: Ellenberg N   G: Gains   L: Losses   R: Re-finds   TF: Tetrad Frequency   RC: Relative Change   CF: Change Factor (weighted)

Some native species of other Broad Habitats appear to be spreading on forestry tracks   Paul Westley

Gillian Beckett

Boundary and linear features (BH3)

Species	36	Average tetrads	184	Mean CF	+6	Significance	0.31
				Increase not significant			

This Broad Habitat includes a range of boundary and linear features, including hedges, roads and railways outside urban areas, walls, lines of trees, earth banks and dry ditches. Urban roads and railways come under 'Built-up areas and gardens' (BH17) and ditches which usually contain water under 'Standing water and canals' (BH13).

Boundaries and linear features have less ecological coherence than most Broad Habitats, and although a large group of species are associated with it only a minority are uniquely assigned to it. Although Boundary and linear features are well represented in many of the Local Change tetrads, it has been found best to treat them for analysis purposes as consisting of fragments of other Broad Habitats. Thus most hedgerow species also occur in Broadleaved woodland, while other species share this Broad Habitat with Arable and horticultural land, Neutral grassland or Built-up areas and gardens. This leaves a residue of just 37 species assigned to BH3 alone. For the purposes of this analysis, only these 37 species are considered. They are mainly robust perennials of roadsides and tracksides, although they also include some light-demanding hedgerow shrubs and climbers that do not penetrate into woodland interiors, and there is an interesting group of annuals.

Changes in Boundaries and linear features, 1950-2004

1950-1986

It is difficult to summarise the changes to such a diverse group of features as those incorporated in this broadest of habitats. One of the few features they share is their linear shape: as habitats that are all edge and no interior they are clearly particularly exposed to influences from the surrounding land. The following list includes some of the changes that affected British hedgerows, roadsides and railways between 1950 and 1986. Not all these operations have necessarily affected the rather small suite of species uniquely assigned to this Broad Habitat.

- Loss of hedgerows, which were deliberately removed by farmers to increase field sizes or gradually deteriorated following unsympathetic management.

- Ploughing of headlands adjacent to hedges, fences, roads and tracks.

- Neglect of hedgerows and cessation of grazing on roadside verges, leading the hedges to become overgrown and the grasslands to revert to scrub.

- Replacement of manual management of roadside verges with mechanical management, and subsequent fluctuations in the degree of management, with a policy in recent decades of minimal cutting.

- Construction of new roads and verges, and disturbance of existing verges during road improvements or other operations such as pipe-laying.

- Reseeding and tree-planting on new roadside verges, including the use of seed mixes containing 'wild flowers' such as *Primula veris*, in addition to the traditional rye grass and white clover mixtures.

- Eutrophication, resulting from an increased volume of traffic on the roads, fertiliser drift from nearby fields or aerial inputs.

- Increased salting of roads in winter.

- Cessation of burning on railway embankments, with subsequent management by infrequent cutting unable to halt the succession to scrub and woodland.

1987-2004

The loss of hedgerows continued into at least the early part of this period: Barr & Gillespie (2000) estimated that 23% of hedges were lost between 1984 and 1990. However, there was no evidence for further net loss of managed hedges between 1990 and 1998 (although remnant hedges decreased by 21% in England and Wales). This apparent stability represents a dynamic equilibrium, with the loss of old hedges (possibly ancient and species-rich) being balanced by the planting of new hedges (which may have a rich mix of native and alien woody species but will lack the herbs associated with older hedgerows). Some hedges have deteriorated into remnants whereas other remnants were restored to hedges. In 1997 some hedges in England and Wales received statutory protection under the Hedgerow Regulations.

Between 1993 and 2002 an extra 227 km of motorways were constructed, an increase of 7%; a total of 974 km of motorways and trunk roads were constructed or improved in the same period (Department for Transport 2003). The new or disturbed embankments or verges offer a pathway for the spread of expanding species.

Earlier studies of changes in the species of Boundaries and linear features

It is more difficult to quantify changes to the species of this Broad Habitat as it has not often been recognised in the British floristic literature. However, in Bedfordshire and Northamptonshire the proportion of extinct species associated with Boundary and linear features is low (Walker & Preston in press). Similarly, the comparison of the BSBI Atlas surveys suggested that these species had done relatively well at the 10-km square scale in England and Wales, although they had declined in Scotland. Floristic studies of changes at a finer scale are also scarce. The Bibury study of roadside verges is referred to under Neutral grassland, and at this site there has been little directional change. However, Wells' (1989) impression in Huntingdonshire that "there has been no systematic study ... but I have the impression that in many areas verges were more grass dominated now, than they were 20 years ago, and are less colourful" is probably widely shared elsewhere. Experimental studies have demonstrated the decline of species richness on uncut verges (Parr & Way 1988), so such a trend would not be unexpected.

One marked and well-studied trend in recent decades has been the spread of halophytes such as *Atriplex littoralis*, *Cochlearia danica* and *Puccinellia distans* along salted roadside verges.

By contrast to the lack of long-term floristic studies, the Countryside Survey has in recent years provided much information specifically related to this Broad Habitat. Hedge plots recorded in 1990 and 1998 showed that hedges with a 'lowland wooded vegetation' showed few significant changes, although there was an increase in ruderal species in these plots. By contrast, the plots with 'tall grass and herb vegetation' in 1990 had a 12% decrease in species diversity, with an increase in the frequency of shade-tolerant species. Roadside verge plots showed a general decline in species richness in England and Wales; infertile sites showed an increase in species associated with higher nutrient levels whereas more fertile vegetation showed a small decrease in plants of fertile vegetation. In Scotland there was an increase in species diversity associated with increased nutrient levels and more disturbance.

The BSBI Local change surveys

As a group, the specialist species of Boundary and linear habitats have shown no significant change between the two Local Change surveys. However, some of the most dramatic changes in species of Boundary and linear features are exhibited by species that also occur in other habitats, and are therefore not included in the following accounts. The spread of *Lactuca serriola* and *L. virosa* on roadsides is dealt with under Built-up areas and gardens (BH 17) and the invasion of halophytes along the edges of major roads under Coastal habitats (BH 18, 19, 21).

There is strong evidence that annual species are out-performing biennials and perennials in the specialised species of this habitat ($F_{2,33}$ = 11.57, $p < 0.001$).

Perennation	No. species	Mean CF	Standard error
Annual	6	+35	9
Biennial	11	+6	5
Perennial	19	-4	4

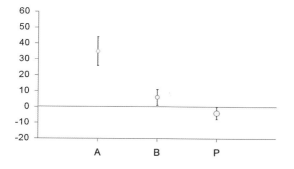

Perhaps surprisingly, there is little difference in performance between the two phytogeographical elements, temperate and southern, which constitute the bulk of the species analysed here ($F_{2,33}$ = 1.25, $p = 0.30$).

Wider Distribution	No. species	Mean CF	Standard error
Northern	3	-13	11
Temperate	22	+6	4
Widespread	0	-	-
Southern	11	+10	8

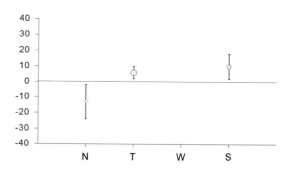

This suite of species is dominated by plants of more or less neutral soil conditions, so there is little to be learnt from the relationship of the change factor to Ellenberg R values ($r = 0.081$, $p = 0.64$).

Ellenberg R	No. species	Mean CF	Standard error
4 (moderately acid)	2	-8	14
5	3	+14	11
6	1	+50	-
7	24	0	4
8 (basic)	6	+19	9

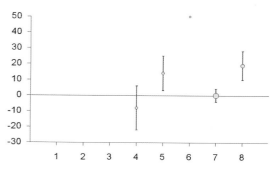

The range of Ellenberg N values is wider, but shows little trend ($r = -0.143$, $p = 0.40$). The surprisingly high mean change factors for the small groups of species with N=2 and N=3 is the result of the high values for three species of dry, nutrient-poor soils, *Filago vulgaris*, *Poa compressa* and *Vulpia bromoides*.

Ellenberg N	No. species	Mean CF	Standard error
2 (infertile)	2	+19	13
3	4	+10	16
4	7	+11	7
5	6	+8	11
6	11	+8	7
7	5	-6	9
8 (extremely fertile)	1	+7	-

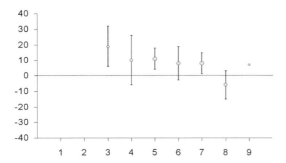

What environmental variables are driving the changes in Boundary and linear features?

For a model based simply on perennation, $R^2 = 41.2\%$. Adding the additional non-climatic variables to this model results in no significant increase in R^2, demonstrating that the effects of perennation are not masking any effects of Ellenberg R or N. Adding the Wider Distribution terms also shows no effect. However, there is a significant increase in R^2 when the two temperature values are added singly. For January temperature $R^2 = 54.5\%$, $p = 0.004$, and for July temperature $R^2 = 50.5\%$, $p = 0.020$. There is a suggestion of an effect for rainfall ($R^2 = 46.0\%$, $p = 0.10$). January temperature shows an effect in combined models with perennation and July temperature ($R^2 = 56.9\%$, $p = 0.039$), and

with perennation and rainfall ($R^2 = 55.9\%$, $p = 0.012$), but neither July temperature nor rainfall is statistically significant in these models.

This analysis therefore suggests that January temperature is the most important of the climatic variables affecting this Broad Habitat.

Species groups

Three species groups are recognised and described below.

Verbascum thapsus colonising a new roadside verge in Wales Richard Pryce

Boundary and linear features (BH3):
classification of species

Ballota nigra group (1.1)

Species	15	Average tetrads	89	Mean CF	+19	Significance	0.02
		Moderately local			**Significant increase**		

This southerly group has prospered more than any other within this Broad Habitat.

Some of the species, such as *Ballota nigra* and *Poa compressa*, are as often found in towns and species of a range of soil types are included in the group. However the most striking feature is that several species of open habitats have increased markedly, and it is difficult to avoid the conclusion that climate change, with drier summers in southeast Britain, has contributed to this change.

Species	Broad Habitats	Native Status	WD	EN	G	L	R	Total	TF	RC	CF	90% Conf. Limits
Cichorium intybus	3	AR	s	5	6	10	4	20	13	-37	-39	47
Rubus caesius	3	N	t	6	50	46	63	159	67	-4	-6	22
Clematis vitalba	3	N	t	5	22	14	90	126	50	-1	-1	14
Bryonia dioica	3	N	s	7	23	8	129	160	79	+2	+3	11
Arctium lappa	3	AR	t	9	37	25	50	112	64	+6	+7	22
Ballota nigra	3	AR	s	6	47	19	118	184	67	+10	+13	14
Poa compressa	3	N	t	4	32	23	9	64	42	+14	+17	35
Sison amomum	3	N	s	5	32	14	42	88	60	+16	+19	21
Verbascum nigrum	3	N	t	6	15	6	12	33	34	+25	+26	33
Smyrnium olusatrum	3	AR	s	7	20	3	31	54	35	+25	+27	17
Asparagus officinalis	3	AR	t	5	19	5	12	36	28	+37	+39	29
Malva neglecta	3	AR	t	7	49	14	33	96	50	+35	+41	20
Geranium pusillum	3	N	t	7	55	9	43	107	53	+39	+45	15
Bromus commutatus	3	N	t	6	36	11	14	61	54	+42	+47	25
Filago vulgaris	3	N	s	4	22	5	8	35	32	+48	+51	29

WD: Wider Distribution   EN: Ellenberg N   G: Gains   L: Losses   R: Re-finds   TF: Tetrad Frequency   RC: Relative Change   CF: Change Factor (weighted)

Smyrnium olusatrum
Alexanders

Mapped Change	+33%	
Relative Change	+25%	±15%
Weighted CF	+27%	±17%
Tetrad Frequency	35%	

Filago vulgaris
Common Cudweed

Mapped Change	+57%	
Relative Change	+48%	±32%
Weighted CF	+51%	±29%
Tetrad Frequency	32%	

Smyrnium olusatrum is an archaeophyte that was formerly cultivated and persists as a cast-out. Until recently natural spread appears to have been largely restricted to sites within a few kilometres of the sea, although there are a few long-established inland colonies. The map suggests that this species has begun to spread at inland sites along roadsides. The species is winter-green and climate change, in particular milder winters, may have contributed to its success.

In the past *Filago vulgaris* has declined in its native habitat of sandy or rocky pasture and it probably continues to decline in such habitats as the habitat is itself declining. However this annual species also colonises sand pits, quarries and more fragmentary nutrient-poor ruderal habitats and it is here that it appears to have increased markedly within its existing range. Climate change may have been a factor in this.

Key to maps   ● Loss   ● Gain   ○ Re-find

         ▨ *New Atlas* distribution

Chaerophyllum temulum group (1.2)

Species	9	Average tetrads	179	Mean CF	+ 1	Significance	0.84
		Moderately widespread		No change			

Although these species have comparable distributions they differ in their ecology and their fortunes reflect this. *Chaerophyllum temulum* is a plant of open ground under shade at woodland edges and on hedgebanks and it has probably declined where eutrophication has led to an explosion of *Galium aparine* and other competitive species. On the other hand *Conium maculatum* and *Vulpia bromoides* exploit open habitats and both have prospered even though the *Conium* favours nutrient-rich ground and the *Vulpia* nutrient-poor ground. The common factor in this success appears to be that they are both favoured by droughts that provide habitat gaps for colonisation.

Species	Broad Habitats	Native Status	WD	EN	G	L	R	Total	TF	RC	CF	90% Conf. Limits
Chenopodium bonus-henricus	3	AR	n	8	13	20	12	45	31	-30	-33	32
Chaerophyllum temulum	3	N	t	7	39	51	193	283	81	-12	-21	12
Armoracia rusticana	3	AR	t	7	31	30	120	181	60	-7	-10	14
Carduus crispus	3	N	t	7	34	28	84	146	54	-3	-4	17
Rosa arvensis	3	N	t	5	46	29	172	247	80	+1	+1	15
Humulus lupulus	3	N	t	8	53	31	97	181	60	+7	+10	18
Conium maculatum	3	AR	s	8	67	35	144	246	69	+8	+13	16
Chelidonium majus	3	AR	t	7	58	32	69	159	51	+13	+17	20
Vulpia bromoides	3	N	s	3	58	24	44	126	42	+25	+32	20

WD: Wider Distribution   EN: Ellenberg N   G: Gains   L: Losses   R: Re-finds   TF: Tetrad Frequency   RC: Relative Change   CF: Change Factor (weighted)

Chenopodium bonus-henricus
Good King Henry

Mapped Change	-22%	
Relative Change	-30%	±38%
Weighted CF	-33%	±32%
Tetrad Frequency	31%	

Vulpia bromoides
Squirrel-tail Fescue

Mapped Change	+33%	
Relative Change	+25%	±18%
Weighted CF	+32%	±20%
Tetrad Frequency	42%	

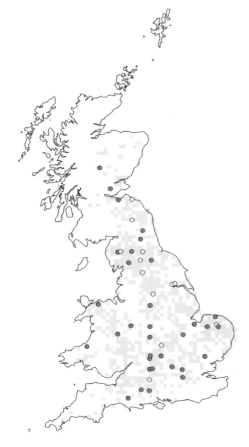

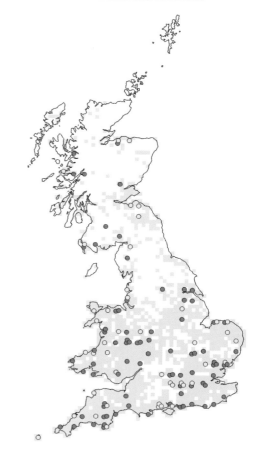

Chenopodium bonus-henricus was formerly cultivated as a vegetable and is very persistent as a cast-out on roadsides near farmsteads where it is widespread but infrequent. It occasionally colonises river gravels but fails to become frequent in such mobile habitats. It has gradually become scarcer following development and other disturbance to roadsides.

The hectad distribution of *Vulpia bromoides* did not change significantly between the two Atlas surveys but these surveys show that this grass is increasing its range in inland areas where it may colonise development sites, quarries and smaller nutrient-poor ruderal habitat fragments. Climate change may have accelerated this trend.

Key to maps ● Loss ● Gain ○ Re-find
▒ *New Atlas* distribution

Stachys sylvatica group (2)

Species	12	Average tetrads	308	Mean CF	- 6	Significance	0.01
		Widespread		Significant decrease			

This is a group of widespread species and it is surprising that they show significant change. The balance is tipped by *Silene latifolia* and *Cytisus scoparius* which are both relatively short-lived perennials favouring somewhat infertile soils. Their limited capacity to reproduce may be a factor in their decline in competitive linear habitats.

Species	Broad Habitats	Native Status	WD	EN	G	L	R	Total	TF	RC	CF	90% Conf. Limits
Silene latifolia	3	AR	s	6	34	53	169	256	71	-16	-25	12
Cytisus scoparius	3	N	t	4	45	57	199	301	64	-11	-21	14
Stachys sylvatica	3	N	t	8	31	24	430	485	92	-4	-15	12
Torilis japonica	3	N	t	7	69	60	230	359	81	-3	-8	18
Anthriscus sylvestris	3	N	n	7	33	16	443	492	94	-2	-7	13
Lepidium heterophyllum	3	N	s	4	19	18	22	59	38	-6	-7	29
Prunus spinosa	3	N	t	6	33	18	386	437	88	-2	-6	11
Alliaria petiolata	3	N	t	8	37	20	344	401	94	-1	-4	11
Arctium minus	3	N	t	5	70	48	308	426	82	0	0	19
Tanacetum vulgare	3	N	n	7	48	38	55	141	39	+2	+2	24
Hypericum humifusum	3	N	t	3	51	39	46	136	48	+4	+6	25
Verbascum thapsus	3	N	t	5	67	45	86	198	53	+7	+11	21

WD: Wider Distribution   EN: Ellenberg N   G: Gains   L: Losses   R: Re-finds   TF: Tetrad Frequency   RC: Relative Change   CF: Change Factor (weighted)

Silene latifolia
White Campion

Mapped Change	- 9%	
Relative Change	-16%	± 8%
Weighted CF	-25%	±22%
Tetrad Frequency	71%	

Silene latifolia is a short-lived plant. It is not very successful as an arable weed and is out-competed in hedgerows. Its seed production is low compared to many annuals of waste ground and it has no special dispersal mechanism. These factors may indicate why it is struggling to maintain its distribution, especially in pastoral areas in the west of Britain.

Key to maps ● Loss ● Gain ○ Re-find
◼ *New Atlas* distribution

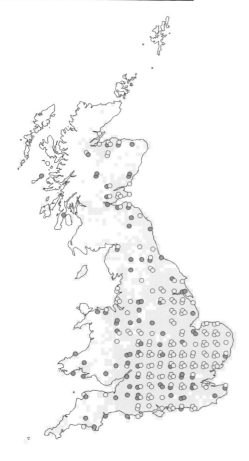

Gillian Beckett

Doubtfully native species and neophytes in Boundary and linear features

One doubtfully native species, *Reseda lutea*, is assigned to this Broad Habitat alone.
There are also several neophytes.

Species	Broad Habitats	Native Status	WD	EN	G	L	R	Total	TF	RC	CF	90% Conf. Limits
Doubtful Status												
Reseda lutea	3	NA	s	5	21	20	49	90	39	-7	-8	20
Neophytes												
Allium triquetrum	3	AN	s	5	24	2	4	30	45	+70	+72	27
Barbarea verna	3	AN		6	9	7	3	19	27	+8	+9	56
Melilotus albus	3	AN		4	11	12	4	27	22	-15	-16	48
Persicaria wallichii	3	AN		6	4	8	4	16	30	-42	-43	48
Petasites fragrans	3	AN		6	28	10	39	77	31	+19	+21	20
Symphytum orientale	3	AN		6	23		7	30	39	+68	+70	10
Symphytum x uplandicum	3	AN		7	89	38	116	243	63	+18	+29	17

WD: Wider Distribution   EN: Ellenberg N   G: Gains   L: Losses   R: Re-finds   TF: Tetrad Frequency   RC: Relative Change   CF: Change Factor (weighted)

Gillian Beckett

Arable and horticultural (BH4)

Species	82	Average tetrads	57	Mean CF	+ 7	Significance	0.10
				Increase marginally significant			

Most commercially cultivated land is included in this Broad Habitat: arable fields, set-aside and fallow land, annual grass leys, areas of perennial crops and intensively managed orchards. The weeds of arable land include a high proportion of archaeophytes, perhaps in part because it is easier to identify arable plants as archaeophytes than plants of more natural habitats. As the habitat itself is archaeophytic, even native species have had to colonise it in the past from other habitats.

Changes in the arable and horticultural habitat, 1950-2004

1950-1986

Agricultural intensification in the second half of the twentieth century led to a series of well-documented changes in British arable land (Stoate 1996, Robinson & Sutherland 2002):

- a decline in mixed farms (with both arable and livestock) leading to increasing separation of arable and pastoral land – in large areas of the north and west small-scale arable cultivation was discontinued, but in the south and east large areas of grassland were converted to arable;

- increasing field sizes, with the removal of hedgerows and reduction in the length of field edges;

- intensification of cereal production, with improved field drainage, the development of increasingly productive cereal varieties and the increasing use of fertilisers and herbicides, all leading to an increasingly competitive cereal sward in which less competitive arable weeds are unable to survive;

- changes in crop preferences, with an increase in wheat production and the introduction of large-scale oil-seed rape cultivation;

- shorter cropping cycles, with the loss of fallow and break crops and the replacement of four-crop rotations with a regime of continuous wheat (two years) and rape (one year) cultivation;

- an increase in the proportion of autumn-sown cereals, especially in England, with a consequent reduction in the area of winter stubbles.

1987-99

The BSBI Monitoring Scheme in 1987-88 came at a turning point in European agriculture. As a result of increases in agricultural productivity, coupled with price support to European farmers, "by 1986, surplus stocks had increased to the point where the cost of their storage and disposal was so high that it was suggested that it would be cheaper to pay farmers not to grow the surplus in the first place" (Firbank *et al.* 1993). A voluntary set-aside programme was introduced in 1989, followed in 1992 by measures which obliged larger arable farmers to set-aside 15% of their land, for which they received an area payment. Although there have been changes in the rules since 1992, the obligation to set-side land has continued. These developments in agricultural policy coincided with increasing concern at the loss of biodiversity on arable land, centred on the decline of farmland birds. A Habitat Action Plan for Cereal Field Margins was prepared in 1995. Farming options designed to favour wildlife include the promotion of winter stubbles and fallow fields, and of cropped and uncropped headlands with restricted fertiliser and herbicide use along field boundaries. There have also been moves to diversify crop habitats, with an increase of game cover crops and even wildflower mixes sown as food for wild birds, bumblebees and other insects. Game cover crops often have their own characteristic weeds, introduced with the seed mixes.

Arable weeds provide the basis for many annual wild-flower seed mixes, which have been widely sown in recent years. Many rarer weeds have been introduced into new areas in this way.

Earlier studies of changes in the species of arable and horticultural land

Long-term declines in the distribution of arable weeds have been identified in many studies. In areas of the north and west the main reason has been habitat loss, as the reduction in small-scale arable cultivation has, not surprisingly, led to the disappearance of its specialist weed species. The only really marked change in the flora of the Hebridean islands of Coll and Tiree between the 1930s and the 1990s, for example, was the decline of the arable flora (Pearman & Preston 2000). In the south and east the proportion of arable land has increased, but agricultural intensification has reduced and modified its weed flora. It is true that the arable plants as a group have not suffered a disproportionate number of extinctions at the vice-county scale. In general the vice-county is too large a unit to show these changes. Arable species tend to persist in buried seed banks, growing to maturity on occasions where they are missed by herbicides, or flourishing temporarily on ground disturbed for other reasons, such as road-building. However, the decrease in the frequency of arable weeds between 1950 and 1987 was obvious to those botanists whose field experience spanned much of this period (e.g. James 1977, Sell 1989, Wells 1989). There is very clear quantitative evidence for the loss of species at the 10-km square scale (Preston *et al.* 2002b, Rich & Woodruff 1996). The species of this Broad Habitat showed the greatest overall decrease between the two BSBI atlas surveys in 1930-69 and 1987-99, and this decrease was marked in all regions of Britain (Preston *et al.* 2003b). The loss of some rare species in this period, and the increase of other species favoured by modern agricultural methods, has also been demonstrated in resurveys of individual fields (Sutcliffe & Kay 2000). The long-term decline of arable weeds has been a pronounced trend in many other European countries (Andreasen *et al.* 1996).

The BSBI Local change surveys

There is evidence of a small overall increase in the group as a whole, with a group mean CF of +7. The species of arable and horticultural land are concentrated in the southeast. The evidence for change in two of the species groups, the lowland *Anagallis arvensis* and the south-eastern *Alopecurus myosuroides* groups, is particularly striking, with 23 of the 50 species in these groups showing marked increases or decreases. Although there is great variation in the changes shown by individual species in all groups, many more arable species show increases than decreases and the *A. arvensis* group as a whole shows a significant overall increase.

In this Broad Habitat, as in Built-up areas and gardens (BH17) but unlike the semi-natural habitats, the majority of species analysed are archaeophytes (species introduced before AD 1500). The mean Change Factors are not significantly different ($F_{1,80} = 1.14$, $p = 0.29$).

History	No. species	Mean CF	Standard error
Native	33	+11	4
Archeophyte	49	+5	4

Fumaria muralis in a field of flax Michael Braithwaite

The very small northern element shows a negative mean Change Factor, differing from the other phytogeographical groups ($F_{3,78} = 3.20$, $p = 0.03$).

Wider Distribution	No. species	Mean CF	Standard error
Northern	7	-19	6
Temperate	24	+8	6
Widespread	8	+6	8
Southern	43	+11	4

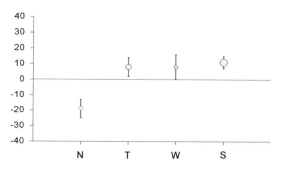

There is little evidence for change related to the pH ($r = -0.046$, $p = 0.68$).

Ellenberg R	No. species	Mean CF	Standard error
4 (moderately acid)	1	-16	-
5	2	+13	22
6	28	+12	5
7	46	+4	4
8 (basic)	5	+10	6

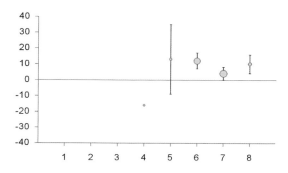

The same is true of nutrient requirements
($r = 0.023$, $p = 0.84$)

Ellenberg N	No. species	Mean CF	Standard error
4 (intermediate fertility)	6	-2	11
5	17	+15	7
6	32	+4	4
7	23	+7	5
8 (very fertile)	4	+16	15

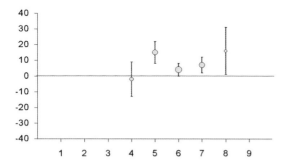

What environmental variables are driving the changes in the Arable and horticultural habitat?

The absence of statistically significant effects of individual variables, including the specific climate variables, provides little scope for further analysis. It suggests that the autecology of the arable species, as summarised by the available descriptors, is not the main factor controlling their distribution in this highly artificial habitat. Studies of change in relation to other biological attributes, such as the extent to which species are adapted to spring or autumn cultivation, might be worthwhile.

The overall results of the BSBI Local Change surveys contrast greatly with the results of the earlier studies, such as the Atlas surveys. Far from showing a continuing decline in arable weeds, the overall picture is one of stability or increase at the tetrad scale. The obvious assumption is that this reflects the relaxation in arable intensification, and the resulting availability of suitable habitats, such as arable in the early stages of set-aside and unsprayed marginal strips. This is doubtless one factor involved, but the detailed accounts of changes in a few vice-counties reported in the Local Assessment of Change (Chapter 7) suggests that much of the turnover in these species relates to plants appearing in disturbed sites on roadsides, reseeded ground and other non-arable habitats. Whatever habitats are involved, we need to know the extent to which the apparent increase in these species represents an increase in self-sustaining populations, as opposed to the appearance of plants from an historic seedbank which is no longer being replenished, or the occurrence of small, casual populations. This is a crucial question in understanding what is happening to these species, and it requires much more detailed research.

Species groups

This Broad Habitat has a largely southern and eastern distribution. It is relatively uniform compared to more complex, semi-natural habitats. Although five main distributional groups are considered, they are less distinctive than the groups recognised in most other Broad Habitats. One species, *Lamium confertum*, separates out as a sixth group, 1.1. It has a northern distribution and appears to be stable.

Arable and horticultural (BH4): classification of species

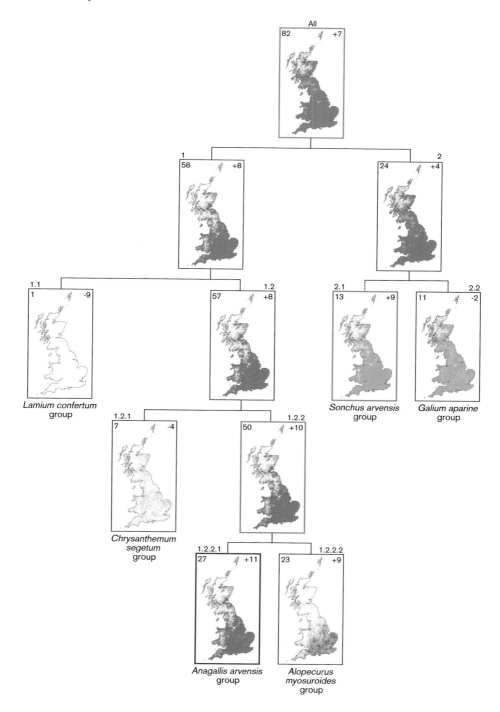

Chrysanthemum segetum group (1.2.1)

Species	7	Average tetrads	57	Mean CF	- 4	Significance	0.63
		Local		**No change**			

The species in this small group are plants of light, acidic soils.

Although change for the group as a whole is not significant, the individual species vary dramatically in their fortunes. Of the five that are specific to the Broad Habitat, the archaeophytes *Galeopsis speciosa* and *Chrysanthemum segetum*, which are thought to be strongly associated with root crops, show marked declines; *Descurainia sophia* and *Fumaria bastardii* appear to be stable whereas the native *Fumaria muralis*, which occurs with many crop species, shows a marked increase.

Galeopsis speciosa in a field of Phacelia Michael Braithwaite

Galeopsis speciosa Bob Ellis

Species	Broad Habitats	Native Status	WD	EN	G	L	R	Total	TF	RC	CF	90% Conf. Limits
Galeopsis speciosa	4	AR	n	7	5	15	16	36	40	-41	-43	22
Chrysanthemum segetum	4	AR	s	5	18	30	21	69	35	-32	-36	26
Scleranthus annuus	4, 8, 10, 16	N	t	4	7	8	6	21	29	-16	-16	48
Descurainia sophia	4	AR	t	6	4	2	15	21	31	+2	+2	30
Fumaria bastardii	4	N	s	6	7	5	5	17	30	+8	+8	54
Viola tricolor	4, 8, 19	N	t	4	38	26	27	91	43	+10	+13	27
Fumaria muralis	4	N	s	6	73	19	49	141	64	+36	+46	17

WD: Wider Distribution   EN: Ellenberg N   G: Gains   L: Losses   R: Re-finds   TF: Tetrad Frequency   RC: Relative Change   CF: Change Factor (weighted)

Chrysanthemum segetum
Corn Marigold

Mapped Change	-24%	
Relative Change	-32%	±28%
Weighted CF	-36%	±26%
Tetrad Frequency	35%	

Galeopsis speciosa
Large-flowered Hemp-nettle

Mapped Change	-32%	
Relative Change	-41%	±23%
Weighted CF	-43%	±22%
Tetrad Frequency	40%	

Chrysanthemum segetum is now only very locally frequent and appears to have declined markedly in its former English strongholds though it has fared rather better near the coast, particularly in Scotland. Plants mature relatively slowly during the season and are easily controlled by weedkillers except in root crops; in cereals it is no longer found in winter wheat crops but it is occasionally prominent in unsprayed corners, summer fallows or marginal strips.

In some parts of eastern Scotland *Galeopsis speciosa* is still a frequent weed of cultivated fields towards the upper limits of cultivation, often on peaty soils. Elsewhere it has become a scarce plant that is declining sharply. It is comparatively late in flowering and only prospers in root crops and in some game and exotic crops such as *Phacelia*.

Key to maps ● Loss ● Gain ○ Re-find
▨ *New Atlas* distribution

Fumaria muralis
Common Ramping-fumitory

Mapped Change	+44%	
Relative Change	**+36%**	±15%
Weighted CF	**+46%**	±17%
Tetrad Frequency	64%	

Descurainia sophia
Flixweed

Mapped Change	+11%	
Relative Change	**+ 2%**	±29%
Weighted CF	**+ 2%**	±30%
Tetrad Frequency	31%	

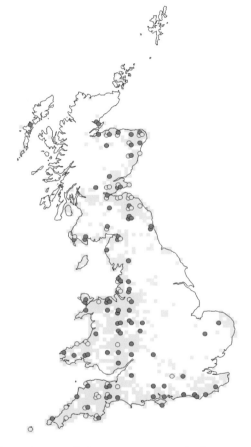

Fumaria muralis is a common weed of cultivated land in eastern Scotland but it is a surprise to find how much it appears to have increased there. In the southwest of England and the Welsh borders there is less cultivated land than in the past and many weeds of such land have decreased. For *Fumaria muralis* to have increased against this trend may well imply the exploitation of alternative habitats such as hedge banks and gardens. However *Fumaria muralis* was formerly a poorly understood taxon and increased awareness may account for some of the recorded gains.

Descurainia sophia is a weed of light soils in the east of the country, with a particular stronghold in and around the East Anglian Breckland. Within this core area it appears to be stable. At the edges of this area, and elsewhere in the country, there is an assortment of losses, re-finds and gains, as might be expected for an arable weed which sometimes occurs as a casual.

Key to maps   ● Loss   ● Gain   ○ Re-find
      ▨ *New Atlas* distribution

Anagallis arvensis group (1.2.2.1)

Species	27	Average tetrads	211	Mean CF	+11	Significance	0.03
		Moderately widespread		**Significant increase**			

These species are frequent in the lowlands of England and Wales, but in Scotland tend to be confined to the east, where the concentrations of arable land are greatest. They include many of the plants most characteristic of the arable habitat and a majority (74%) are archaeophytes.

Five species are specific to the Broad Habitat. Of these, *Lamium hybridum* shows a marked increase, possibly spreading north in response to climate change; *Anagallis arvensis*, *Anchusa arvensis* and *Viola arvensis* appear stable and only *Raphanus raphanistrum*, which favours root crops, shows a marked decline.

A further 15 species may also occur in ruderal habitats but are primarily arable weeds. Of these *Stachys arvensis*, *Matricaria recutita*, *Euphorbia helioscopia*, *Papaver dubium*, *Veronica agrestis*, *Avena fatua*, and *Papaver rhoeas* all show a significant increase. These are mainly plants that would be expected to recover in areas where they are scarce under set-aside or agri-environment options, but (as discussed above) there is some evidence that changes in species such as *Papaver rhoeas* relate to the colonisation of disturbed, non-arable habitats. *Matricaria recutita* has been sown in quantity as a wildflower spectacle along new roads and *Avena fatua* is well known to be a problem weed in cereal crops where it may have been favoured by reduced rotation of crops. *Convolvulus arvensis*, *Fallopia convolvulus*, *Lamium amplexicaule*, *Thlaspi arvense* and *Urtica urens* are more or less stable while, of those species that show a decline, *Agrostis gigantea* is poorly recorded and the losses of *Chaenorhinum minus* may relate to other habitats.

Three species also occur in wet places and even in arable fields are mainly found in damp corners. Of these *Chenopodium rubrum* and *Persicaria lapathifolia* appear to have been increasing whereas *Mentha arvensis* seems to have been decreasing, suggesting that it is more dependent on the arable habitat than the other two and that fields are now better drained.

Stachys arvensis, Field Woundwort Simon Harrap

Species	Broad Habitats	Native Status	WD	EN	G	L	R	Total	TF	RC	CF	90% Conf. Limits
Chaenorhinum minus	3, 4, 17	AR	t	4	27	37	20	84	39	-26	-31	28
Mentha arvensis	4, 11	N	n	6	44	55	44	143	48	-19	-26	23
Agrostis gigantea	3, 4	AR	s	7	62	65	47	174	63	-11	-17	27
Lamium amplexicaule	3, 4	AR	s	6	37	36	44	117	51	-7	-9	24
Convolvulus arvensis	3, 4	N	s	6	38	28	226	292	82	-3	-5	12
Fallopia convolvulus	3, 4	AR	w	5	68	57	169	294	78	-2	-4	18
Thlaspi arvense	3, 4	AR	t	6	48	41	60	149	54	-1	-2	22
Anchusa arvensis	4	AR	t	5	26	21	51	98	43	-2	-2	21
Urtica urens	4, 17	AR	s	8	54	43	83	180	56	0	+1	22
Viola arvensis	4	AR	t	6	66	41	198	305	79	+3	+5	17
Anisantha sterilis	3, 4, 17	AR	s	7	50	16	281	347	91	+4	+9	11
Papaver rhoeas	3, 4	AR	s	6	52	22	176	250	74	+6	+10	13
Raphanus raphanistrum	4, 19	N	s	6	61	42	66	169	80	+7	+11	22
Fumaria officinalis	3, 4	AR	s	6	80	55	100	235	65	+7	+11	22
Avena fatua	3, 4	AR	s	7	64	34	122	220	74	+9	+14	17
Anagallis arvensis	4	N	s	5	74	36	190	300	82	+8	+15	15
Veronica agrestis	3, 4, 17	AR	t	7	54	39	26	119	51	+11	+15	29
Persicaria lapathifolia	4, 11	N	s	7	83	44	105	232	67	+13	+22	19
Veronica hederifolia	1, 3, 4, 17	AR	s	6	94	42	207	343	88	+11	+23	17
Papaver dubium	3, 4	AR	s	5	78	42	79	199	57	+15	+24	20
Euphorbia helioscopia	4, 17	AR	s	6	90	39	162	291	74	+13	+25	16
Chenopodium rubrum	4, 11	N	t	8	72	43	39	154	62	+18	+27	25
Matricaria recutita	3, 4	AR	s	7	93	44	113	250	83	+17	+28	18
Lamium hybridum	4	AR	t	6	48	18	42	108	55	+25	+31	20
Euphorbia peplus	4, 17	AR	s	6	100	32	153	285	76	+20	+35	15
Stachys arvensis	3, 4	AR	s	5	37	17	15	69	39	+30	+35	27
Atriplex prostrata	3, 4, 19, 21	N	w	7	130	38	115	283	80	+31	+53	16

WD: Wider Distribution EN: Ellenberg N G: Gains L: Losses R: Re-finds TF: Tetrad Frequency RC: Relative Change CF: Change Factor (weighted)

Chaenorhinum minus
Small Toadflax

Mapped Change	-18%	
Relative Change	-26%	±31%
Weighted CF	-31%	±28%
Tetrad Frequency	39%	

Lamium hybridum
Henbit Dead-nettle

Mapped Change	+33%	
Relative Change	+25%	±18%
Weighted CF	+31%	±20%
Tetrad Frequency	55%	

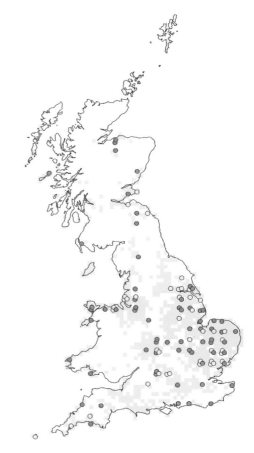

Chaenorhinum minus has a low proportion of re-finds and appears to be declining, a trend also reported in the *New Atlas*. In arable it is more or less confined to infertile, chalky soils. It can be an elusive plant and its habitats on waste ground are very subject to change. Access to railway property is more strictly controlled than in the past, and such property will only have been viewed from a distance: it is still believed to hold substantial populations. However while disused lines were previously places where *Chaenorhinum minus* could be found readily, they have now grassed over or been converted to other uses.

Lamium hybridum is recorded as having increased markedly and this may well be a true trend as it favours light soils and low summer rainfall areas. It appears to have increased in the east and to have spread west. This may reflect changing climate, though the introduction of set-aside is also likely to have favoured this species.

Key to maps ● Loss ● Gain ○ Re-find

░ *New Atlas* distribution

Matricaria recutita
Scented Mayweed

Mapped Change	+24%	
Relative Change	+17%	±12%
Weighted CF	+28%	±18%
Tetrad Frequency	83%	

Matricaria recutita is a species that has enjoyed a vogue of popularity with the highway authorities and has been sown in quantity along new roads and motorways. Not surprisingly it has turned up in arable land in areas where it was unknown. There it has sometimes prospered and its success may also owe something to warmer summers. Whether the increase recorded between the two surveys will be maintained is thus an open question.

Stachys arvensis
Field Woundwort

Mapped Change	+38%	
Relative Change	+30%	±30%
Weighted CF	+35%	±27%
Tetrad Frequency	39%	

Stachys arvensis was shown by the *New Atlas* to have declined over a long period. These surveys show evidence of a marked and rather unexpected resurgence, particularly near the coast. This is a species of waste places as well as arable fields and the distribution suggests that both habitats may be involved in the increase.

Key to maps ● Loss ● Gain ○ Re-find
▨ *New Atlas* distribution

Alopecurus myosuroides group (1.2.2.2)

Species	23	Average tetrads	65	Mean CF	+ 9	Significance	0.39
		Moderately local		**Increase not significant**			

These species are concentrated in southern and eastern England, and many are characteristic of light, calcareous soils. Like the more widespread *Anagallis arvensis* group, a majority of species (83%) are archaeophytes. 11 members of the group are specific to the Broad Habitat and a further 6 also occur in ruderal habitats but are primarily arable weeds.

There is a very wide range of fortunes in the individual species, and the mean change factor is not significantly different from that of the flora as a whole. *Centaurea cyanus* has been frequently introduced in wildflower seed mixes and consequently shows a marked increase. If this is discounted, the mean change factor is reduced to +6.

Chenopodium ficifolium, Coronopus squamatus, Chenopodium polyspermum, Kickxia elatine and *Petroselinum segetum* all show marked increases, possibly related to the increase in game cover crops and to other agri-environment options, while *Alopecurus myosuroides* has spread north as a problem weed of cereal crops. *Euphorbia exigua, Fumaria densiflora, Kickxia spuria, Papaver argemone* and *Lepidium campestre* all appear to be stable. *Sinapis alba* is now sometimes sown as a game crop but shows little change. *Anthemis arvensis* and *Silene noctiflora* show very marked declines and may be among the weeds least able to exploit soil with high nitrogen levels.

Picris echioides is at least as much a ruderal as an arable weed and has been spreading rapidly. *Mercurialis annua* has also apparently been increasing, but probably mainly as a garden weed. Climate change could be a factor in the colonisation by these two species.

Species	Broad Habitats	Native Status	WD	EN	G	L	R	Total	TF	RC	CF	90% Conf. Limits
Anthemis arvensis	3, 4	AR	s	6	5	11	1	17	36	-59	-63	52
Silene noctiflora	4	AR	t	6	4	11	3	18	34	-59	-60	44
Anthemis cotula	4	AR	s	6	20	27	11	58	48	-27	-31	33
Erysimum cheiranthoides	3, 4	AR	n	7	16	23	15	54	48	-27	-30	30
Legousia hybrida	4	AR	s	4	4	7	9	20	30	-27	-28	36
Papaver argemone	4	AR	s	5	8	9	4	21	28	-16	-17	52
Vicia tetrasperma	3, 4, 6	N	t	6	44	37	67	148	66	-2	-2	21
Sinapis alba	3, 4	AR	s	6	22	20	4	46	36	-1	-1	44
Lepidium campestre	3, 4, 17	AR	t	6	11	9	8	28	29	+2	+2	45
Euphorbia exigua	4	AR	s	5	23	17	28	68	50	+3	+4	28
Orobanche minor	4, 5	N	s	6	12	10	3	25	19	+5	+5	52
Fumaria densiflora	4	AR	s	5	6	4	5	15	47	+10	+10	55
Alopecurus myosuroides	4	AR	s	6	44	22	91	157	81	+9	+11	16
Kickxia spuria	4	AR	s	5	23	13	24	60	61	+13	+14	27
Coronopus squamatus	3, 4	AR	s	7	66	16	100	182	73	+23	+31	13
Petroselinum segetum	3, 4	N	s	6	10	3	7	20	30	+33	+34	38
Mercurialis annua	3, 4, 17	AR	s	7	30	9	24	63	45	+31	+34	23
Kickxia elatine	4	AR	s	5	42	15	26	83	56	+32	+37	22
Anthriscus caucalis	3, 4, 8	N	t	5	23	9	10	42	45	+34	+37	31
Picris echioides	3, 4	AR	s	6	77	9	89	175	73	+34	+44	11
Chenopodium polyspermum	4	AR	t	8	63	15	33	111	61	+42	+50	18
Chenopodium ficifolium	4	AR	t	7	47	11	14	72	53	+51	+57	22
Centaurea cyanus	3, 4, 17	AR	t	5	11	2	2	15	17	+61	+62	42

WD: Wider Distribution   EN: Ellenberg N   G: Gains   L: Losses   R: Re-finds   TF: Tetrad Frequency   RC: Relative Change   CF: Change Factor (weighted)

Silene noctiflora, Night-flowering Catchfly Simon Harrap

Anthemis arvensis
Corn Chamomile

Mapped Change	-50%	
Relative Change	-59%	±73%
Weighted CF	-63%	±52%
Tetrad Frequency	36%	

Silene noctiflora
Night-flowering Catchfly

Mapped Change	-50%	
Relative Change	-59%	±55%
Weighted CF	-60%	±44%
Tetrad Frequency	34%	

Anthemis arvensis is infrequent even within its limited range in arable fields on light calcareous soils in the southeast. In common with other archaeophytes of such habitats its long-term decline has probably continued.

Silene noctiflora is primarily an annual of arable ground on infertile soils in the south. It is unsurprising that losses appear to have continued a severe long-term decline and that, of the remaining sites, those near the coast have fared best.

Key to maps ● Loss ● Gain ○ Re-find
▨ *New Atlas* distribution

Chenopodium ficifolium
Fig-leaved Goosefoot

Mapped Change	+59%	
Relative Change	+51%	±24%
Weighted CF	+57%	±22%
Tetrad Frequency	53%	

The strong expansion within and beyond the former range of *Chenopodium ficifolium* shown by the *New Atlas* is confirmed. It is difficult to assess the extent to which it was previously under-recorded. The reasons for any increase are unclear.

Key to maps   ● Loss   ● Gain   ○ Re-find
       ■ *New Atlas* distribution

Gillian Beckett

Chenopodium polyspermum
Many-seeded Goosefoot

Mapped Change	+50%	
Relative Change	+42%	±17%
Weighted CF	+50%	±18%
Tetrad Frequency	61%	

Chenopodium polyspermum shows a similar trend to *Chenopodium ficifolium* except that the spread has been within its existing distribution. It is a much more distinctive species and we can therefore be much more confident that this is a genuine increase. One factor in the expansion of both species might be their ability to mature rapidly after crops are harvested in August, setting seed in the increasingly mild autumn and early winter months.

Key to maps ● Loss ● Gain ○ Re-find
▨ *New Atlas* distribution

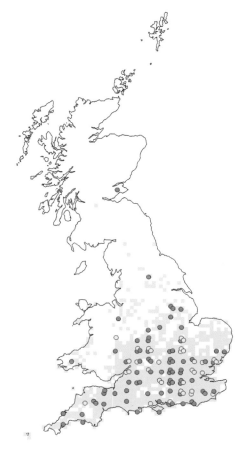

Bob Ellis

Sonchus arvensis group (2.1)

Species	13	Average tetrads	382	Mean CF	+ 9	Significance	0.07
		Widespread		Increase marginally significant			

This is a group of very widespread species. They occur throughout lowland Britain, although they are rarer in lowland districts of northern Scotland than elsewhere, and most of the typical weeds of winter wheat fields are found in this group. The majority (62%) are native. Only two plants are specific to the Broad Habitat, *Chenopodium album* and *Sonchus arvensis*, and these appear to be stable. Of those that also occur in ruderal habitats, *Atriplex patula*, *Geranium dissectum* and *Sonchus oleraceus*, which may all be able to thrive where nitrogen levels are high, show an increase while *Geranium molle*, *Lamium purpureum*, *Sinapis arvensis*, *Sisymbrium officinale* and *Tripleurospermum inodorum* appear to be stable. No member of the group shows a significant decline.

Species	Broad Habitats	Native Status	WD	EN	G	L	R	Total	TF	RC	CF	90% Conf. Limits
Geranium molle	3, 4	N	s	5	67	57	222	346	73	-3	-7	18
Sinapis arvensis	3, 4, 17	AR	t	7	68	55	204	327	77	-2	-4	18
Chenopodium album	4	N	w	7	69	50	294	413	90	-1	-2	19
Lamium purpureum	3, 4, 17	AR	t	7	62	42	311	415	87	-1	-2	17
Sonchus arvensis	4	N	t	6	65	43	252	360	77	+1	+1	17
Elytrigia repens	3, 4, 19	N	w	7	62	34	357	453	87	+1	+4	19
Sisymbrium officinale	3, 4, 17	AR	s	7	57	27	281	365	84	+3	+6	14
Tripleurospermum inodorum	4, 17	AR	t	6	82	49	286	417	94	+3	+9	20
Atriplex patula	3, 4	N	w	7	92	51	220	363	82	+7	+16	19
Sonchus oleraceus	3, 4	N	s	7	80	33	306	419	87	+6	+18	16
Geranium dissectum	3, 4	AR	s	6	68	15	291	374	83	+9	+20	11
Aphanes arvensis agg.	4, 8, 16	N	t	4	99	58	129	286	65	+11	+22	21
Bromus hordeaceus	4, 6	N	s	4	98	38	297	433	91	+9	+28	17

WD: Wider Distribution   EN: Ellenberg N   G: Gains   L: Losses   R: Re-finds   TF: Tetrad Frequency   RC: Relative Change   CF: Change Factor (weighted)

Geranium dissectum
Cut-leaved Crane's-bill

Mapped Change	+15%	
Relative Change	+ 9%	± 5%
Weighted CF	+20%	±11%
Tetrad Frequency	83%	

Bromus hordeaceus
Soft Brome

Mapped Change	+15%	
Relative Change	+ 9%	± 6%
Weighted CF	+28%	±17%
Tetrad Frequency	91%	

Geranium dissectum is very frequent within its range and shows evidence of a slight expansion of its range to the north. Its ability to thrive in disturbed nutrient-rich habitats is probably assisting this spread and the areas in which the increases have occurred suggest that set-aside may be the habitat most implicated in this change.

Over much of its range *Bromus hordeaceus* is a plant of disturbed, moderately nutrient-rich sites. The map suggests a degree of flux, especially around the edges of its distribution, with gains very much outnumbering losses. It is also found in more natural, seasonally droughted vegetation on shallow soils, especially near the sea.

Key to maps ● Loss ● Gain ○ Re-find
　　　　　　　 New Atlas distribution

Capsella bursa-pastoris group (2.2)

Species	11	Average tetrads	459	Mean CF	- 2	Significance	0.42
		Very widespread		**No change**			

These species are even more widespread than those of the *Sonchus arvensis* group. The majority (80%) are native and are as much plants of ruderal habitats as arable weeds. Only *Spergula arvensis*, the scarcest of the group, is solely listed for arable in *PLANTATT* and this appears to be more or less stable, in contrast to the sharp decline over a longer period shown in the *New Atlas*. Two species, *Capsella bursa-pastoris* and *Galium aparine*, are amongst the very common species for which the adjustment made to reflect the more thorough recording in the second survey is not fully applicable, and for which the Change Factor therefore appears to provide an exaggerated estimate of decline.

Species	Broad Habitats	Native Status	WD	EN	G	L	R	Total	TF	RC	CF	90% Conf. Limits
Galeopsis tetrahit agg.	3, 4	N	n	6	69	78	235	382	79	-9	-23	19
Capsella bursa-pastoris	4, 17	AR	w	7	39	33	426	498	91	-4	-17	15
Galium aparine	3, 4, 17	N	t	8	15	6	495	516	90	-3	-16	16
Persicaria maculosa	3, 4	N	t	7	72	61	343	476	91	-3	-12	23
Spergula arvensis	4	N	w	5	73	69	95	237	59	-5	-9	23
Senecio vulgaris	3, 4, 17	N	s	7	47	33	400	480	89	-2	-9	17
Equisetum arvense	3, 4	N	n	6	60	38	419	517	91	-1	-3	25
Myosotis arvensis	3, 4	AR	n	6	69	48	342	459	87	-1	-2	21
Polygonum aviculare agg.	3, 4, 17	N	w	6	52	23	450	525	94	+1	+5	22
Sonchus asper	3, 4	N	s	6	75	19	404	498	91	+7	+28	16
Veronica arvensis	3, 4, 16	N	s	5	117	58	285	460	86	+9	+33	24

WD: Wider Distribution   EN: Ellenberg N   G: Gains   L: Losses   R: Re-finds   TF: Tetrad Frequency   RC: Relative Change   CF: Change Factor (weighted)

Spergula arvensis
Corn Spurrey

Mapped Change	+ 2%	
Relative Change	- 5%	±16%
Weighted CF	- 9%	±23%
Tetrad Frequency	59%	

Spergula arvensis was shown by the *New Atlas* to have declined markedly over much of England since 1960 and the tetrad distribution confirms its scarcity there, where it has become something of a coastal species. In eastern Scotland however it remains very frequent and indeed is sometimes a troublesome weed in arable fields, its principal habitat. Adjustment for the relative over-recording of Local Change over the Monitoring Scheme survey results in a net recorded gain being converted into an adjusted net loss, but this loss is below the confidence limits for significance in Britain as a whole. However the map suggests some decline at the fringes of its range in central England.

Key to maps   ● Loss   ● Gain   ○ Re-find
       ▨ *New Atlas* distribution

Gillian Beckett

Doubtfully native species and neophytes in the Arable and horticultural habitat

Although there is only a small group of Doubtfully native species and neophytes ascribed to this habitat, many of them are very frequent.

Species	Broad Habitats	Native Status	WD	EN	G	L	R	Total	TF	RC	CF	90% Conf. Limits
Doubtful Status												
Aethusa cynapium	3, 4, 17	NA	t	6	53	40	124	217	69	0	0	17
Brassica nigra	3, 4	NA	t	6	24	21	19	64	38	-1	-2	30
Solanum nigrum	4	NA	s	8	90	24	90	204	79	+29	+42	15
Neophytes												
Amaranthus retroflexus	3, 4, 17	AN		7	18	2	0	20	30	+80	-	-
Amsinckia micrantha	4	AN		3	13	2	6	21	33	+49	+51	33
Anisantha diandra	3, 4, 19	AN	s	4	23		4	27	50	+77	+78	12
Barbarea intermedia	4	AN		7	19	15	9	43	41	+6	+7	39
Claytonia perfoliata	4, 17, 19	AN		5	14	10	12	36	32	+7	+7	38
Conyza canadensis	3, 4, 17, 19	AN		6	78	6	38	122	57	+54	+63	13
Coronopus didymus	4, 17	AN		7	80	18	63	161	64	+36	+46	15
Diplotaxis muralis	3, 4, 16, 17	AN		6	19	9	18	46	34	+19	+20	29
Epilobium ciliatum	3, 4, 17	AN		6	128	54	183	365	86	+17	+41	19
Galinsoga parviflora	4, 17	AN		7	12	3	1	16	26	+61	+64	41
Galinsoga quadriradiata	3, 4, 17	AN		6	18	6	2	26	33	+51	+56	36
Matricaria discoidea	3, 4	AN		7	38	29	470	537	94	-3	-19	19
Veronica persica	3, 4, 17	AN		7	76	34	275	385	88	+6	+15	16
Veronica polita	4, 17	AN	s	5	42	28	22	92	52	+14	+17	28

WD: Wider Distribution   EN: Ellenberg N   G: Gains   L: Losses   R: Re-finds   TF: Tetrad Frequency   RC: Relative Change   CF: Change Factor (weighted)

Richard Pryce

Improved grassland (BH5)

Species	5	Average tetrads	139	Mean CF	+25	Significance	0.09
					Increase marginally significant		

These grasslands covered by this Broad Habitat are species-poor, grass-dominated swards, usually managed intensively for agriculture or recreation. They are either deliberately sown or derived from more semi-natural communities by the application of fertilisers and selective herbicides. Most of the grassland in Britain comes under this Broad Habitat but it is notoriously species-poor, often dominated by the sown mixtures of agriculturally selected cultivars of *Lolium perenne* and *Trifolium repens*.

Over 20 Improved grassland species, including both *Lolium perenne* and *Trifolium repens*, are amongst the very common plants excluded from the analysis of the Local Change results. This removes more than half the species listed for this Broad Habitat, and reduces its representation to a small and uncharacteristic suite of species. The sample is too small to analyse in the usual detail.

Changes in improved grassland habitats, 1950-2004

1950-1986
The changes to this habitat came as a result of the intensification of agriculture in the 20th century.

- Great expansion in the area of improved grassland, resulting from the agricultural improvement of semi-natural grassland, and the expansion of grassland into areas of moorland in the uplands.

- Intensification of improved grassland swards, with better field drainage, an increased frequency of ploughing and reseeding, the use of less diverse seed mixtures and the increased application of nitrogenous fertilisers.

- The change from hay to silage and haylage as the major grass crops, combined with a change in stock management so that they are kept in "feeding units" rather than allowed to graze in the traditional way.

1987-2004
There has been little change in the management of improved grassland in this period. The Countryside Survey results show that the overall area of Improved grassland in Britain showed little change between 1990 and 1998 (Haines-Young *et al.* 2000). There is a high turnover of land attributable to this Broad Habitat, but losses (primarily to arable land) are balanced by gains (from arable land, neutral and acidic grasslands).

81

Earlier studies of changes in the species of improved grassland habitats

Improved grassland is not a habitat which interests many British botanists! It has rarely been treated as a separate category in analyses of floristic change, and the fact that its component species are so common would make change difficult to detect at the county level. By contrast, its very abundance means that it is well represented in the Countryside Survey samples. Between 1990 and 1998 there was evidence for the loss of species from less fertile stands attributed to Improved grassland in England and Wales, apparently associated with nutrient enrichment (Haines-Young *et al.* 2000).

The BSBI Local change surveys

As discussed above, the most characteristic species of this Broad Habitat are not included amongst those analysed here. *Cerastium glomeratum*, the species showing the greatest change, is discussed in the species accounts.

Species	Broad Habitats	Native Status	WD	EN	G	L	R	Total	TF	RC	CF	90% Conf. Limits
Orobanche minor	4, 5	N	s	6	12	10	3	25	19	+5	+5	52
Rumex pulcher	3, 5, 6	N	s	7	8	5	7	20	24	+11	+12	47
Hordeum secalinum	5	N	t	6	38	24	40	102	60	+10	+12	24
Veronica serpyllifolia	3, 5, 11	N	n	5	106	48	361	515	92	+7	+36	27
Cerastium glomeratum	3, 5	N	s	5	145	37	284	466	86	+20	+60	17

WD: Wider Distribution   EN: Ellenberg N   G: Gains   L: Losses   R: Re-finds   TF: Tetrad Frequency   RC: Relative Change   CF: Change Factor (weighted)

Doubtfully native species and neophytes in Improved grassland

Two neophytes are ascribed to this Broad Habitat.

Species	Broad Habitats	Native Status	WD	EN	G	L	R	Total	TF	RC	CF	90% Conf. Limits
Neophytes												
Crepis vesicaria	3, 5, 6, 17	AN		7	54	35	94	183	72	+5	+8	19
Trifolium hybridum	3, 5	AN		6	45	78	49	172	56	-34	-49	21

WD: Wider Distribution   EN: Ellenberg N   G: Gains   L: Losses   R: Refinds   TF: Tetrad Frequency   RC: Relative Change   CF: Change Factor (weighted)

Cerastium glomeratum
Sticky Mouse-ear

Mapped Change	+25%	
Relative Change	+20%	± 6%
Weighted CF	+60%	±17%
Tetrad Frequency	86%	

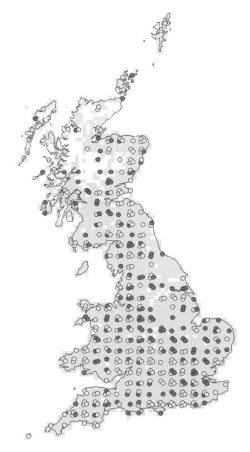

Cerastium glomeratum has probably benefited from the general rise in nitrogen levels in the countryside, including hill areas, and it is indeed in the hill areas where it has increased most markedly, colonising vehicle tracks and disturbed grassland. The large increase was also evident in the *New Atlas*.

Veronica serpyllifolia
Thyme-leaved Speedwell

Mapped Change	+12%	
Relative Change	+ 7%	± 6%
Weighted CF	+36%	±27%
Tetrad Frequency	92%	

Veronica serpyllifolia is virtually ubiquitous at both hectad and tetrad scale except in the arable heartland of eastern England and in the northern hills, but is not always plentiful and may be overlooked. There is strong evidence of spread into eastern England where roadsides and ruderal habitats may have been colonised rather than extensive grassland.

Key to maps ● Loss ● Gain ○ Re-find
▨ *New Atlas* distribution

Neutral grassland (BH6)

Species	79	Average tetrads	208	Mean CF	0	Significance	0.39
				No change			

All unimproved and semi-improved grassland on circumneutral soils is included in this Broad Habitat. Neutral grassland may occur as extensive areas, often in enclosed fields, or as narrow strips along linear features such as cliff tops, green lanes and roadside verges. The Broad Habitat includes tall and ungrazed grasslands (such as those dominated by *Arrhenatherum elatius*), hay meadows and pastures, the less maritime coastal cliff grassland, coastal grazing marshes, periodically flooded grassland on riparian flood plains and permanently moist or waterlogged grassland. Other inland grasslands are allocated to Calcareous grassland (BH7), Acidic grassland (BH8) and Improved grassland (BH5). Maritime coastal grasslands on thin, rocky soils belong to the Supralittoral rock Broad Habitat (BH18).

Changes in the Neutral grassland habitat, 1950-2004

1950-1986

There have been major changes to British neutral grasslands since 1950. These have included:

- the agricultural improvement of grassland in pastoral areas, with the elimination of many broad-leaved species either directly by ploughing and reseeding or with herbicides or indirectly by increasing fertiliser applications;

- increasing grazing pressure in pastoral regions, brought about by increases in the productivity of the grassland and a greater tendency to maintain high stock numbers by supplementary winter feeding;

- the change from hay to silage or haylage production in pastoral areas;

- the loss of grazing on linear swards, including cliff slopes and roadside verges, even in areas of intensive pastoral farming;

- drainage improvements to wet grassland;

- replacement of manual management of roadside verges with mechanical management, and subsequent fluctuations in the degree of management, with a policy in recent decades of minimal cutting;

- the conversion of grassland to arable land in areas where arable cultivation predominates, a reflection of the loss of mixed farming and the polarisation of the countryside into arable and pastoral zones;

- losses to roads, housing, industry, gravel extraction and other land uses;

- increasing fragmentation of species-rich neutral grasslands, with many stands reduced to small, remnant patches;

- the cessation of grazing on remaining fragments of grassland in arable areas, a result of the loss of agricultural stock and the reduction in rabbit populations by myxomatosis;

- the eutrophication of grasslands by fertiliser drift from surrounding arable land, aerial deposition or, in the case of seasonally flooded grassland, by increasingly nitrate-rich floodwaters.

As a result of these changes extensive swards of species-rich neutral grassland had been more or less eliminated from many inland counties by the time of the Monitoring Scheme in 1987-88.

1987-2004

Since 1986 the largest driving force of change is believed to have been the continued increase in nitrogen levels in the soil. Extensive grassland areas are normally grazed by sheep, cattle or horses, and while grazing levels were high over most of the period between the two surveys there have been reductions in recent years as a result of Foot and Mouth disease and in response to subsidy changes. There appears to have been an increase in horse paddocks in many urban or suburban fringes, although there are no statistics on changes in the number of horses in Britain during the period. By contrast grassland in linear features has often remained ungrazed.

Conservation attention was focussed on this Broad Habitat by BAP Habitat Action Plans for Lowland meadows and Upland hay meadows, drafted in 1998. Much effort has been devoted to the restoration or recreation of these habitats. In view of the contrasting influences on the habitat in this period, some contradictory species trends can be expected.

Earlier studies of changes in the species of Neutral grassland

Although the dramatic decline in the area of species-rich neutral grassland has been well documented, trends in the distribution of its component species are less frequently discussed. The Broad Habitat itself is not one of the classic 'types of British vegetation' and authors discussing species changes do not always discuss it; even if they do, its definition varies from author to author. Lacking a large suite of characteristic species, it has never received the lavish attention paid by both floristic botanists and ecologists to Calcareous grassland (BH7). The species of neutral grassland tend to be widespread plants, its few charismatic species (e.g. *Fritillaria meleagris*, *Orchis morio*) too rare to be analysed in the current survey.

At the 10-km square scale, comparison of the two BSBI Atlas surveys, in 1930-69 and 1987-99, showed a very slight overall change in neutral grassland species (Preston *et al.* 2002b); the pattern was variable within regions with some showing a relative increase of neutral grassland species and others a relative decrease (Preston *et al.* 2003b).

Two long-term studies of Neutral grassland, the Park Grass experiment at Rothamsted (Dodd *et al.* 1995) and A. J. Willis' observations on broad roadside verges at Bibury (Dunnett *et al.* 1998), have demonstrated the essential stability of neutral grassland under a stable management regime. Changes such as the 'outbreaks' of some species at Rothamsted and the responses of the vegetation at Bibury to climatic fluctuations took place against the background of a stable grassland matrix. By contrast, there was a clear trend in the 4 m^2 plots of the Countryside Survey for a decrease in species-richness between 1990 and 1998, with the loss of species of nutrient-poor conditions ('stress-tolerant species') and a corresponding increase in competitive species (Haines-Young *et al.* 2000).

The BSBI Local change surveys

This group of species as a whole is stable with a group mean change factor of 0. However, the relatively small group of Neutral grassland annuals has been more successful than the perennials ($F_{2,77} = 6.59$, $p = 0.002$).

Perennation	No. species	Mean CF	Standard error
Annual	13	+20	8
Biennial	7	-4	7
Perennial	60	-4	3

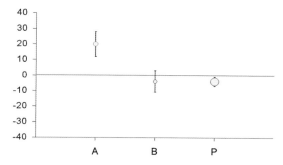

A striking difference in the trends shown by northern and southern species in Britain is revealed by the mean change index for the four broad phytogeographical groups ($F_{3,76} = 3.22$, $p = 0.027$).

Wider Distribution	No. species	Mean CF	Standard error
Northern	18	-11	4
Temperate	40	-1	3
Widespread	1	-14	-
Southern	21	+11	6

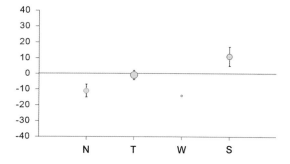

The northern species have clearly done less well than the southern. The sole widespread species, *Euphrasia officinalis* agg., is rather unusual as it represents an aggregate of many species with specialised habitats. The accounts of the species groups provide further details of these changes.

There is no clear difference in trends shown by species with pH over the rather narrow range of Ellenberg R values spanned by the neutral grassland species ($r = 0.085$ $p = 0.68$).

Ellenberg R	No. species	Mean CF	Standard error
5 (moderately acid)	11	-6	5
6	24	-4	5
7	39	+5	3
8 (basic)	6	-13	10

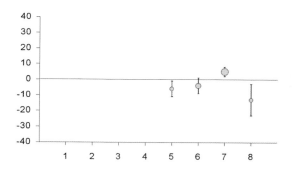

However, there is a very clear tendency for the species of less fertile habitats (as measured by Ellenberg N value) to have declined ($r = 0.25$, $p = 0.024$).

Ellenberg N	No. species	Mean CF	Standard error
2 (very infertile)	3	-15	6
3	10	-6	7
4	22	-2	5
5	22	-2	5
6	19	+4	6
7	3	+11	7
8 (very fertile)	1	+49	-

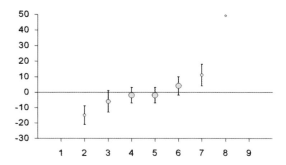

Ranunculus parviflorus, Small-flowered Buttercup, appears to be making a recovery
Richard Pryce

What environmental variables are driving the changes in Neutral grassland?

In a model including both perennation and Ellenberg N, $R^2 = 19.2\%$ with significant effects of perennation after allowing for N ($p = 0.004$) and N after allowing for perennation ($p = 0.041$). Ellenberg R shows no effect either individually or after allowing for perennation and N.

In a model including perennation, Ellenberg N and the Wider Distribution, $R^2 = 30.3\%$ and each term is statistically significant (perennation: $p = 0.008$; N: $p = 0.031$; Distribution: $p = 0.013$). After allowing for N and perennation there is a significant effect of January temperature ($R^2 = 28.1\%$, $p = 0.003$), July temperature ($R^2 = 27.9\%$, $p = 0.004$) and rainfall ($R^2 = 23.7\%$, $p = 0.038$). The statistical significance of N is reduced when adding either July temperature ($p = 0.15$) or rainfall ($p = 0.12$).

Allowing for Wider Distribution reduces the statistical significance of the three direct temperature variables January temperature ($p = 0.13$), July temperature ($p = 0.094$) and rainfall ($p = 0.43$). Conversely, the statistical significance of Wider Distribution is reduced after allowing for climatic variables January temperature ($p = 0.20$), July temperature ($p = 0.15$) and rainfall ($p = 0.067$). So, there is some confounding of Wider Distribution and the climatic variables, especially January and July temperatures, and the statistical analysis cannot disentangle their effects.

The results of the current survey clearly suggest that annual species are increasing when compared with perennials. Eutrophication and climate change are suggested as the drivers of change in neutral grasslands, although the precise climatic factors are unclear.

Species groups

Five species groups are considered.

Neutral grassland (BH6):
classification of species

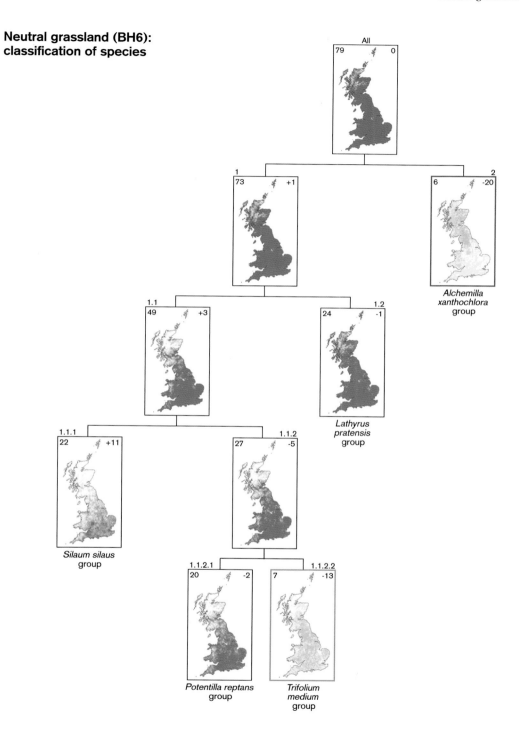

Silaum silaus group (1.1.1)

Species	22	Average tetrads	55	Mean CF	+11	Significance	0.17
		Local			Increase not significant		

Although the species in this group share the predominantly southerly range of those of the *Potentilla reptans* group (1.1.2.1), they are much less frequent plants (as the total number of tetrads in which they have been recorded demonstrates). Many are plants of seasonally parched grassland on light soils, and there are concentrations of these species in some coastal areas; others are plants of heavy clay soils.

Two species that show a decrease are more frequent in calcareous grassland, *Centaurea scabiosa* and *Pastinaca sativa*. *Medicago sativa* also shows a decrease, but most of the records probably relate to sown crops or casual occurrences following cultivation rather than to native or naturalised populations in grassland.

Allium vineale, *Bromus racemosus*, *Carex divulsa*, *Carex spicata* and *Torilis nodosa* show marked increases but probably on tracksides or roadsides rather than in extensive grassland. *Oenanthe pimpinelloides* and *Ranunculus parviflorus* are notably nitrogen tolerant and show a marked increase in poached grassland. Many of these species are favoured by dry summers, and both *Oenanthe pimpinelloides* and *Torilis nodosa* have Mediterranean distributions in Europe.

Genista tinctoria, Dyer's Greenweed Bob Ellis

Torilis nodosa, Knotted Hedge-parsley Gillian Beckett

Species	Broad Habitats	Native Status	WD	EN	G	L	R	Total	TF	RC	CF	90% Conf. Limits
Centaurea scabiosa	6, 7	N	t	3	11	27	62	100	45	-26	-30	12
Pastinaca sativa	3, 6, 7	N	t	5	19	31	47	97	48	-24	-28	18
Genista tinctoria	6	N	t	2	6	9	9	24	19	-25	-26	38
Pimpinella major	6	N	t	6	8	12	15	35	37	-23	-25	30
Medicago sativa	3, 6	N	s	5	18	23	20	61	37	-20	-23	29
Carduus tenuiflorus	3, 6	N	s	4	5	5	5	15	18	-9	-9	56
Carduus nutans	6, 7	N	t	5	26	24	46	96	41	-5	-6	22
Vicia tetrasperma	3, 4, 6	N	t	6	44	37	67	148	66	-2	-2	21
Agrimonia procera	1, 3, 6	N	t	5	9	8	3	20	20	0	0	53
Platanthera chlorantha	1, 6	N	t	4	5	4	7	16	11	0	0	47
Senecio erucifolius	3, 6	N	t	5	36	23	94	153	63	+2	+3	17
Lathyrus nissolia	3, 6, 7	N	t	6	15	12	10	37	35	+3	+4	40
Silaum silaus	6	N	t	4	16	12	17	45	29	+4	+4	34
Trifolium fragiferum	6	N	s	6	12	9	10	31	30	+5	+5	41
Rumex pulcher	3, 5, 6	N	s	7	8	5	7	20	24	+11	+12	47
Crepis biennis	3, 6	N	t	6	8	5	3	16	26	+19	+19	56
Allium vineale	3, 6, 7	N	t	6	42	14	45	101	46	+24	+29	19
Oenanthe pimpinelloides	6	N	s	3	7	0	12	19	44	+28	+29	12
Carex spicata	3, 6, 7	N	t	4	41	14	28	83	45	+31	+36	22
Carex divulsa	3, 6, 7	N	s	6	48	10	30	88	65	+41	+46	18
Bromus racemosus	3, 6	N	t	8	12	3	4	19	28	+48	+49	40
Torilis nodosa	3, 6	N	s	6	20	1	6	27	31	+65	+66	24
Ranunculus parviflorus	6	N	s	5	13	0	4	17	30	+68	+69	14

WD: Wider Distribution EN: Ellenberg N G: Gains L: Losses R: Re-finds TF: Tetrad Frequency RC: Relative Change CF: Change Factor (weighted)

Pimpinella major, Greater Burnet-saxifrage Gillian Beckett

Genista tinctoria
Dyer's greenweed

Mapped Change	-17%	
Relative Change	-25%	±45%
Weighted CF	-26%	±38%
Tetrad Frequency	25%	

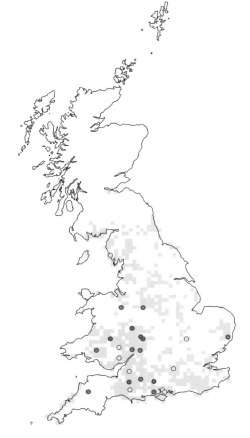

Pimpinella major
Greater Burnet-saxifrage

Mapped Change	-15%	
Relative Change	-23%	±34%
Weighted CF	-25%	±30%
Tetrad Frequency	37%	

This map gives a clear message as to how scarce *Genista tinctoria* is at tetrad scale, indeed it is so scarce that LC survey results are not able to show significant change. There is strong independent evidence for the decline of this species, suggesting that at least some of the apparent losses on the map are all too probably real: both over- and under-grazing may be to blame, coupled with habitat losses.

That part of the range of *Pimpinella major* that lies in hilly districts appears to be stable while the part that lies in more intensively farmed arable areas appears to have suffered a significant decline as small fragments of grassland become degraded.

Oenanthe pimpinelloides
Corky-fruited Water-dropwort

Mapped Change	+37%	
Relative Change	+28%	±10%
Weighted CF	+29%	±12%
Tetrad Frequency	44%	

Ranunculus parviflorus
Small-flowered buttercup

Mapped Change	+76%	
Relative Change	+68%	±10%
Weighted CF	+69%	±14%
Tetrad Frequency	30%	

Oenanthe pimpinelloides appears to be a rather improbable benefactor of the popularity of horse culture and the amenity paddocks associated with it, as it is a specialist of poached grassland subject to the sort of disturbance that is provided by grazing horses.

Ranunculus parviflorus was formerly more widespread in southern England but had retreated to the west by 1930. This evidence of a marked recovery in a limited area is somewhat unexpected.

Key to maps ● Loss ● Gain ○ Re-find ▨ *New*
Atlas distribution

Allium vineale
Wild Onion

Mapped Change	+32%	
Relative Change	+24%	±17%
Weighted CF	+29%	±19%
Tetrad Frequency	46%	

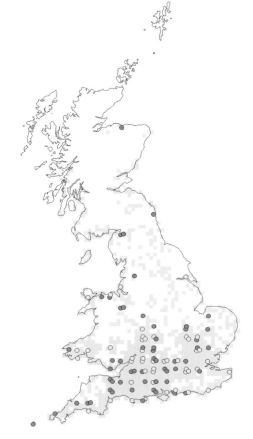

Torilis nodosa
Knotted Hedge-parsley

Mapped Change	+73%	
Relative Change	+65%	±22%
Weighted CF	+66%	±24%
Tetrad Frequency	31%	

Allium vineale is normally dispersed by bulbils and depends on water or transport of material largely by man to extend its distribution. The suggestion of increased frequency mainly within the existing range of the species is in line with these constraints. *Allium vineale* is favoured by dry summers which help to open vegetation gaps for the bulbils to establish. An example of colonisation not evident from this survey has been its recent spread on sandy banks along the River Tweed and its tributary the Teviot.

Torilis nodosa is seen to have increased markedly in recent years. It is a plant of dry banks on the coast, seasonally droughted edges of roadside verges (often on compacted, shallow soil adjoining concrete kerbs) and waste places inland. Climate change could be a possible factor in its apparent increase.

Key to maps ● Loss ● Gain ○ Re-find ▧ *New Atlas* distribution

Potentilla reptans group (1.1.2.1)

Species	20	Average tetrads	209	Mean CF	- 2	Significance	0.44
		Moderately widespread		**No change**			

These species are widespread in lowland England and Wales, but thin out rapidly north of the border and are almost absent from the Scottish Highlands.

The species in this group which show the greatest decline include several plants thought to be intolerant of high nutrient levels, including *Agrimonia eupatoria*, *Knautia arvensis*, *Silene vulgaris*, and *Stachys officinalis*.

Two of the species with marked increases, *Lysimachia nummularia* and *Malva moschata*, are affected by garden escapes. *L. nummularia* was formerly cultivated but has often been discarded, and such cast-outs have been noticed spreading in the wild. *M. moschata* is commonly grown in gardens and it is a very common constituent of wildflower mixes; it is increasingly found on road margins and other areas where such seed has been sown. The similar garden plant *M. alcea* may occasionally have been recorded in error for this species. *Carex hirta* also shows a marked increase (see species account).

The two species of *Festuca* included are an interesting contrast: *Festuca arundinacea* has increased markedly and flourishes in unmown linear habitats while *Festuca pratensis* which is now seldom sown and favours damp grazed grassland shows a decrease.

Knautia arvensis, Field Scabious Michael Braithwaite

Silene vulgaris, Bladder Campion Bob Ellis

Species	Broad Habitats	Native Status	WD	EN	G	L	R	Total	TF	RC	CF	90% Conf. Limits
Silene vulgaris	3, 6	N	s	5	18	44	78	140	50	-29	-36	12
Festuca pratensis	6	N	n	6	68	84	57	209	60	-19	-34	26
Daucus carota	6, 7	N	s	3	30	40	112	182	52	-14	-20	14
Knautia arvensis	6, 7	N	t	4	31	40	102	173	55	-14	-19	15
Stachys officinalis	6, 7	N	t	3	29	38	101	168	56	-14	-19	14
Agrimonia eupatoria	6	N	s	4	29	37	163	229	65	-11	-17	11
Linaria vulgaris	3, 6	N	n	6	31	38	137	206	55	-11	-17	13
Tragopogon pratensis	6	N	t	5	57	50	181	288	82	-4	-7	16
Potentilla reptans	6	N	s	5	30	20	314	364	91	-3	-7	9
Hypericum hirsutum	6, 7	N	t	5	28	24	66	118	50	-4	-5	18
Potentilla anglica	6	N	t	5	35	32	31	98	52	-4	-5	27
Pulicaria dysenterica	6, 11	N	s	4	43	31	126	200	65	0	0	15
Trisetum flavescens	6, 7	N	t	4	63	47	120	230	68	+1	+2	20
Juncus inflexus	6, 11	N	s	5	52	23	220	295	79	+4	+7	13
Primula veris	6, 7	N	t	3	53	30	115	198	61	+6	+9	17
Vicia hirsuta	3, 6	N	t	6	76	51	119	246	66	+6	+10	20
Lysimachia nummularia	6, 11, 14	N	t	5	66	37	46	149	58	+18	+25	23
Carex hirta	6	N	t	6	93	34	152	279	71	+17	+30	15
Festuca arundinacea	6, 7	N	s	6	97	43	123	263	63	+17	+30	18
Malva moschata	6	N	t	4	69	19	60	148	51	+31	+40	16

WD: Wider Distribution EN: Ellenberg N G: Gains L: Losses R: Re-finds TF: Tetrad Frequency RC: Relative Change CF: Change Factor (weighted)

Festuca pratensis
Meadow Fescue

Mapped Change	-11%	
Relative Change	-19%	±19%
Weighted CF	-34%	±26%
Tetrad Frequency	60%	

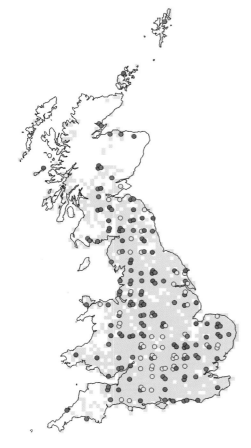

Festuca arundinacea
Tall Fescue

Mapped Change	+25%	
Relative Change	+17%	±11%
Weighted CF	+30%	±18%
Tetrad Frequency	63%	

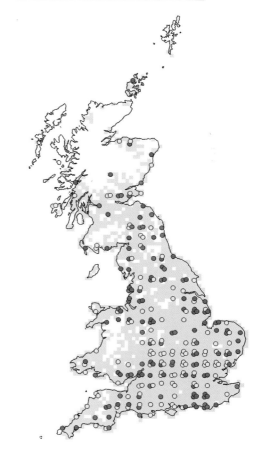

Festuca pratensis is not an easily recorded grass. It is not readily picked out vegetatively and its flowering heads are soon mown on roadsides and grazed in pastures. It is shown to be decreasing. This may partly be because it cannot compete in tall vegetation and has been lost from waterside habitats where these are unmanaged. It seems to be unable to compete on roadsides except in more upland areas, probably as a result of eutrophication favouring more aggressive species.

Festuca arundinacea is seen to be only frequent at tetrad scale on neutral or basic soil in the lowlands. It appears to be increasing within its range, probably as it is competitive in nutrient-rich grassland in linear features which are unmown but subject to disturbance.

Key to maps ● Loss ● Gain ○ Re-find ▨ *New*
Atlas distribution

Silene vulgaris
Bladder Campion

Mapped Change	-21%	
Relative Change	-29%	±11%
Weighted CF	-36%	±12%
Tetrad Frequency	50%	

Carex hirta
Hairy Sedge

Mapped Change	+24%	
Relative Change	+17%	± 9%
Weighted CF	+30%	±15%
Tetrad Frequency	71%	

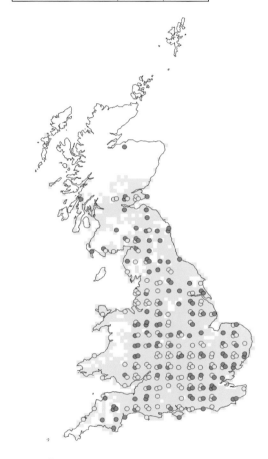

Although not a strict calcicole, the distribution of *Silene vulgaris* shows that it is frequent only on chalk and limestone. The sharp decline even in core areas suggests that the grassy field margins where this species was formerly familiar are often now too eutrophic to provide the open vegetation structure it requires.

Carex hirta is mainly a lowland species which avoids the most acidic soils but is very tolerant of disturbance and a very effective coloniser of slightly-damp partly-improved grassland with some disturbance from livestock. It also grows in some ruderal habitats and its young shoots may even grow up through asphalt paths. This survey provides striking evidence of increased frequency across its whole range.

Key to maps ● Loss ● Gain ○ Re-find ▪ *New*
Atlas distribution

Trifolium medium group (1.1.2.2)

Species	7	Average tetrads	94	Mean CF	-13	Significance	0.05
		Moderately local		Decrease marginally significant			

This is an interesting group of species which are most frequent in the uplands of England and Wales, but are absent from large areas in the Scottish Highlands. Many of them are found in species-rich grassland on limestone or other calcareous substrates in areas with high rainfall, and hence strong leaching at the soil surface. These habitats have suffered greatly from agricultural improvement and from reduced grazing on valley sides and coastal slopes.

Persicaria bistorta has declined but some losses are likely to relate to former introductions of a species that was once cultivated. *Helictotrichon pubescens* is not a very competitive species and is likely to have been affected by drainage and eutrophication. *Saxifraga granulata* is even more stress-tolerant and it has suffered severe losses (see species account).

Species	Broad Habitats	Native Status	WD	EN	G	L	R	Total	TF	RC	CF	90% Conf. Limits
Saxifraga granulata	6, 7	N	t	4	7	15	12	34	22	-38	-40	30
Helictotrichon pubescens	6, 7	N	t	3	32	39	28	99	37	-19	-23	26
Persicaria bistorta	6	N	n	6	17	21	33	71	36	-16	-18	23
Sanguisorba officinalis	6	N	n	5	16	17	41	74	44	-10	-11	21
Cruciata laevipes	6	N	t	5	22	18	122	162	59	-5	-6	12
Ophioglossum vulgatum sens. lat.	6	N	t	3	19	17	6	42	15	-1	-1	40
Trifolium medium	6	N	n	4	65	46	67	178	51	+7	+10	23

WD: Wider Distribution EN: Ellenberg N G: Gains L: Losses R: Re-finds TF: Tetrad Frequency RC: Relative Change CF: Change Factor (weighted)

Saxifraga granulata
Meadow Saxifrage

Mapped Change	-30%	
Relative Change	-38%	±33%
Weighted CF	-40%	±30%
Tetrad Frequency	22%	

Persicaria bistorta
Common Bistort

Mapped Change	- 7%	
Relative Change	-16%	±24%
Weighted CF	-18%	±23%
Tetrad Frequency	50%	

Saxifraga granulata is not a frequent plant at hectad or tetrad scale except in East Anglia and along some coasts, especially in eastern Scotland. The coastal tetrads are little sampled in this survey and this may have increased the proportion of losses recorded away from its heartland in East Anglia. The species exploits dry grassy or rocky places as well as damp burnside grassland, and its decline reflects the continuing losses of unimproved, nutrient-poor, basic or neutral grassland.

While *Persicaria bistorta* is assumed to be native in an area centred on Lancashire and Cumbria, and is frequent there, it is usually found in other areas as isolated patches that are more or less obviously relicts of former cultivation. These former introductions may be in decline.

Key to maps ● Loss ● Gain ○ Re-find ■ *New Atlas* distribution

Lathyrus pratensis group (1.2)

Species	24	Average tetrads	402	Mean CF	- 1	Significance	0.45
		Widespread		**No change**			

This is the least specialised and most widely distributed group of species which are representative of this Broad Habitat, and many are frequent thoughout Britain outwith the Scottish Highlands.

Although the area of species-rich neutral grassland habitat is usually thought to be in decline, this is not reflected in the mean change factor which is not significantly different from the overall mean. This may in part reflect the abundance of many species and in part the contribution to the mean made by some rather exceptional members of the group.

Damp grassland species that show losses are *Alopecurus geniculatus*, *Cardamine pratensis*, *Potentilla anserina* and *Rhinanthus minor*. The grassland and woodland-edge species *Conopodium majus* also shows a decline. There are also intriguing probable losses in the very familiar *Cynosurus cristatus* and *Vicia sepium*. The first may be attributable, at least in part, to the effects of the adjustment for over-recording in the second survey on such a common species, but it is interesting that *Vicia sepium* may be so scarce in such arable areas as Lincolnshire to have suffered losses at the tetrad scale.

Geranium pratense has increased but is often an introduction outside its native range. *Bromus hordeaceus*, *Myosotis discolor* and *Trifolium dubium* also show an increase but these are annual species of a variety of habitats and the increases may well relate to ruderal situations. *Plantago coronopus* is predominantly coastal though its increases may relate to the colonisation of road verges.

Trifolium dubium, Lesser Trefoil Simon Harrap

Rhinanthus minor, Yellow-rattle Bob Ellis

Species	Broad Habitats	Native Status	WD	EN	G	L	R	Total	TF	RC	CF	90% Conf. Limits
Rhinanthus minor	6	N	n	4	55	75	152	282	55	-16	-28	16
Vicia sepium	3, 6	N	n	6	51	59	338	448	83	-8	-25	16
Conopodium majus	1, 6	N	t	5	59	66	293	418	79	-8	-23	17
Cynosurus cristatus	6	N	t	4	64	57	413	534	90	-4	-23	29
Cardamine pratensis	6, 11	N	n	4	70	62	394	526	90	-3	-21	30
Potentilla anserina	6	N	n	6	33	27	427	487	85	-4	-16	12
Alopecurus geniculatus	6	N	n	6	79	76	233	388	74	-5	-15	21
Succisa pratensis	6	N	t	2	57	50	255	362	68	-4	-10	16
Luzula campestris	6	N	t	2	95	80	301	476	85	-2	-9	31
Rumex crispus	3, 6, 19	N	s	6	56	40	409	505	88	-2	-9	22
Centaurea nigra	6, 7	N	t	5	34	16	471	521	91	-1	-7	15
Lathyrus pratensis	6	N	n	5	48	26	445	519	92	-1	-3	21
Phleum pratense sens. lat.	3, 6	N	s	6	72	51	362	485	94	-1	-3	24
Alopecurus pratensis	6	N	n	7	62	41	347	450	91	0	-2	19
Stellaria graminea	6	N	n	4	74	46	322	442	86	+1	+5	21
Leucanthemum vulgare	6, 7	N	n	4	81	53	266	400	79	+2	+6	21
Odontites vernus	6	N	t	5	80	56	154	290	66	+3	+7	20
Vicia sativa	6	N	s	4	84	52	243	379	85	+4	+9	20
Ranunculus bulbosus	6, 7	N	s	4	98	56	172	326	74	+9	+19	20
Geranium pratense	6	N	n	7	58	25	81	164	50	+16	+22	17
Plantago coronopus	3, 6, 18	N	s	4	42	14	65	121	42	+18	+22	16
Myosotis discolor	6	N	t	3	89	47	84	220	56	+17	+27	20
Bromus hordeaceus	4, 6	N	s	4	98	38	297	433	91	+9	+28	17
Trifolium dubium	6	N	t	5	96	37	343	476	90	+8	+30	20

WD: Wider Distribution EN: Ellenberg N G: Gains L: Losses R: Re-finds TF: Tetrad Frequency RC: Relative Change CF: Change Factor (weighted)

Rhinanthus minor
Yellow-rattle

Mapped Change	- 9%	
Relative Change	-16%	±10%
Weighted CF	-28%	±16%
Tetrad Frequency	55%	

Trifolium dubium
Lesser Trefoil

Mapped Change	+13%	
Relative Change	+ 8%	± 5%
Weighted CF	+30%	±20%
Tetrad Frequency	90%	

Rhinanthus minor is an annual dependent on relatively infertile grassland with some disturbance such as cattle grazing and, at least today, it is generally associated with wetter pastures. Such habitats are on the decline at least on the fringes of the range of *R. minor*, and its losses are not unexpected.

Trifolium dubium is very frequent indeed across most of its range and shows a slight but distinct increase, particularly at the edges of upland areas. Here such features as recent forestry access roads may have allowed colonisation.

Key to maps ● Loss ● Gain ○ Re-find ▨ *New Atlas* distribution

Alchemilla xanthochlora group (2)

Species	6	Average tetrads	127	Mean CF	-20	Significance	0.00
		Moderately local		**Significant decrease**			

This is the most northerly group of neutral grassland species. *Scilla verna* is a coastal plant, but the other five species form a characteristic northern grassland group that all favour slightly damp to very damp grassland and are characteristic of species-rich northern hay meadows.

The five non-maritime species appear to have suffered heavy losses. They are all species that are unlikely to remain competitive where nitrogen levels are high. This adds to the evidence for decline in this group of species (e.g. Jefferson 2005, Valle Pacha 2004). Colonies of *Cirsium heterophyllum* are incredibly persistent and it is thus not a surprise to note that any decrease is not significant. There are insufficient data to draw conclusions on trends in the distribution of *Scilla verna*.

Cirsium heterophyllum, Melancholy Thistle Bob Ellis

Species	Broad Habitats	Native Status	WD	EN	G	L	R	Total	TF	RC	CF	90% Conf. Limits
Alchemilla glabra	6, 15, 16	N	n	4	16	40	125	181	75	-22	-30	8
Alchemilla xanthochlora	6, 7	N	t	4	19	30	45	94	57	-23	-27	19
Scilla verna	6, 10	N	t	3	2	4	11	17	29	-22	-22	25
Geranium sylvaticum	6, 16	N	n	5	14	18	42	74	63	-15	-17	19
Euphrasia officinalis agg.	6, 7, 8, 10	N	w	3	49	50	236	335	68	-7	-14	14
Cirsium heterophyllum	6, 16	N	n	5	18	17	27	62	53	-6	-7	27

WD: Wider Distribution EN: Ellenberg N G: Gains L: Losses R: Re-finds TF: Tetrad Frequency RC: Relative Change CF: Change Factor (weighted)

Geranium sylvaticum
Wood Crane's-bill

Mapped Change	- 7%	
Relative Change	-15%	±19%
Weighted CF	-17%	±19%
Tetrad Frequency	63%	

Geranium sylvaticum is a northern species that is more typical of slightly upland areas than of the hills as such. These are areas that have been subject to much change including drainage, conifer afforestation and agricultural intensification. While *G. sylvaticum* is relatively resilient to change there is a suggestion here of an erosion at the fringes of its distribution.

Key to maps ● Loss ● Gain ○ Re-find
■ *New Atlas* distribution

Bob Ellis

Doubtfully native species and neophytes in Neutral grassland

Two doubtfully native species and two neophytes have been assigned to this habitat.

Species	Broad Habitats	Native Status	WD	EN	G	L	R	Total	TF	RC	CF	90% Conf. Limits
Doubtful Status												
Dipsacus fullonum sens. lat.	3, 6, 17	NA	t	7	87	26	123	236	70	+22	+34	14
Ranunculus sardous	3, 6, 13	NA	t	7	8	7	9	24	35	-3	-3	42
Neophytes												
Crepis vesicaria	3, 5, 6, 17	AN		7	54	35	94	183	72	+5	+8	19
Medicago sativa subsp. *sativa*	3, 6	AN		5	11	25	18	54	37	-41	-45	24

WD: Wider Distribution   EN: Ellenberg N   G: Gains   L: Losses   R: Re-finds   TF: Tetrad Frequency   RC: Relative Change   CF: Change Factor (weighted)

Gillian Beckett

Calcareous grassland (BH7)

Species	102	Average tetrads	130	Mean CF	- 6	Significance	0.00
				Significant decrease			

This Broad Habitat comprises grassland over shallow, lime-rich soils, usually derived from underlying chalk or limestone rocks. The habitat is characterised by many specialist species. Unlike its counterpart, Acid Grassland (BH8), montane calcareous grassland is included within this Broad Habitat.

Changes in the Calcareous grassland habitat, 1950-2004

1950-1986

Many of the changes to calcareous grassland in the post-war years are similar to those which have affected Neutral grassland. They include:

- the agricultural improvement of grassland in pastoral areas;

- increasing grazing pressure in pastoral regions, brought about by increases in the productivity of the grassland and a greater tendency to maintain high stock numbers by supplementary winter feeding, the latter leading to a net input of nutrients even into otherwise unfertilised swards;

- the increasing dominance of coarse species such as *Brachypodium pinnatum* (for reasons which are unclear) and *Bromopsis erecta* (which increases when levels of grazing are low);

- the conversion of grassland to arable land, leading to extreme fragmentation of the habitat which in many areas is reduced to small patches or linear strips;

- losses to quarrying of chalk and limestone;

- the cessation of grazing on the remaining fragments of grassland in arable areas, following the loss of agricultural stock and the reduction in rabbit populations by myxomatosis, the eventual result being the replacement of grassland by scrub;

- increased nutrient inputs into fragmentary and relict grassland areas from aerial inputs and fertiliser drift.

As a result of these changes, many surviving calcareous grasslands have become taller and ranker than they were.

1987-2004

In the period since 1987 the direct destruction of species-rich grassland has slowed, as the habitat has long been valued and good examples therefore tend to be designated as SSSIs. Lowland and Upland calcareous grasslands are both BAP Priority Habitats, and large areas have been restored or 'recreated' in recent years as a result of Countryside

Stewardship, Environmentally Sensitive Area or EU LIFE agreements. However, the more insidious threats, such as eutrophication and under-grazing, remain and there are great problems in managing those fragments of calcareous grassland which lie in an arable landscape. Minor sites such as small chalk pits, which often provide refuges for calcareous grassland species but are not sufficiently important to merit statutory protection, have continued to lose grassland species because of infilling or scrub colonisation.

Earlier studies of changes in the species of Calcareous grassland

Calcareous grassland has long been recognised as suffering severe losses. In southern English vice-counties the relatively few detailed studies suggest that the proportion of extinct species tends to be similar to the overall proportion of species lost from the county. The exceptions are counties such as Middlesex and Northamptonshire where the habitat is very localised, and where losses have been greater than average (James 1997, McCollin *et al.* 2000, Preston 2000, Walker & Preston in press). However, many calcareous species have declined, even if not to extinction: in Hertfordshire 12% of the chalk grassland species have become extinct, but a further 29% are declining (James 1997). At the 10-km square scale, this decline is certainly evident. Calcareous grassland species showed a decline in all British regions between the two BSBI Atlas surveys, in 1930-69 and 1987-99 (Preston *et al.* 2002b, 2003b). The decline of some uncommon species, such as *Orchis ustulata* and *Pulsatilla vulgaris*, has been well documented (Foley 1992, Wells 1968).

The BSBI Local change surveys

There is clear evidence for an overall decline of species in this habitat. As the studies of the species groups show, the plants with the most restricted distributions have shown the most severe declines. Against this pattern of decline must be set small groups of species that are flourishing and showing substantial gains.

The perennation of the species and the broad phytogeographical groupings throw some light on these changes. As with Neutral grassland (BH6), there is a significant difference between plants with different perennation ($F_{2,99} = 3.12$, $p = 0.049$), with the small group of annual species contrasting with the less successful biennials and perennials.

Perennation	No. species	Mean CF	Standard error
Annual	8	+10	6
Biennial	11	-16	6
Perennial	83	-6	3

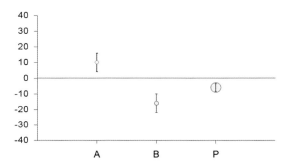

There are also differences in relationship to phytogeography ($F_{3,98} = 9.27$, $p < 0.001$) as the large northern and temperate elements in the calcareous grassland flora have declined, whereas southern species have increased. These southern species include *Anacamptis pyramidalis*, *Catapodium rigidum*, *Ophrys apifera* and *Sherardia arvensis*, species which perhaps share a tendency to exploit barer areas in calcareous turf and an ability to exploit rather ruderal sites as well as classic calcareous grassland.

Wider Distribution	No. species	Mean CF	Standard error
Northern	29	-12	4
Temperate	56	-9	3
Widespread	1	-14	-
Southern	16	+19	6

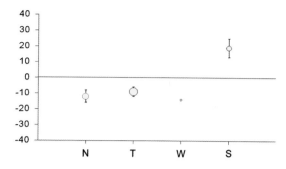

The differences in Change Factor with respect to pH preference are not statistically significant ($r = -0.22$, $p = 0.779$). However, the trend in relation to Ellenberg N values is very clear ($r = 0.276$, $p = 0.007$), with the large groups requiring low fertility habitats having declined and the small groups which benefit from more fertile soils showing a positive Change Factor.

Ellenberg N	No. species	Mean CF	Standard error
2 (very infertile)	31	-10	3
3	34	-10	4
4	21	+1	0.5
5	9	-5	7
6	5	+18	12
7 (very fertile)	2	+12	9

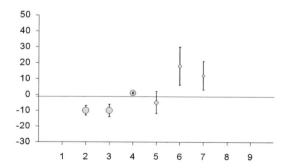

What environmental variables are driving the changes in Calcareous grassland?

The results of this survey confirm the continuing decline of many calcareous grassland species. In particular, they provide evidence of the loss of species in upland grasslands, in areas where there has hitherto been less evidence of loss (in part perhaps because the historical record of plant distribution is much more fragmentary). However, the survey also highlights the hitherto undocumented spread of some southern species.

Modelling the relationship of the Change Factor to the environmental variables suggests that both Ellenberg N ($R^2 = 7.1\%$, p = 0.007) and perennation ($R^2 = 5.9\%$, p = 0.049) are significant non-climatic variables. For a model combining these two variables, $R^2 = 11.9\%$. Addition of the Wider Distribution variable and one climatic variable, mean January temperate, adds greatly to the explanatory power of the model ($R^2 = 33.7\%$, with all four variables statistically significant). No effects of mean July temperature or annual rainfall can be detected. It is interesting that the January temperature term does not completely replace the rather general distributional category, as after allowing for January temperature there is still an effect of phytogeography. This suggests that there may be a further factor, correlated with Wider Distribution, which is influencing the changes in Calcareous grassland species.

This analysis therefore suggests that amongst the factors driving change in Calcareous grassland are eutrophication and climate change, with the important feature of climate being January temperature. Annuals and plants of southerly distribution are the main beneficiaries.

Species groups

Five groups of species are recognised.

Calcareous grassland (BH7):
classification of species

Viola hirta group (1.1.1)

Species	27	Average tetrads	42	Mean CF	- 11	Significance	0.01
		Local			Significant decrease		

This group comprises species with distributions that are concentrated in those areas of England and Wales with chalk and limestone rocks. The group includes many of the classic chalk grassland species.

Most of the species in the group show a pronounced decline, probably associated with continued habitat loss and the degradation through eutrophication and lack of grazing of the remaining habitat fragments. As the sample data is quite limited for individual species it is unwise to pick out species with especially large changes for special comment, but the overall trend is clear and as pronounced as any shown by this survey.

Three species appear to have increased: *Geranium sanguineum* and *Convallaria majalis* have probably gained through garden escapes while *Anacamptis pyramidalis* has probably colonised ruderal sites as well as extensive grassland.

Scabiosa columbaria, Small Scabious Gillian Beckett

Species	Broad Habitats	Native Status	WD	EN	G	L	R	Total	TF	RC	CF	90% Conf. Limits
Arabis hirsuta	7, 16	N	n	3	7	18	10	35	27	-48	-50	29
Bromopsis erecta	7	N	t	3	9	26	32	67	47	-38	-41	16
Saxifraga granulata	6, 7	N	t	4	7	15	12	34	22	-38	-40	30
Cirsium acaule	7	N	t	3	9	22	28	59	47	-34	-37	19
Gentianella amarella	7	N	n	2	7	12	11	30	24	-30	-32	33
Hippocrepis comosa	7	N	t	2	1	4	11	16	26	-29	-29	13
Cirsium eriophorum	7	N	t	5	5	9	13	27	39	-27	-28	30
Helictotrichon pratense	7	N	t	2	15	22	20	57	35	-25	-28	27
Inula conyzae	7, 16	N	t	3	8	13	17	38	25	-25	-27	28
Scabiosa columbaria	7	N	t	2	7	13	26	46	36	-24	-25	20
Campanula glomerata	7	N	t	3	5	7	7	19	30	-23	-24	44
Helictotrichon pubescens	6, 7	N	t	3	32	39	28	99	37	-19	-23	26
Asperula cynanchica	7	N	t	2	1	3	14	18	32	-20	-21	12
Cynoglossum officinale	7, 19	N	t	6	3	5	14	22	24	-19	-20	25
Carlina vulgaris	7	N	t	2	8	11	19	38	22	-18	-20	27
Viola hirta	7	N	t	2	18	19	32	69	43	-10	-12	25
Filipendula vulgaris	7	N	t	2	5	5	13	23	22	-9	-9	35
Origanum vulgare	7, 16	N	s	4	24	20	28	72	36	-1	-1	26
Brachypodium pinnatum	7	N	t	3	14	10	22	46	42	+3	+3	30
Geranium columbinum	3, 7	N	t	7	14	11	12	37	29	+3	+3	39
Helianthemum nummularium	7	N	t	2	15	9	35	59	35	+4	+4	23
Blackstonia perfoliata	7	N	s	2	13	9	18	40	30	+4	+5	33
Lithospermum officinale	1, 3, 7	N	t	5	7	5	5	17	19	+8	+8	54
Koeleria macrantha sens. lat.	7	N	t	2	26	17	27	70	34	+9	+10	27
Convallaria majalis	1, 7	N	n	5	12	5	6	23	25	+30	+32	41
Anacamptis pyramidalis	7	N	s	3	23	3	17	43	28	+42	+44	21
Geranium sanguineum	7, 16	N	t	3	13	4	3	20	23	+48	+50	41

WD: Wider Distribution   EN: Ellenberg N   G: Gains   L: Losses   R: Re-finds   TF: Tetrad Frequency   RC: Relative Change   CF: Change Factor (weighted)

Bromopsis erecta
Upright Brome

Mapped Change	-29%	
Relative Change	-38%	±16%
Weighted CF	-41%	±16%
Tetrad Frequency	47%	

Cirsium acaule
Dwarf Thistle

Mapped Change	-26%	
Relative Change	-34%	±19%
Weighted CF	-37%	±19%
Tetrad Frequency	47%	

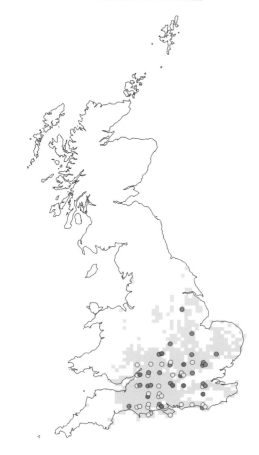

Although *Bromopsis erecta* has increased in abundance at some sites, where its coarse mats replaced more species-rich chalk grassland in recent decades, the tetrad results suggest that this has not been accompanied by range expansion. Indeed, the evidence suggests a marked decline which may be due to its replacement by other dominant grasses following eutrophication in the eastern part of its range.

Cirsium acaule remains relatively frequent in the core area of its distribution but is scarcer and declining towards the east, where its grassland habitat has suffered further losses and degradation related to lack of grazing and eutrophication.

Key to maps   ● Loss   ● Gain   ○ Re-find
       ▓ *New Atlas* distribution

Gentianella amarella
Autumn Gentian

Mapped Change	-22%	
Relative Change	-30%	±38%
Weighted CF	-32%	±33%
Tetrad Frequency	24%	

Scabiosa columbaria
Small Scabious

Mapped Change	-15%	
Relative Change	-24%	±21%
Weighted CF	-25%	±20%
Tetrad Frequency	36%	

Gentianella amarella is scarce at tetrad scale even within its limited range. Despite the small sample size the very marked decline is seen to be possibly significant. Losses may be due to both over- and under-grazing and to eutrophication.

Scabiosa columbaria requires calcareous grassland that is neither too much nor too little grazed. Such requirements are exacting in the present countryside and this species appears to be probably in sharp decline especially in the east of its range.

Key to maps ● Loss ● Gain ○ Re-find
░ *New Atlas* distribution

Anacamptis pyramidalis
Pyramidal Orchid

Mapped Change	+50%	
Relative Change	+42%	±20%
Weighted CF	+44%	±21%
Tetrad Frequency	28%	

Anacamptis pyramidalis is generally scarce at tetrad scale within its range but there appear to be limited areas where it is more frequent and it is in these areas where it is found to have been increasing very markedly. The gains may have occurred more often in recently created habitats than in old-established grassland: in several areas it is a conspicuous colonist of recently constructed roadside verges. Remarkably, only 3 apparent losses have been recorded.

Key to maps   ● Loss   ● Gain   ○ Re-find
         ▨ *New Atlas* distribution

Bob Ellis

Viola odorata group (1.1.2)

Species	33	Average tetrads	121	Mean CF	+ 4	Significance	0.62
		Moderately widespread		**Increase not significant**			

Although these species share the southerly range of the *Viola hirta* group, they are much more widespread within that range as they are less restricted to chalk and limestone soils.

The 8 species that show losses are typical of calcareous grassland but share the rather wider habitat range characteristic of the *Viola odorata* group as a whole. Again, habitat fragmentation followed by eutrophication is thought to be the main causes of decline.

Of the 8 species that show gains the very marked increase in *Ophrys apifera* stands out as the most extreme. Like *Anacamptis pyramidalis* most of the gains may relate to ruderal situations. The remaining species include a group that have probably exploited vegetation gaps in linear habitats that are more drought-prone in summer than formerly. These are *Carex divulsa, Carex muricata, Sherardia arvensis, Carex spicata, Allium vineale* and *Catapodium rigidum*. *Viola odorata* is often cultivated and its increase is likely to relate to colonies close to gardens.

Sherardia arvensis, Field Madder Simon Harrap

Ophrys apifera, Bee Orchid Richard Pryce

Species	Broad Habitats	Native Status	WD	EN	G	L	R	Total	TF	RC	CF	90% Conf. Limits
Centaurea scabiosa	6, 7	N	t	3	11	27	62	100	45	-26	-30	12
Pastinaca sativa	3, 6, 7	N	t	5	19	31	47	97	48	-24	-28	18
Linaria repens	3, 7	AR	t	5	7	9	3	19	19	-25	-27	53
Orchis mascula	1, 7, 16	N	t	4	27	37	36	100	32	-22	-27	23
Leontodon hispidus	7	N	t	3	45	55	110	210	63	-14	-20	17
Daucus carota	6, 7	N	s	3	30	40	112	182	52	-14	-20	14
Knautia arvensis	6, 7	N	t	4	31	40	102	173	55	-14	-19	15
Stachys officinalis	6, 7	N	t	3	29	38	101	168	56	-14	-19	14
Plantago media	7	N	t	3	24	30	68	122	54	-14	-17	17
Sanguisorba minor	7	N	s	3	14	17	65	96	46	-12	-14	14
Ononis repens	7	N	t	3	27	27	65	119	40	-8	-10	19
Carduus nutans	6, 7	N	t	5	26	24	46	96	41	-5	-6	22
Hypericum hirsutum	6, 7	N	t	5	28	24	66	118	50	-4	-5	18
Clinopodium vulgare	7	N	t	4	28	23	57	108	50	-2	-3	20
Epipactis helleborine	1, 7	N	t	4	21	17	18	56	30	+2	+2	33
Leontodon saxatilis	7	N	s	3	47	39	35	121	44	+2	+2	28
Trisetum flavescens	6, 7	N	t	4	63	47	120	230	68	+1	+2	20
Lathyrus nissolia	3, 6, 7	N	t	6	15	12	10	37	35	+3	+4	40
Medicago lupulina	7, 17	N	t	4	53	20	284	357	85	+4	+8	12
Primula veris	6, 7	N	t	3	53	30	115	198	61	+6	+9	17
Centaurium erythraea	7, 19	N	s	3	63	41	84	188	52	+7	+11	20
Galium mollugo	7	N	n	4	48	20	132	200	65	+8	+12	14
Serratula tinctoria	7	N	t	2	17	11	13	41	28	+12	+13	35
Picris hieracioides	7	N	t	3	20	11	23	54	38	+13	+14	28
Echium vulgare	7	N	t	4	16	9	15	40	24	+14	+15	33
Viola odorata	7	N	t	7	62	24	115	201	67	+14	+20	15
Catapodium rigidum	7, 17	N	s	2	32	14	24	70	32	+24	+27	25
Allium vineale	3, 6, 7	N	t	6	42	14	45	101	46	+24	+29	19
Carex spicata	3, 6, 7	N	t	4	41	14	28	83	45	+31	+36	22
Sherardia arvensis	7, 16	N	s	4	64	19	51	134	51	+31	+39	17
Carex muricata	3, 7, 8	N	s	4	30	10	10	50	35	+42	+46	28
Carex divulsa	3, 6, 7	N	s	6	48	10	30	88	65	+41	+46	18
Ophrys apifera	7	N	s	3	25	3	14	42	24	+48	+51	22

WD: Wider Distribution   EN: Ellenberg N   G: Gains   L: Losses   R: Re-finds   TF: Tetrad Frequency   RC: Relative Change   CF: Change Factor (weighted)

Centaurea scabiosa
Greater Knapweed

Mapped Change	-18%	
Relative Change	-26%	±11%
Weighted CF	-30%	±12%
Tetrad Frequency	45%	

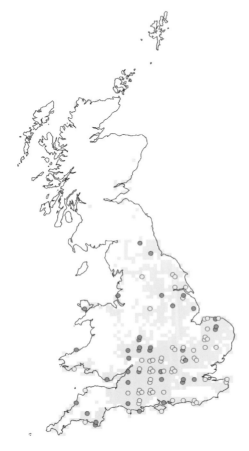

Leontodon hispidus
Rough Hawkbit

Mapped Change	- 6%	
Relative Change	-14%	±13%
Weighted CF	-20%	±17%
Tetrad Frequency	63%	

Centaurea scabiosa has a distribution that follows that of calcareous rocks. While it remains very frequent in its heartlands it has clearly been declining at the limits of its range where suitable habitat may only be found as small fragments vulnerable to eutrophication and many other changes.

Leontodon hispidus is a characteristic plant of basic grassland. This is a habitat only now represented in many areas by fragments on banks and tracksides where it is very vulnerable to eutrophication and small-scale disturbance. *L. hispidus* is more resilient than many calcicoles but has still experienced probable losses.

Key to maps   ● Loss   ● Gain   ○ Re-find
            ▦ *New Atlas* distribution

Sherardia arvensis
Field Madder

Mapped Change	+39%	
Relative Change	+31%	±15%
Weighted CF	+39%	±17%
Tetrad Frequency	51%	

Ophrys apifera
Bee Orchid

Mapped Change	+56%	
Relative Change	+48%	±21%
Weighted CF	+51%	±22%
Tetrad Frequency	24%	

Sherardia arvensis has a similar ecology to *Geranium pusillum* with both species showing a marked increase. The gains may be concentrated in the built-up environment rather than more natural grassland communities and indeed some of the apparent losses may relate to real losses of such habitat.

Ophrys apifera has a distribution that is very similar to that of *Anacamptis pyramidalis* but is somewhat more eastern. Like that species it is scarce over much of its range and is increasing markedly but, unlike *Anacamptis pyramidalis*, its increase has been mainly by an extension of its range to the north and west, as has already been reported in the *New Atlas*. It is probable that many of its new colonies are on disturbed sites rather than native grassland. It is remarkable that only three colonies found in the first survey have not been re-found.

Key to maps   ● Loss   ● Gain   ○ Re-find
         ▨ *New Atlas* distribution

Pilosella officinarum group (1.2.1)

Species	15	Average tetrads	336	Mean CF	- 3	Significance	0.27
		Widespread		Decrease not significant			

This group of widespread plants is much less specific to calcareous grassland than the preceding groups, and most species are also found in neutral or even acid grasslands.

The species with most losses are *Briza media*, *Viola riviniana*, *Pimpinella saxifraga*, *Campanula rotundifolia* and *Anthyllis vulneraria*. In many areas of Britain chalk grassland is the main habitat of all these species except for *Viola riviniana* (which is equally frequent in woodland), and all are expected to be adversely affected by factors which lead to ranker grassland swards, including eutrophication.

In contrast the two species with most gains, *Festuca arundinacea* and *Ranunculus bulbosus*, are thought to be tolerant of eutrophication.

Species	Broad Habitats	Native Status	WD	EN	G	L	R	Total	TF	RC	CF	90% Conf. Limits
Briza media	7	N	t	3	30	46	105	181	53	-18	-25	14
Viola riviniana	1, 7, 16	N	t	4	59	54	417	530	88	-4	-24	26
Pimpinella saxifraga	7	N	t	3	39	52	113	204	55	-15	-23	15
Campanula rotundifolia	7	N	n	2	39	51	213	303	67	-11	-21	12
Anthyllis vulneraria	7	N	n	2	17	24	51	92	30	-17	-20	18
Fragaria vesca	1, 7	N	t	4	59	61	200	320	69	-8	-15	17
Centaurea nigra	6, 7	N	t	5	34	16	471	521	91	-1	-7	15
Carex flacca	7, 11	N	s	2	103	80	234	417	75	+1	+2	29
Pilosella officinarum	7	N	t	2	101	75	238	414	76	+2	+5	27
Crepis capillaris	7	N	t	4	76	48	294	418	81	+2	+5	20
Leucanthemum vulgare	6, 7	N	n	4	81	53	266	400	79	+2	+6	21
Galium verum	7	N	n	2	71	37	241	349	69	+5	+10	16
Hypericum perforatum	7	N	s	5	76	43	176	295	74	+6	+12	17
Ranunculus bulbosus	6, 7	N	s	4	98	56	172	326	74	+9	+19	20
Festuca arundinacea	6, 7	N	s	6	97	43	123	263	63	+17	+30	18

WD: Wider Distribution EN: Ellenberg N G: Gains L: Losses R: Re-finds TF: Tetrad Frequency RC: Relative Change CF: Change Factor (weighted)

Briza media
Quaking-grass

Mapped Change	-11%	
Relative Change	-18%	±11%
Weighted CF	-25%	±14%
Tetrad Frequency	53%	

Campanula rotundifolia
Harebell

Mapped Change	- 5%	
Relative Change	-11%	± 7%
Weighted CF	-21%	±12%
Tetrad Frequency	67%	

Briza media is much less frequent towards the southeast. It favours infertile calcareous grassland and shows evidence of marked decline in the areas in which it is scarce. There such grassland is only likely to survive where it is protected from eutrophication and agricultural improvement by physical features.

Campanula rotundifolia is almost ubiquitous at tetrad scale in its core areas but is rather scarce at tetrad scale in much of the south and east of England and some of Wales and west Scotland. This puts into perspective its near absence in the southwest of England and in the northwest of Scotland. Its distribution appears to be limited by a demand for infertile habitats to suppress potential dominants and for sharp drainage, especially in high rainfall areas. There is evidence from the map of net decline at the fringes of the distribution, especially in East Anglia.

Key to maps ● Loss ● Gain ○ Re-find
▨ *New Atlas* distribution

Linum catharticum group (1.2.2)

Species	11	Average tetrads	220	Mean CF	-10	Significance	0.04
		Moderately widespread		**Significant decrease**			

The species in this group are short in stature and found in infertile grassland with a wide range of soil reaction. This is reflected in the distribution of the group, with concentrations in areas of the north and west with acidic soils as well as in areas of chalk and limestone.

The decline in this group is very substantial. The species are amongst those thought to be vulnerable to eutrophication. The only species with an increase is *Danthonia decumbens*, which can be remarkably elusive, and the increase is likely to relate to better recording.

Species	Broad Habitats	Native Status	WD	EN	G	L	R	Total	TF	RC	CF	90% Conf. Limits
Polygala vulgaris	7	N	t	3	31	44	53	128	38	-21	-27	20
Alchemilla xanthochlora	6, 7	N	t	4	19	30	45	94	57	-23	-27	19
Alchemilla filicaulis	7, 15, 16	N	n	3	30	37	34	101	48	-18	-22	24
Festuca ovina agg.	7, 8	N	n	2	72	71	301	444	79	-6	-19	21
Euphrasia officinalis agg.	6, 7, 8, 10	N	w	3	49	50	236	335	68	-7	-14	14
Linum catharticum	7	N	t	2	56	55	172	283	56	-7	-12	17
Thymus polytrichus	7, 16	N	n	2	27	27	187	241	56	-7	-11	10
Carex caryophyllea	7	N	t	2	47	42	63	152	48	-3	-5	22
Veronica officinalis	7, 8	N	n	4	77	59	208	344	71	0	-1	19
Gymnadenia conopsea	7, 11	N	n	3	19	15	18	52	29	+2	+3	33
Danthonia decumbens	7, 8	N	t	2	90	39	117	246	58	+17	+29	17

WD: Wider Distribution   EN: Ellenberg N   G: Gains   L: Losses   R: Re-finds   TF: Tetrad Frequency   RC: Relative Change   CF: Change Factor (weighted)

Polygala vulgaris
Common Milkwort

Mapped Change	-13%	
Relative Change	-21%	±19%
Weighted CF	-27%	±20%
Tetrad Frequency	38%	

Thymus polytrichus
Wild Thyme

Mapped Change	0%	
Relative Change	-7%	±7%
Weighted CF	-11%	±10%
Tetrad Frequency	56%	

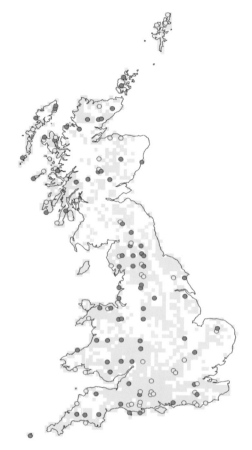

Polygala vulgaris is notably scarce within its range at the tetrad scale and it is something of a surprise to find that it appears to be more frequent on the Pennine limestones than on the chalk in the south. Losses are evident throughout its range suggesting that subtle changes, such as the effect of atmospheric nitrogen on upland communities, may have been relevant alongside habitat loss as such.

The tetrad distribution map emphasises how much *Thymus polytrichus* is a plant of skeletal soils in the north and how infrequent it is as a component of chalk and limestone grassland in the south. The apparent losses are concentrated in the south where losses to more competitive species following eutrophication and reduced grazing may be the most significant cause of change.

Key to maps   ● Loss   ● Gain   ○ Re-find
　　　　　 ▦ *New Atlas* distribution

Selaginella selaginoides group (2)

Species	16	Average tetrads	45	Mean CF	-15	Significance	0.00
		Local		Significant decrease			

This group of species is characteristically found on the calcareous rocks of the north and west. The species are predominantly plants of upland and montane habitats.

This group shows a particularly clear trend of decline with no species showing an increase. The species are all stress-tolerant and would be expected to suffer from competition where there are increased soil nutrients and less extreme climate conditions. Many of their losses relate to localities at the fringe of their ranges, in less montane conditions where such pressures are likely to be greatest.

Species	Broad Habitats	Native Status	WD	EN	G	L	R	Total	TF	RC	CF	90% Conf. Limits
Viola lutea	7, 8, 16	N	n	2	3	18	13	34	46	-57	-59	16
Melica nutans	1, 7, 16	N	n	3	4	9	5	18	35	-44	-46	42
Coeloglossum viride	7	N	n	2	5	8	8	21	25	-27	-28	40
Botrychium lunaria	7, 16	N	n	2	6	8	5	19	16	-24	-25	49
Saxifraga oppositifolia	7, 15, 16	N	n	2	1	4	17	22	49	-23	-24	10
Persicaria vivipara	7, 15	N	n	2	6	9	21	36	55	-18	-20	24
Alchemilla alpina	7, 15, 16	N	n	3	6	10	40	56	82	-16	-18	14
Galium boreale	7, 16	N	n	3	13	16	24	53	62	-16	-17	26
Rubus saxatilis	1, 7, 16	N	n	4	12	13	16	41	36	-12	-13	33
Juniperus communis	7, 10, 15, 16	N	n	3	19	19	37	75	45	-8	-9	23
Gentianella campestris	7	N	n	3	10	10	12	32	36	-9	-9	38
Saxifraga aizoides	7, 11, 15, 16	N	n	2	9	6	34	49	67	-1	-2	20
Saxifraga hypnoides	7, 15, 16	N	n	3	8	7	5	20	29	-1	-1	50
Antennaria dioica	7, 10	N	n	2	18	12	39	69	52	+2	+3	23
Selaginella selaginoides	7, 11	N	n	2	34	16	78	128	76	+8	+10	16
Thalictrum alpinum	7, 11, 15, 16	N	n	3	12	6	21	39	58	+10	+10	28

WD: Wider Distribution EN: Ellenberg N G: Gains L: Losses R: Re-finds TF: Tetrad Frequency RC: Relative Change CF: Change Factor (weighted)

124

Viola lutea
Mountain Pansy

Mapped Change	-48%	
Relative Change	-57%	±16%
Weighted CF	-59%	±16%
Tetrad Frequency	46%	

Galium boreale
Northern Bedstraw

Mapped Change	- 8%	
Relative Change	-16%	±29%
Weighted CF	-17%	±26%
Tetrad Frequency	62%	

Viola lutea is more frequent in the northern part of its range. It has declined very sharply right across its range, losing half its tetrads. Coniferisation of marginal upland areas may be one cause of decline, but *Viola lutea* is sensitive to grazing levels: it may not flower if grazing is heavy and may be replaced by more competitive species if grazing is relaxed.

Although *Galium boreale* is a predominantly montane plant it has many lowland populations, typically on rocks by rivers but also in other habitats. The relatively high incidence of apparent gains suggests that some populations are overlooked. The apparent net losses probably relate in the main to the relict lowland populations, reflecting the effect of disturbance on plants no longer in a stable community.

Key to maps ● Loss ● Gain ○ Re-find
▨ *New Atlas* distribution

Doubtfully native species and neophytes in Calcareous grassland

One doubtfully native species occurs preferentially in Chalk grassland, *Onobrychis viciifolia*.
A variant which may be native grows in Chalk grassland, whereas introduced variants also occur
in other habitats, including reseeded roadside verges. There is also one species which is treated as
a neophyte in the *New Atlas* and assigned to Chalk grassland, amongst other habitats,
Ornithogalum angustifolium.

Species	Broad Habitats	Native Status	WD	EN	G	L	R	Total	TF	RC	CF	90% Conf. Limits
Doubtful Status												
Onobrychis viciifolia	7	NA	t	3	7	6	5	18	24	0	0	51
Neophytes												
Ornithogalum angustifolium	1, 3, 7, 8	AN	s	4	42	22	10	74	42	+30	+38	30

WD: Wider Distribution   EN: Ellenberg N   G: Gains   L: Losses   R: Re-finds   TF: Tetrad Frequency   RC: Relative Change   CF: Change Factor (weighted)

Scrub invading calcareous grassland Richard Pryce

Robin Stevenson

Acid grassland (BH8)

Species	39	Average tetrads	187	Mean CF	- 3	Significance	0.23
				Decrease not significant			

Grasslands on acidic soils in the lowlands, and below the tree-line in upland areas, are included here. Acid grassland is an extensive habitat in the north and west, where acidic rocks and pastoral farming predominate. It is often present in a mosaic with heathland habitats. In much of the south it is highly localised, and particularly associated with sand in habitats that are often much disturbed and may be vulnerable. Over much of its range this Broad Habitat lacks a large suite of characteristic species, a strong contrast with Calcareous grassland (BH7).

Changes in the Acid grassland habitat, 1950-2004

1950-1986

The changes affecting these grasslands are broadly similar to those that have influenced the other grassland Broad Habitats. The main differences arise from the concentration of the acidic grasslands in pastoral areas, which means that loss of grazing land has been less of a factor than habitat modification. The main changes include:

- large-scale afforestation in both the lowlands and the uplands;

- spread of bracken, *Pteridium aquilinum*, in the uplands;

- agricultural improvement of grazed grasslands, especially in areas closest to farmsteads;

- changes in the composition of established grassland, with a reduction in species diversity, probably attributable to the increased deposition of atmospheric nitrogen (Stevens *et al.* 2004);

- increased intensity of grazing in many northern and western areas, leading to the expansion of species-poor acid grassland communities into areas of heathland;

- conversion of grassland to arable in the south and east, even in areas of sandy soil which would be unable to sustain arable crops without irrigation;

- loss of grasslands in southern and eastern England to sand and gravel extraction and to housing and industrial estates;

- loss of grazing on common lands and other grasslands in the south, as traditional land uses have stopped and rabbit numbers have never recovered to pre-myxomatosis levels, leading to the development of rank swards, scrub or woodland on previously grazed grasslands;

- increasing fragmentation, with many stands reduced to small, remnant patches.

1987-2004

Between 1990 and 1998 the CEH Countryside Survey reported a net loss of 10% of Acid grassland in the UK. Most losses were in the uplands of England and Wales, mainly as a result of the change from Acid grassland to Improved grassland (BH5); gains came from Dwarf shrub heath (BH10) and Bog (BH12). Although the net direction of the change is clear, this oversimplifies a more complex set of changes: in some places Acid grassland was lost during this period to Bog and Dwarf Shrub heath.

Sheep densities have fallen since the early 1990s when 'headage payments' (payments per animal) were replaced by area payments, removing the incentive to maximise stocking rates. The outbreak of Foot and Mouth disease in 2001 caused a further reduction in grazing in affected upland areas, at least temporarily, with dramatic changes to the appearance of grasslands in northern England (Corner 2004, Roberts 2003). In recent years large areas of arable have been allowed to revert to grass-heath, under agri-environment agreements, and this has created or restored areas of species-poor acid grassland, as has the felling of some conifer woodland.

Earlier studies of changes in the species of Acid grassland

Comparison of the results of the two BSBI Atlas surveys showed that there had been a relative loss of Acid grassland species at the 10-km square scale in all areas except Highland Scotland. There was a clear geographical pattern to the results, with very slight losses in lowland Scotland, somewhat greater losses in Wales and Northern England and much greater losses further south and east (Preston et al. 2003b). This ties in with the results obtained by studies at the county scale, which show that species of acid grassland and heathland have suffered a disproportionate level of extinction in the historical period in S.E. England (Dony 1977, James 1997, Preston 2000, Walker & Preston in press).

Sample Acid grassland plots recorded by the Countryside Survey teams in 1990 and again in 1998 showed an increase in species characteristic of more fertile conditions and a reduction in frequency of species associated with lower nutrient levels (Haines-Young et al. 2000).

The BSBI Local change surveys

There is much less difference in the performance of annual and perennial species in Acid grassland than in Neutral or Calcareous grassland ($F_{2,36} = 0.80$, $p = 0.46$).

Perennation	No. species	Mean CF	Standard error
Annual	15	+4	7
Biennial	2	-5	15
Perennial	22	-7	5

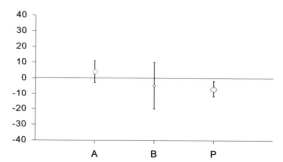

The mean change factors for the three large phytogeographical groups show that the northern species have done badly, temperate species show little overall change but southern species have done relatively well ($F_{3,35} = 4.05$, $p = 0.014$). At first sight this might appear to be at variance with the results of previous studies, which indicate that the loss of acid grassland species has been greatest in the south and east. However, there is clear evidence that the losses of at least some of the northern species are taking place at the southern fringes of their range (see species account for *Potentilla erecta* below). The extreme value for the two widespread species results from the decline of *Euphrasia officinalis* agg., a complex of more local taxa, and *Rumex acetosella*.

Wider Distribution	No. species	Mean CF	Standard error
Northern	10	-20	5
Temperate	18	+3	5
Widespread	2	-33	18
Southern	9	+10	10

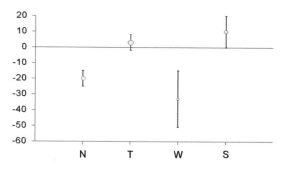

There is no significant trend with Ellenberg R values ($r = -0.21$ $p = 0.20$), although only the less acidic soils (R=6) show a positive mean change factor

Ellenberg R	No. species	Mean CF	Standard error
2 (very acid)	4	-7	1
3	8	-5	8
4	11	-5	8
5	9	-14	11
6 (weakly acid)	7	+19	7

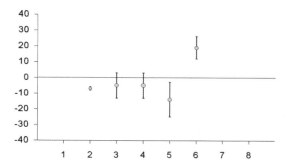

There is, however, a clear trend with fertility preferences: species associated with the more infertile habitats (N1-3) show a decline whereas those found in more fertile habitats (N4-6) have increased ($r = 0.34$, $p < 0.036$).

Ellenberg N	No. species	Mean CF	Standard error
1 (very infertile)	1	-9	-
2	16	-4	7
3	12	-19	5
4	6	+13	9
5	3	+30	11
6 (fertile)	1	+12	-

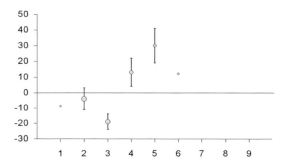

What environmental variables are driving the changes in Acid grassland?

A model based solely on Ellenberg N has an R^2 of 11.4%. Models including Ellenberg N and each of the other non-climatic variables show slightly reduced statistical significance for effects of N but no effects of the other variables. Including N and Wider Distribution increases the value of R^2 considerably, to 33.7%, with significant effects of both factors ($p = 0.051$ and 0.018 respectively). However, adding each of the climate variables to a model based on N fails to show effects of January temperature ($R^2 = 17.6\%$, $p = 0.11$), July temperature ($R^2 = 14.4\%$, $p = 0.27$) or rainfall ($R^2 = 11.6\%$, $p = 0.78$). The differences attributable to Wider Distribution do not appear to be associated with the climate variables, suggesting that this term may be acting as a surrogate for a factor that has not been included in the analysis.

In conclusion, eutrophication is the only driver of change in Acidic grassland which emerges with any clarity from the analysis.

Species groups

Two main species groups are considered. These separate very effectively the widespread species of the north and west from the much more localised plants concentrated on light, sandy soils in the south and east. Both main groups show a preponderance of losses but a small number of species with gains affect their overall significance.

Acid grassland (BH8): classification of species

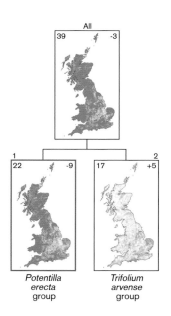

Potentilla erecta group (1)

Species	22	Average tetrads	299	Mean CF	- 9	Significance	0.04
		Widespread		**Significant decrease**			

Seven species show a decrease. These include many of those most characteristic of this habitat and the location of the losses, which tend to be at the southern limits of a species range, suggest that the main cause is the eutrophication or destruction of habitat fragments away from more extensive examples.

Carex pilulifera shows the largest increase. If this is a real change it may relate to movement towards grassland in grassland/heath mosaics in response to grazing pressure. *Danthonia decumbens* has also increased but was probably poorly recorded in the first survey. The increase of *Aphanes arvensis* agg. may well relate to ruderal and arable habitats rather than to acid grassland, while those of *Senecio sylvaticus* and *Carex binervis* may relate to conifer forestry.

Potentilla erecta, Tormentil Gillian Beckett

Rumex acetosella, Sheep's Sorrel Gillian Beckett

Species	Broad Habitats	Native Status	WD	EN	G	L	R	Total	TF	RC	CF	90% Conf. Limits
Viola lutea	7, 8, 16	N	n	2	3	18	13	34	46	-57	-59	16
Rumex acetosella	8, 9, 16	N	w	3	47	87	346	480	83	-15	-51	15
Galium saxatile	8, 9	N	t	3	27	47	323	397	77	-11	-28	8
Potentilla erecta	8	N	n	2	29	42	385	456	80	-9	-28	10
Agrostis canina sens. lat.	8, 11	N	n	3	72	80	186	338		-10	-22	19
Jasione montana	8, 10	N	t	2	12	17	36	65	42	-18	-20	20
Festuca ovina agg.	7, 8	N	n	2	72	71	301	444	79	-6	-19	21
Euphrasia officinalis agg.	6, 7, 8, 10	N	w	3	49	50	236	335	68	-7	-14	14
Aira praecox	8, 16	N	s	2	69	70	133	272	58	-8	-14	20
Nardus stricta	8	N	n	2	24	24	240	288	74	-7	-12	8
Lathyrus linifolius	8, 16	N	t	3	37	38	126	201	57	-8	-12	15
Luzula multiflora	8	N	n	3	57	48	266	371	76	-3	-8	16
Deschampsia flexuosa	8, 10	N	n	3	41	32	282	355	78	-3	-8	12
Polygala serpyllifolia	8, 10, 12	N	t	2	41	35	182	258	66	-4	-7	13
Juncus squarrosus	8, 12	N	t	2	29	17	220	266	74	-2	-3	10
Veronica officinalis	7, 8	N	n	4	77	59	208	344	71	0	-1	19
Digitalis purpurea	8, 9	N	s	5	66	32	396	494	89	+2	+10	21
Carex binervis	8, 10, 16	N	t	2	53	21	173	247	68	+7	+12	13
Senecio sylvaticus	2, 8, 9	N	t	6	58	40	53	151	47	+8	+12	24
Aphanes arvensis agg.	4, 8, 16	N	t	4	99	58	129	286	65	+11	+22	21
Danthonia decumbens	7, 8	N	t	2	90	39	117	246	58	+17	+29	17
Carex pilulifera	8	N	t	2	93	38	122	253	66	+18	+31	17

WD: Wider Distribution   EN: Ellenberg N   G: Gains   L: Losses   R: Re-finds   TF: Tetrad Frequency   RC: Relative Change   CF: Change Factor (weighted)

Carex pilulifera
Pill Sedge

Mapped Change	+26%	
Relative Change	+18%	±11%
Weighted CF	+31%	±17%
Tetrad Frequency	66%	

Galium saxatile
Heath Bedstraw

Mapped Change	- 5%	
Relative Change	-11%	± 3%
Weighted CF	-28%	± 8%
Tetrad Frequency	77%	

Carex pilulifera is frequent in dry grassy places where there is a mosaic of grassland and moorland. Increased grazing of such areas may have been a factor favouring this species, leading to an increase within its established range. Currently grazing levels have fallen again and this trend might reverse.

Galium saxatile is very widespread and plentiful in moorland and unimproved upland grassland but in lowland areas it is dependent on pockets of acid vegetation in heathland or woodland. Here, at the fringes of its distribution, there is firm evidence of a progressive decline.

Key to maps ● Loss ● Gain ○ Re-find
▨ *New Atlas* distribution

Potentilla erecta
Tormentil

Mapped Change	- 3%	
Relative Change	- 9%	± 3%
Weighted CF	-28%	±10%
Tetrad Frequency	80%	

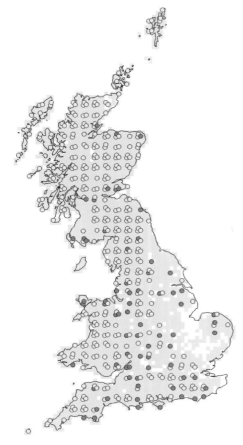

Potentilla erecta has a very similar distribution to *Galium saxatile* and shows the same trend, that of a progressive decline at the fringes of its distribution while it remains very widespread and plentiful where there is moorland or hill grassland.

Rumex acetosella
Sheep's Sorrel

Mapped Change	- 9%	
Relative Change	-15%	± 5%
Weighted CF	-51%	±15%
Tetrad Frequency	83%	

Rumex acetosella is demonstrated to be not nearly as ubiquitous as the *New Atlas* suggests. Not only is it distinctly scarce in eastern England but also it is by no means ubiquitous in the peat-covered regions of the north of Scotland. In eastern England it is in steep decline, presumably a victim of eutrophication and the conversion of unproductive soils to forestry and other uses.

Key to maps ● Loss ● Gain ○ Re-find
▓ *New Atlas* distribution

Trifolium arvense group (2)

Species	17	Average tetrads	43	Mean CF	- 5	Significance	0.76
		Local		Decrease not significant			

This group contains a high proportion of annuals. The species with decreases are *Vicia lathyroides*, *Trifolium arvense*, *Cerastium arvense* and *Myosotis ramosissima*. These are all stress-tolerant species, often growing in small pockets of dry or rocky grassland within larger areas of improved grassland where they are vulnerable to eutrophication.

The species with large increases are *Spergularia rubra*, which is an effective colonist of forestry and other roads, *Carex muricata*, of which subsp. *lamprocarpa* is spreading in various ruderal habitats near roads, *Trifolium micranthum*, which is nutrient-tolerant and found increasingly in lawns and other closely-mown grass swards, and *Anthriscus caucalis*, another nutrient-tolerant species whose gains may in part relate to set-aside or agri-environment options in its alternative arable habitat. The more modest apparent gains of *Cerastium semidecandrum* are less easy to explain, as it appears to be similar to the species showing losses.

Species	Broad Habitats	Native Status	WD	EN	G	L	R	Total	TF	RC	CF	90% Conf. Limits
Vicia lathyroides	8, 19	N	t	3	3	8	5	16	25	-47	-48	41
Trifolium arvense	8	N	s	2	15	24	17	56	29	-30	-34	28
Cerastium arvense	8	N	n	3	8	14	16	38	38	-28	-30	28
Scleranthus annuus	4, 8, 10, 16	N	t	4	7	8	6	21	29	-16	-16	48
Myosotis ramosissima	8, 16	N	s	3	18	20	15	53	28	-14	-16	33
Viola canina	8, 10	N	n	2	11	11	7	29	27	-9	-9	45
Agrostis curtisii	8, 10	N	s	1	3	3	9	15	40	-9	-9	40
Ornithopus perpusillus	8	N	t	3	15	14	16	45	28	-5	-6	33
Festuca filiformis	8	N	t	2	15	10	11	36	34	+11	+12	38
Trifolium striatum	8	N	s	2	14	10	6	30	24	+11	+12	44
Viola tricolor	4, 8, 19	N	t	4	38	26	27	91	43	+10	+13	27
Sagina subulata	8, 10	N	t	4	10	6	7	23	26	+15	+16	44
Cerastium semidecandrum	8, 18, 19	N	t	3	24	16	10	50	29	+15	+17	35
Anthriscus caucalis	3, 4, 8	N	t	5	23	9	10	42	45	+34	+37	31
Trifolium micranthum	8, 17	N	s	5	32	11	11	54	34	+40	+45	27
Carex muricata	3, 7, 8	N	s	4	30	10	10	50	35	+42	+46	28
Spergularia rubra	8, 17	N	s	2	44	15	16	75	37	+40	+47	24

WD: Wider Distribution   EN: Ellenberg N   G: Gains   L: Losses   R: Re-finds   TF: Tetrad Frequency   RC: Relative Change   CF: Change Factor (weighted)

Cerastium arvense, Field Mouse-ear Bob Ellis

Trifolium arvense, Hare's-foot Clover Gillian Beckett

Cerastium arvense
Field Mouse-ear

Mapped Change	-20%	
Relative Change	-28%	±31%
Weighted CF	-30%	±28%
Tetrad Frequency	38%	

Trifolium arvense
Hare's-foot Clover

Mapped Change	-22%	
Relative Change	-30%	±32%
Weighted CF	-23%	±28%
Tetrad Frequency	29%	

Cerastium arvense is infrequent even on the calcareous soils within its eastern distribution. The decline evident in the *New Atlas* is shown to include a probable recent element likely to be related to eutrophication and loss of the grassland fragments in which it is found.

Trifolium arvense is infrequent within much of its limited range, though less so in coastal areas. This was a species that prospered on ballast when the railways were first constructed but is now controlled by weedkillers and its apparent marked decline may reflect relatively poor success in other open microhabitats found in waste places.

Key to maps   ● Loss   ● Gain   ○ Re-find
■ *New Atlas* distribution

Spergularia rubra
Sand Spurrey

Mapped Change	+48%	
Relative Change	+40%	±26%
Weighted CF	+47%	±24%
Tetrad Frequency	37%	

Spergularia rubra is a species that once seemed to be set to decline because of the general reduction in infertile habitats but it has recently made a considerable resurgence. It is particularly successful in colonising forestry tracks from where it is doubtless spread by contractors' vehicles.

Key to maps ● Loss ● Gain ○ Re-find
■ *New Atlas* distribution

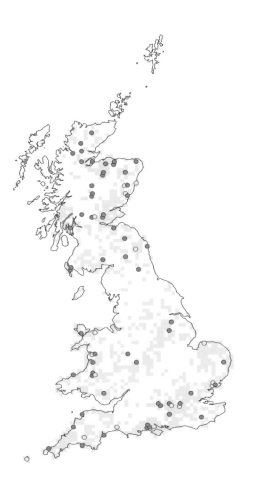

Simon Harrap

Doubtfully native species and neophytes in Acid grassland
A single neophyte is attributed to this Broad Habitat.

Species	Broad Habitats	Native Status	WD	EN	G	L	R	Total	TF	RC	CF	90% Conf. Limits
Neophytes												
Ornithogalum angustifolium	1, 3, 7, 8	AN	s	4	42	22	10	74	42	+30	+38	30

WD: Wider Distribution   EN: Ellenberg N   G: Gains   L: Losses   R: Re-finds   TF: Tetrad Frequency   RC: Relative Change   CF: Change Factor (weighted)

E.L. Swann

Bracken (BH9)

Species	9	Average tetrads	362	Mean CF	- 8	Significance	0.25
						Decrease not significant	

This Broad Habitat simply covers continuous stands of bracken, *Pteridium aquilinum*. Bracken increased in area greatly during the 20th century, apparently in response to the changing management of upland areas. However, trends in recent decades have been less clear-cut. The Countryside Survey results suggested a marked decline between 1984 and 1990, but no significant change in the next 8-year period (Haines-Young *et al.* 2000).

Very few other vascular plants compete successfully in continuous bracken and the list of species with any preference for this Broad Habitat is therefore very short. It is much too small a sample to be analysed statistically. Species accounts for *Pteridium aquilinum* and *Ceratocapnos claviculata* are provided here, and *Galium saxatile* and *Rumex acetosella* are dealt with under Acid grassland (BH8).

Species	Broad Habitats	Native Status	WD	EN	G	L	R	Total	TF	RC	CF	90% Conf. Limits
Rumex acetosella	8, 9, 16	N	w	3	47	87	346	480	83	-15	-51	15
Galium saxatile	8, 9	N	t	3	27	47	323	397	77	-11	-28	8
Pteridium aquilinum	1, 9	N	t	3	28	30	419	477	83	-6	-21	10
Hyacinthoides non-scripta	1, 9	N	t	6	52	47	324	423	83	-5	-13	16
Teucrium scorodonia	1, 9, 16	N	s	3	33	32	237	302	64	-6	-12	11
Holcus mollis	1, 3, 9	N	t	3	84	55	330	469	89	+1	+6	25
Digitalis purpurea	8, 9	N	s	5	66	32	396	494	89	+2	+10	21
Senecio sylvaticus	2, 8, 9	N	t	6	58	40	53	151	47	+8	+12	24
Ceratocapnos claviculata	1, 9	N	t	5	27	8	30	65	33	+25	+28	21

WD: Wider Distribution   EN: Ellenberg N   G: Gains   L: Losses   R: Re-finds   TF: Tetrad Frequency   RC: Relative Change   CF: Change Factor (weighted)

Pteridium aquilinum
Bracken

Mapped Change	0%	
Relative Change	- 6%	± 3%
Weighted CF	-21%	±10%
Tetrad Frequency	83%	

Ceratocapnos claviculata
Climbing Corydalis

Mapped Change	+33%	
Relative Change	+25%	±20%
Weighted CF	+28%	±21%
Tetrad Frequency	33%	

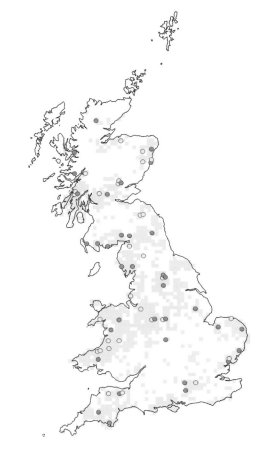

Pteridium aquilinum is very widespread and frequent at tetrad scale except in the fen country of eastern England where it is largely absent. In the arable land round the edge of this area these is a faint suggestion of decline. The trend should be interpreted with caution as the over-recording adjustment could be excessive for such a conspicuous and usually abundant species.

The suggestion of increase in *Ceratocapnos claviculata* is intriguing. In the *New Atlas* it was believed that the increase related to better recording but this is one of the few species that can colonise conifer plantations, at least when the trees are relatively mature, so conifer woodland may be becoming an increasingly frequent habitat of this species. There are likely to be regional differences as it is also found in a variety of other woodland and rocky habitats, sometimes with bracken.

Key to maps   ● Loss   ● Gain   ○ Re-find
▓ *New Atlas* distribution

Robin Stevenson

Dwarf shrub heath (BH10)

Species	39	Average tetrads	190	Mean CF	- 5	Significance	0.01
				Significant decrease			

These are dry or wet, lowland or upland heathlands dominated by dwarf shrubs in the Ericaceae, such as *Calluna vulgaris* and species of *Erica*, or by *Ulex minor*. Coastal heaths are included here, but heaths on exposed mountain ridges and summits are classified as Montane habitats (BH15).

Changes in the Dwarf shrub heath habitat, 1950-2004

1950-1986

In the lowlands this habitat has been in gradual decline for centuries. The gradual loss of Dorset heathland, described by Norman Moore in 1962, has become the classic example of habitat fragmentation. Long regarded as 'waste', heathland was targeted by the advocates of enclosure and agricultural improvement as early as the late 18th century, and by 1950 the heathlands of southern England had already become greatly reduced in extent. In the following years, the main changes to heaths in the uplands and lowlands included:

- large-scale afforestation of both lowland and upland heathland;

- agricultural improvement, with the conversion of heathland to pasture, either directly (through ploughing and reseeding) or indirectly (though heavy grazing pressure), or to arable land;

- the spread of bracken, *Pteridium aquilinum;*

- losses to building development, road construction and mineral extraction, largely in the lowlands;

- reduction in grazing pressure and consequent loss of shorter vegetation, with the heathland becoming rank or being colonised by native broadleaved trees or by conifers from nearby plantations;

- increasing fragmentation of heathland as a result of losses from the above causes, with the reduction of many surviving heaths to small and remnant patches;

- changes in the hydrology of some wet heaths caused by falling water tables and the drainage of adjacent land;

- intensive management of upland heathland by burning ('muirburn'), eliminating many fire-sensitive species;

- increased inputs of nitrogen from atmospheric sources.

A resurvey of heathland sites in Dorset originally recorded by Ronald Good in 1931-37 showed that by 1990-93 65% survived and the rest had been lost, primarily to agriculture (22%) and forestry (7%). The greatest losses were in the heathland communities on more fertile soils on ground which is not waterlogged, including grassy heathlands, as these had been preferentially taken for agricultural use. Most of the remaining sites (78%) were protected as nature reserves or SSSIs (Byfield & Pearman 1996). In N.E. Scotland David Welch selected 32 heathland study sites in 1969-70; by 1995, 23 (72%) were still heathland, the remainder having been lost, most (22%) to ploughing and reseeding (Welch & Scott 1995).

1987-2004

The factors outlined above have continued to operate. The CEH Countryside Survey reported a net loss of 4% of heathland between 1990 and 1998. Some of this was doubtless the result of overgrazing, perhaps coupled with burning or eutrophication (Haines-Young *et al.* 2000). It is difficult to separate the roles of overgrazing and eutrophication in the degradation of heathland, as the interplay between these two factors is important (see Montane habitats, BH15). On the positive side, both Lowland heath and Upland heath are UK Biodiversity Action Plan Priority Habitats. Heathland has been re-established on areas which were formerly arable land or conifer plantations under the Environmentally Sensitive Areas and Countryside Stewardship schemes.

Earlier studies of changes in the species of Dwarf shrub heath

The loss of lowland heathland in England has resulted in a high proportion of species extinctions at the county scale (Dony 1974, 1977, Greenwood 2003, James 1997, Preston 2000, Walker & Preston in press). Even in lowland Scotland, where the habitat survives, the rarer heathland species have declined, "unable to withstand the combined assault of high sheep numbers and regular muirburn" (Braithwaite 2004). At the 10-km scale, the comparison of the two Atlas surveys suggested a greater decline in species of this Broad Habitat than of any other except Arable and horticultural land (Preston *et al.* 2003).

The effects of the lack of management on heathland species in Dorset were highlighted by the resurvey in 1990-93 of Good's 1931-7 sites. Many small species restricted to specialist heathland microhabitats had declined catastrophically, surviving only where sites were grazed or disturbed by a range of other activities (from bombing on military ranges to horse riding). The losses had been greater on more fertile sites, where successional changes proceeded more rapidly (Byfield & Pearman 1996).

Sample plots studied by the Countryside Survey in 1990 and 1998 showed an increase in species characteristic of more fertile situations, and reduced abundance of those characteristic of more nutrient-poor conditions (Haines-Young *et al.* 2000).

The BSBI Local change surveys

The Local Change Surveys provide evidence of a continued whittling away of the edges of the heathland habitat in lowland areas and of more pronounced decline in a very few specialist species. However the adjustment made to reflect the more thorough recording in the second survey is not fully applicable to the commonest moorland species and the extent of the decline indicated by the Change Factor appears to be overstated. The gains shown by a few moorland species seem to relate either to their occurrence in other habitats or to incomplete survey data for elusive species.

Almost all heathland species have northern or temperate distributions, and they have declined to a similar extent ($F_{3,35} = 0.26$, $p = 0.85$).

Wider Distribution	No. species	Mean CF	Standard error
Northern	20	-5	4
Temperate	16	-4	3
Widespread	1	-15	-
Southern	2	-12	3

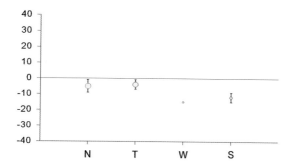

The trends in relation to pH and fertility requirements need to be interpreted with caution, because of the small sample sizes. Although there is a suggestion that the species of relatively base-rich heathland have shown the most severe decline, the trend is not statistically significant ($r = -0.23$, $p = 0.17$).

Ellenberg R	No. species	Mean CF	Standard error
1 (very acid)	2	+5	10
2	13	-3	5
3	6	-4	5
4	7	-7	6
5	7	-8	4
6 (weakly acid)	4	-11	14

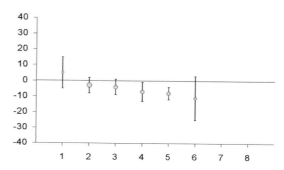

The range of Ellenberg N values in this Broad Habitat is very narrow, and again there is no significant trend ($r = 0.083$, $p = 0.61$).

Ellenberg N	No. species	Mean CF	Standard error
1 (very infertile)	5	-10	2
2	18	-3	5
3	13	-7	3
4 (infertile)	3	+3	10

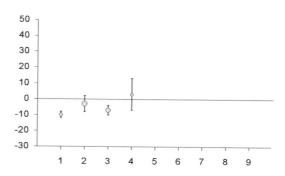

What environmental variables are driving the changes in Dwarf shrub heath?

Although the Change Factors show no significant correlations with the ecological and distribution variables, modelling individual climatic variables shows some effects. The Change Factor shows a decrease with increasing January temperature ($r = -0.31$, $p = 0.057$) and July temperature ($r = -0.37$, $p = 0.019$) and an increase with increasing rainfall ($r = 0.41$, $p = 0.009$). Modelling shows that rainfall accounts for most variation ($R^2 = 17.0\%$, $p = 0.009$) followed by July temperature ($R^2 = 13.9\%$, $p = 0.019$) and then January temperature ($R^2 = 9.5\%$, $p = 0.057$). For a model with July temperature and rainfall, $R^2 = 17.1\%$, but neither July temperature ($p = 0.88$) nor rainfall ($p = 0.25$) is statistically significant. In other words, although there is good evidence of a trend in relation to both factors, the effects are statistically indistinguishable from these data.

There is therefore a suggestion that changes in Dwarf shrub heath may be related to climatic effects, although it seems possible that this relationship is not a causal effect but simply represents the pressures on heathland in warmer, drier areas. There is no suggestion that other ecological effects tested by the models are implicated.

Species groups

Three species groups are considered.

Dwarf shrub heath (BH10) classification of species

Ulex gallii group (1.1)

Species	6	Average tetrads	44	Mean CF	-11	Significance	0.01
		Local		**Significant decrease**			

None of the species in this small group of predominantly southwestern species shows an increase. However, the decline of *Scilla verna* is based on a small data sample and *Jasione montana* is the only other species showing an individual decline.

Jasione montana, Sheep's-bit Bob Ellis

Species	Broad Habitats	Native Status	WD	EN	G	L	R	Total	TF	RC	CF	90% Conf. Limits
Scilla verna	6, 10	N	t	3	2	4	11	17	29	-22	-22	25
Jasione montana	8, 10	N	t	2	12	17	36	65	42	-18	-20	20
Viola canina	8, 10	N	n	2	11	11	7	29	27	-9	-9	45
Agrostis curtisii	8, 10	N	s	1	3	3	9	15	40	-9	-9	40
Ulex gallii	10	N	t	2	21	18	57	96	53	-4	-5	19
Rosa pimpinellifolia	10, 16, 19	N	t	3	12	10	17	39	26	-2	-2	32

WD: Wider Distribution   EN: Ellenberg N   G: Gains   L: Losses   R: Re-finds   TF: Tetrad Frequency   RC: Relative Change   CF: Change Factor (weighted)

Erica cinerea group (1.2)

Species	16	Average tetrads	272	Mean CF	- 8	Significance	0.00
		Widespread		**Significant decrease**			

This group includes the plants most typical of *Calluna* heath. While the habitat persists over large areas of northern and western Britain, it has continued to be whittled away by ploughing at its lowland edges. There is consistent evidence of decline covering both the species of well-drained banks, such as *Erica cinerea*, and those of peaty places, such as *Erica tetralix*. However the adjustment made to reflect the more thorough recording in the second survey is not fully applicable to such common species and the extent of the decline indicated by the Change Factor appears to be overstated. Only *Carex binervis* shows a gain, which may relate to forestry rides.

Species	Broad Habitats	Native Status	WD	EN	G	L	R	Total	TF	RC	CF	90% Conf. Limits
Pedicularis sylvatica	10, 12, 14	N	t	2	24	40	161	225	60	-15	-23	10
Solidago virgaurea	10, 16	N	n	3	30	41	121	192	53	-14	-20	13
Calluna vulgaris	10, 12	N	n	2	23	26	301	350	70	-7	-15	7
Aira caryophyllea	10, 16	N	s	2	29	32	38	99	31	-12	-15	24
Euphrasia officinalis agg.	6, 7, 8, 10	N	w	3	49	50	236	335	68	-7	-14	14
Erica tetralix	10, 12	N	t	1	27	28	203	258	68	-7	-12	10
Vaccinium myrtillus	10, 16	N	n	2	27	25	237	289	77	-6	-11	9
Erica cinerea	10	N	t	2	21	18	191	230	60	-6	-9	8
Salix repens	10, 19	N	n	3	24	23	69	116	45	-7	-9	17
Deschampsia flexuosa	8, 10	N	n	3	41	32	282	355	78	-3	-8	12
Polygala serpyllifolia	8, 10, 12	N	t	2	41	35	182	258	66	-4	-7	13
Blechnum spicant	1, 2, 10, 16	N	t	3	45	32	258	335	78	-2	-5	13
Hypericum pulchrum	10, 16	N	t	3	63	47	224	334	70	-1	-2	16
Ulex europaeus	10	N	t	3	56	26	336	418	75	+2	+6	15
Carex ovalis	3, 10	N	n	4	80	51	184	315	68	+4	+9	19
Carex binervis	8, 10, 16	N	t	2	53	21	173	247	68	+7	+12	13

WD: Wider Distribution   EN: Ellenberg N   G: Gains   L: Losses   R: Re-finds   TF: Tetrad Frequency   RC: Relative Change   CF: Change Factor (weighted)

Calluna vulgaris
Heather

Mapped Change	- 1%	
Relative Change	- 7%	± 3%
Weighted CF	-15%	± 7%
Tetrad Frequency	70%	

While *Calluna vulgaris* is widespread and abundant over much of its range, losses are evident at the edges of its distribution where tiny remnants of former moorland die out in a changed landscape. However the statistics overstate the extent of the change in this very common species.

Key to maps   ● Loss   ● Gain   ○ Re-find
          ▦ *New Atlas* distribution

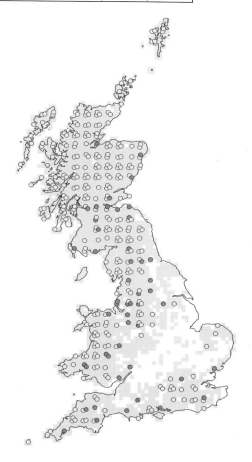

Bob Ellis

Lycopodium clavatum group (2)

Species	17	Average tetrads	53	Mean CF	0	Significance	0.62
		Local		No change			

This is a group of local species which share a predominantly northern distribution but are specialists of differing micro-habitats. *Platanthera bifolia*, as much a woodland-edge species as one of the open moorland, shows a marked decrease which is probably a long-term response to the very uniform management of much of the moorland habitat as grouse moor by muirburn.

The two species with increases, *Listera cordata* and *Pinguicula lusitanica*, are both somewhat elusive species and their apparent gains may well both relate to more thorough recording in the second survey.

Listera cordata, Lesser Twayblade Simon Harrap

Platanthera bifolia, Lesser Butterfly-orchid Bob Ellis

Species	Broad Habitats	Native Status	WD	EN	G	L	R	Total	TF	RC	CF	90% Conf. Limits
Platanthera bifolia	1, 10	N	n	2	4	10	5	19	25	-49	-50	40
Gnaphalium sylvaticum	3, 10	N	n	3	6	7	6	19	27	-16	-17	49
Trichophorum cespitosum	10, 12	N	n	1	17	25	155	197	68	-12	-17	8
Scleranthus annuus	4, 8, 10, 16	N	t	4	7	8	6	21	29	-16	-16	48
Juniperus communis	7, 10, 15, 16	N	n	3	19	19	37	75	45	-8	-9	23
Rubus chamaemorus	10, 12	N	n	1	6	5	26	37	57	-5	-6	22
Empetrum nigrum	10, 12, 15	N	n	1	24	18	121	163	63	-3	-5	12
Trientalis europaea	1, 2, 10	N	n	3	14	10	38	62	77	-1	-1	21
Genista anglica	10	N	t	2	5	3	18	26	30	0	0	29
Arctostaphylos uva-ursi	10, 15	N	n	2	12	9	22	43	63	0	0	30
Antennaria dioica	7, 10	N	n	2	18	12	39	69	52	+2	+3	23
Vaccinium vitis-idaea	2, 10, 15	N	n	2	20	9	72	101	63	+4	+5	15
Cryptogramma crispa	10, 15, 16	N	n	3	8	5	10	23	36	+8	+8	41
Lycopodium clavatum	10	N	n	2	23	14	19	56	51	+13	+15	30
Sagina subulata	8, 10	N	t	4	10	6	7	23	26	+15	+16	44
Pinguicula lusitanica	10, 11	N	t	2	16	7	14	37	50	+22	+23	31
Listera cordata	2, 10, 12	N	n	2	38	11	17	66	65	+41	+46	24

WD: Wider Distribution   EN: Ellenberg   NG: Gains   L: Losses   R: Re-finds   TF: Tetrad Frequency   RC: Relative Change   CF: Change Factor (weighted)

Doubtfully native species and neophytes in Dwarf shrub heath

Two neophytes are assigned to this Broad Habitat.

Species	Broad Habitats	Native Status	WD	EN	G	L	R	Total	TF	RC	CF	90% Conf. Limits
Neophytes												
Cotoneaster simonsii	3, 10, 16, 17	AN		4	50	17	11	78	42	+46	+56	24
Rhododendron ponticum	1, 10, 16	AN		3	55	28	111	194	49	+9	+13	16

WD: Wider Distribution   EN: Ellenberg N   G: Gains   L: Losses   R: Re-finds   TF: Tetrad Frequency   RC: Relative Change   CF: Change Factor (weighted)

Bob Ellis

Wetland habitats (BH11, 13 & 14 in part)

Species	178	Average tetrads	169	Mean CF	0	Significance	0.29
				No change			

Wetland habitats are covered by three Broad Habitats in the BAP classification.

Broad Habitat 11, Fen, marsh and swamp, comprises plant communities that are dependent on periodically, seasonally or permanently high ground-water levels. These include reedbeds, swamps, fens, flushes, springs and marshes. The very wide range of habitats covered by this definition extends from the lowlands to the mountains, and includes substrates which range from acidic to highly calcareous and from nutrient-poor to nutrient-rich. However, species found in very acidic lowland valley-mires have been included in BH12, Bog.

Broad Habitat 13, Standing water and canals, covers the aquatic vegetation of natural lakes, meres and pools, and of man-made water bodies such as reservoirs, canals, gravel pits and artificial ponds. Ditches that are wet for most of the year are also included here. *Broad Habitat 14, Rivers and streams,* includes the riparian and aquatic vegetation of running waters in both the lowland and the upland zones.

There is considerable overlap between the plants in these three Broad Habitats, so rather than treat them separately we have adopted a different approach. Their species have been divided into two groups. The first includes 'wetland plants', species of fens, flushes and other waterside habitats, which grow in moist or wet soils but are not usually found in permanent water. The other group is the true aquatics - submerged or emergent plants rooted in more or less permanent water or floating on the water surface. The division is made on Ellenberg F (moisture) values, with species with F values less than 11 included in the first group and those with F=10-12 in the second. The species with F=10, plants of shallow water which may be dry for extensive periods, are thus included in both groups.

Changes in wetland habitats, 1950-2004

1950-1986

The main changes in wetland habitats include the following.

- Drainage, both of large areas and of damp field corners and other small sites.

- Creation of some water bodies, including large reservoirs and flooded gravel pits; loss of some smaller water bodies and creation of others (probably resulting in an overall loss in this period).

- Eutrophication of both standing and flowing waters, both because of the general background increase in nutrients and because of pollution from 'point sources'.

- Reduced grazing of fens and waterside habitats, especially in eastern, arable areas but also in pastoral areas where stock are now more frequently fenced away from the water's edge, leading to taller swards (especially when coupled with eutrophication).

- Canalisation of streams and rivers and protection of channel banks with artificial piling, reducing or eliminating the marginal emergent vegetation.

- Planting of conifers in the uplands, with the elimination of flushes and shading of streamsides.

- Spread of naturalised alien plants, especially tall herbs on riversides.

- Planting of ornamental native aquatics in garden ponds, village ponds and around lakes, with the subsequent possibility of their escape or of the deliberate release of surplus material into 'wilder' habitats.

In addition to changes induced by human activity, appreciable changes attributable to natural succession may take place in a few decades in mesotrophic or eutrophic waters where there is a rapid input of silt; on the other hand the vegetation of oligotrophic waters may remain unchanged for decades (Spence 1964). There is obviously a potential for increases in nutrient inputs or silt inputs caused by human activities in the catchment to accelerate these natural processes.

1987-2004

There has been a deliberate attempt to reverse some of the above trends in recent years. Countryside Survey results suggest an increase in the number of inland water bodies of c. 4% between 1990 and 1998. This reflects a dynamic equilibrium with small water bodies, in particular, being created in some places and destroyed in others: it is thought that some 24,000 lowland ponds were lost but 37,000 created between 1990 and 1998 (Haines-Young et al. 2000). Although this represents a reversal of earlier trends, the degree to which 37,000 new ponds are an adequate substitute for 24,000 old ones probably differs from species to species.

There is now a greater appreciation of the importance of water catchments. During this period buffer zones were introduced between sprayed agricultural land and ditch and pond margins, originally on a voluntary basis in Environmentally Sensitive Areas and under Countryside Stewardship schemes; they are now compulsory. This is perhaps reflected in the improvement in the biological condition of rivers and streams noted by the Countryside Survey between 1990 and 1998 (Haines-Young et al. 2000). A few canalised waterbodies have been returned to a more natural course, although most engineered watercourses remain in their artificial state.

Earlier studies of changes in the species of wetland habitats

The criteria used to identify wetland species in the Local Change analysis preclude an exact comparison with earlier studies but most studies of county floras include an approximately equivalent group of wetland plants. In terms of county extinctions, species of Fens, marshes and swamps (BH 11) have suffered fewer extinctions in Bedfordshire and Northamptonshire than those of most Broad Habitats, whereas in Middlesex the number of extinctions approximates to the county average and in Cambridgeshire and Hertfordshire it is somewhat higher (James 1997, Preston 2000, Walker & Preston in press). The Lancashire and Cheshire area may be exceptional in the extent to which the creation of new wetland habitats has led to a marked expansion of the wetland flora in the historic period (Greenwood 1999). There is, within the broad spectrum of wetland species, considerable variation in the performance of different ecological groups. In lowland England plants of acidic wetlands have shown many more losses than those of habitats which are either calcareous or eutrophic or both (Mountford 1994); in Berwickshire plants of muddy watersides are currently "in catastrophic decline" (Braithwaite 2004).

At the national level, comparisons of the two Atlas datasets are to some extent hampered by variations in recording intensity, discussed in more detail under Aquatic plants. However, in England, where such variations are least, there is evidence for a moderate loss of Fen, marsh and swamp species at 10-km scale between 1930-69 and 1987-99 (Preston *et al.* 2003b).

Streamside plots recorded in 1990 and again in 1998 by the Countryside Survey teams demonstrated some of the most marked examples of change detected in the entire survey. The 10 x 1 metre plots alongside the edge of streams, ditches and small rivers showed a reduction in species-richness, an increase in species of eutrophic conditions and an increase in competitive, tall-growing vegetation, especially woody species such as *Crataegus monogyna* and *Rubus fruticosus*. Herbs that did well in the period included *Calystegia sepium* and *Poa trivialis*; those losing out included *Galium palustre* and *Myosotis scorpioides* (Haines-Young *et al.* 2000).

The BSBI Local change surveys

Most wetland species are perennials; the minority of annual species have a similar mean Change Factor to the perennials ($F_{2,175} = 1.28$, $p = 0.28$).

Perennation	No. species	Mean CF	Standard error
Annual	20	0	5
Biennial	4	-16	7
Perennial	154	+1	2

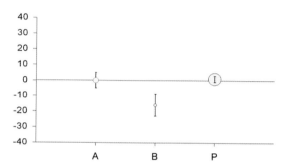

There is little difference in the mean Change Factors of Northern, Temperate and Southern species ($F_{3,173} = 1.17$, $p = 0.32$)

Wider Distribution	No. species*	Mean CF	Standard error
Northern	68	-3	2
Temperate	72	+1	3
Widespread	5	+4	7
Southern	32	+6	3

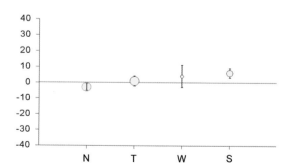

*The hybrid, *Stachys* × *ambigua* has no phytogeographical classification and is therefore excluded from this analysis.

There is a suggestion that plants of habitats with low pH have done less well than those of more base-rich habitats ($r = 0.13$, $p = 0.093$).

Ellenberg R	No. species	Mean CF	Standard error
2 (very acid)	2	-31	27
3	7	-7	7
4	14	+4	4
5	27	-2	3
6	55	-2	3
7	67	+5	3
8 (basic)	6	-7	8

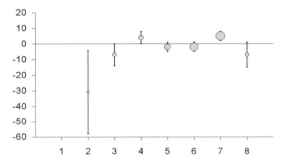

There is a more pronounced indication that the wetland plants of nutrient-poor habitats have done rather less well than those of more nutrient-rich sites ($r = 0.16$, $p = 0.032$).

Ellenberg N	No. species	Mean CF	Standard error
1 (very infertile)	4	-6	19
2	30	-2	3
3	26	-4	4
4	23	-9	4
5	29	+8	4
6	26	+3	5
7	33	+5	3
8 (very fertile)	7	+2	5

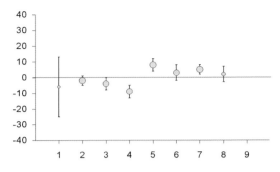

What environmental variables are driving the changes in Wetland habitats?

In modelling the non-climatic variables, a consistent effect of Ellenberg N emerges, but there is little evidence of an effect of any of the other variables. For a model with N alone, $R^2 = 2.6\%$. Neither Wider Distribution nor any of the individual climate variables show an effect when added to the basic model with N.

The analysis therefore shows fairly strong evidence of an effect of Ellenberg N, although the variation accounted for is relatively small. This suggests that eutrophication is the main driver of change that we have detected in this habitat.

Species groups

The species groups recognised below provide further insight into the changes in these habitats. The trend in widespread and lowland species has been in favour of competitive, nitrogen-tolerant plants at the expense of stress-tolerant ones. The more upland groups contain plants of hill flushes and here there has also been a decline of stress-tolerant species but less opportunity for colonisation so diversity has tended to decrease. Riversides are amongst the most dynamic of Britain's plant communities as they are directly affected by the levels of nutrient running off adjacent land and the continuous habitat provides the opportunity for rapid colonisation by any species favoured by the changing conditions. The change in the wetland habitats may relate to riversides and ditches.

Wetland habitats (BH11, 13 & 14 in part): classification of species

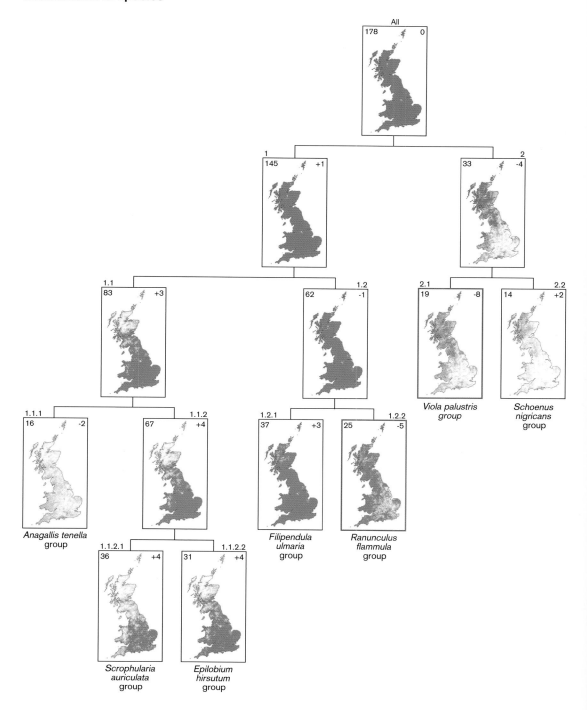

Anagallis tenella group (1.1.1)

Species	16	Average tetrads	36	Mean CF	- 2	Significance	0.53
		Local		No change			

Most of the species in this western group are rather low plants which grow in winter-flooded areas, shallow water or low swards on moist or damp soils. *Carex vesicaria* is the only tall emergent with the capacity to dominate a stand of vegetation.

The greatest losses are shown by *Eleocharis uniglumis*, *Apium inundatum*, *Dactylorhiza incarnata* and *Oenanthe lachenalii*. The first loss is unexpected and may relate to recording bias, the second and third continue a long-term decline, the fourth continues a long-term decline of its inland populations. All the losses may be related to more eutrophic conditions.

All the gains may relate to recording bias between the two surveys or chance effects as the samples involved are small.

Species	Broad Habitats	Native Status	WD	EN	G	L	R	Total	TF	RC	CF	90% Conf. Limits
Eleocharis uniglumis	11	N	t	4	3	11	7	21	26	-53	-54	30
Apium inundatum	11, 13	N	t	4	3	7	7	17	18	-37	-38	37
Dactylorhiza incarnata	11	N	n	2	14	19	7	40	27	-28	-31	38
Oenanthe lachenalii	11	N	s	5	4	6	6	16	21	-25	-26	46
Osmunda regalis	1, 11	N	s	4	7	9	12	28	23	-18	-19	35
Chrysosplenium alternifolium	11, 14	N	n	6	10	12	12	34	28	-17	-18	36
Anagallis tenella	11	N	s	3	15	16	33	64	33	-10	-12	24
Stellaria nemorum	1, 14	N	n	7	7	6	9	22	31	-2	-2	42
Ranunculus omiophyllus	11	N	s	4	28	20	29	77	58	+6	+7	27
Hypericum elodes	11	N	t	2	10	3	19	32	39	+16	+16	25
Lythrum portula	11, 13	N	t	3	28	15	27	70	38	+15	+17	26
Carex vesicaria	11	N	n	4	7	4	4	15	14	+19	+19	54
Scutellaria minor	11	N	s	2	19	7	23	49	39	+20	+22	25
Wahlenbergia hederacea	11, 14	N	s	3	9	3	11	23	52	+21	+22	33
Samolus valerandi	11	N	s	5	13	6	9	28	22	+23	+24	37
Stachys x ambigua	3, 14	NH		6	25	11	8	44	31	+34	+38	32

WD: Wider Distribution   EN: Ellenberg N   G: Gains   L: Losses   R: Re-finds   TF: Tetrad Frequency   RC: Relative Change   CF: Change Factor (weighted)

Apium inundatum
Lesser Marshwort

Mapped Change	-29%	
Relative Change	-37%	±41%
Weighted CF	-38%	±37%
Tetrad Frequency	18%	

Dactylorhiza incarnata
Early Marsh-orchid

Mapped Change	-19%	
Relative Change	-28%	±49%
Weighted CF	-31%	±38%
Tetrad Frequency	27%	

Although *Apium inundatum* was only recorded in 17 tetrads over the two surveys the apparent decline is so marked as to be notable. This result confirms the continuing decline reported in the *New Atlas* with eutrophication perhaps having become the main driver of change now that there is more awareness of the conservation value of the small water bodies that this species frequents.

Although the reported change in *Dactylorhiza incarnata* is below the level of significance the clusters of apparent losses are so striking and so much in line with the trend reported in the *New Atlas* that they are notable, seemingly pointing to the great vulnerability of the small base-rich flushes at low altitude favoured by this species.

Key to maps ● Loss ● Gain ○ Re-find
▨ *New Atlas* distribution

Scrophularia auriculata group (1.1.2.1)

Species	36	Average tetrads	62	Mean CF	+ 4	Significance	0.64
		Local		Increase not significant			

This group includes species from a wide range of lowland aquatic habitats.

The three species with significant losses are *Oenanthe aquatica*, *Rorippa sylvestris*, and *Hippuris vulgaris*. The first continues a long-term decline, the second shows a very unexpected trend, and the third had not changed for the *New Atlas*. *Oenanthe fistulosa*, like *Dactylorhiza incarnata* and *Oenanthe lachenalii* in the previous group, is a low herb which may have declined as eutrophication and a reduction in grazing has led to denser, taller swards in wetland sites.

Three of the species with a high positive Change factor, *Lysimachia nummularia*, *Rumex hydrolapathum* and *Ranunculus lingua*, are commonly introduced. Several are notably tolerant of eutrophic conditions, such as *Catabrosa aquatica*, *Chenopodium rubrum* and *Berula erecta*, and tolerance of eutrophic conditions may be part of the reason for the success of others.

Rorippa sylvestris, Creeping Yellow-cress Gillian Beckett

Oenanthe fistulosa, Tubular Water-dropwort Bob Ellis

Species	Broad Habitats	Native Status	WD	EN	G	L	R	Total	TF	RC	CF	90% Conf. Limits
Oenanthe aquatica	11	N	t	6	4	9	3	16	25	-50	-52	48
Rorippa sylvestris	11, 14	N	t	7	13	27	13	53	30	-43	-48	28
Hippuris vulgaris	11, 13	N	n	4	7	13	11	31	18	-34	-35	32
Oenanthe fistulosa	11	N	t	6	6	9	7	22	23	-27	-28	42
Typha angustifolia	11	N	t	7	11	14	7	32	25	-23	-25	41
Bidens tripartita	11, 13	N	t	7	10	11	11	32	21	-13	-14	38
Veronica catenata	13, 14	N	t	8	21	22	25	68	42	-10	-12	28
Ranunculus sceleratus	11, 13, 14	N	n	8	42	41	81	164	57	-7	-10	19
Calamagrostis epigejos	3, 11	N	n	6	13	13	16	42	28	-8	-9	34
Schoenoplectus tabernaemontani	11, 13	N	s	7	9	9	8	26	23	-9	-9	44
Rorippa amphibia	11, 13, 14	N	t	8	8	7	9	24	26	-3	-3	42
Veronica anagallis-aquatica	13, 14	N	s	7	27	24	21	72	38	-2	-2	29
Pulicaria dysenterica	6, 11	N	s	4	43	31	126	200	65	0	0	15
Juncus subnodulosus	11	N	s	4	6	5	6	17	17	0	0	50
Glyceria maxima	11	N	t	8	26	18	76	120	45	0	0	16
Carex otrubae	11	N	s	7	35	23	91	149	47	+2	+2	17
Bidens cernua	13, 14	N	t	7	15	12	10	37	32	+3	+4	40
Carex riparia	11, 14	N	t	7	26	18	40	84	38	+4	+5	24
Epilobium roseum	1, 3, 14, 17	N	t	7	20	16	6	42	38	+7	+8	42
Myosoton aquaticum	11, 13, 14	N	t	8	27	19	25	71	42	+7	+8	28
Rorippa palustris	11, 13	N	n	7	34	24	25	83	37	+9	+11	28
Alisma lanceolatum	13	N	s	7	8	6	2	16	25	+11	+12	60
Scrophularia auriculata	11, 14	N	s	7	54	18	144	216	71	+11	+16	13
Berula erecta	11	N	t	7	19	11	15	45	25	+15	+16	32
Thalictrum flavum	11	N	n	5	6	3	6	15	16	+16	+17	49
Salix triandra	11, 13, 14	AR	t	5	14	9	6	29	26	+16	+18	43
Ranunculus lingua	11	N	t	7	10	7	2	19	14	+16	+18	54
Rumex hydrolapathum	11	N	t	6	19	9	17	45	27	+19	+21	30
Scirpus sylvaticus	1, 11	N	t	6	10	4	10	24	21	+21	+22	36
Lysimachia nummularia	6, 11, 14	N	t	5	66	37	46	149	58	+18	+25	23
Carex acuta	11	N	n	5	10	6	2	18	22	+25	+26	52
Chenopodium rubrum	4, 11	N	t	8	72	43	39	154	62	+18	+27	25
Dactylorhiza praetermissa	11	N	t	3	22	6	23	51	28	+27	+29	23
Catabrosa aquatica	13, 14	N	n	7	13	6	6	25	25	+28	+30	41
Carex strigosa	1, 14	N	t	6	9	3	6	18	25	+31	+32	42
Carex pseudocyperus	11	N	t	6	16	4	8	28	27	+41	+43	33

WD: Wider Distribution   EN: Ellenberg N   G: Gains   L: Losses   R: Re-finds   TF: Tetrad Frequency   RC: Relative Change   CF: Change Factor (weighted)

Rorippa sylvestris
Creeping Yellow-cress

Mapped Change	-35%	
Relative Change	-43%	±32%
Weighted CF	-48%	±28%
Tetrad Frequency	30%	

Catabrosa aquatica
Whorl-grass

Mapped Change	+37%	
Relative Change	+28%	±49%
Weighted CF	+30%	±41%
Tetrad Frequency	25%	

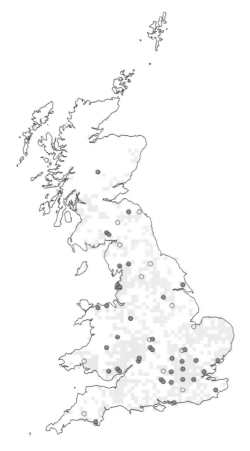

Rorippa sylvestris was reported by the *New Atlas* as increasing. The dramatic losses shown by these surveys are wholly unexpected though the riversides that are the most favoured habitat may have less open habitat than in the past, being increasingly colonised by *Impatiens glandulifera* and grasses such as *Phalaris arundinacea* and *Glyceria maxima* in response to rising nutrient levels.

While only recorded in 25 tetrads over the two surveys *Catabrosa aquatica* shows an intriguing possibility of increase. This species is relatively tolerant of modest eutrophication and has recently colonised the muddy margins of several new ponds in the Scottish Borders where it was once feared almost extinct.

Key to maps   ● Loss   ● Gain   ○ Re-find
░ *New Atlas* distribution

Epilobium hirsutum group (1.1.2.2)

Species	30	Average tetrads	164	Mean CF	+ 4	Significance	0.64
		Moderately widespread		**Increase not significant**			

This group, though widespread, thins out in the acidic uplands, reflecting the tendency of the species to favour relatively eutrophic habitats.

Of the species with losses, that of *Mentha arvensis* probably relates to its alternative arable habitat, that of *Listera ovata* to its woodland and grassland habitats and those of *Valeriana dioica* and *Carex disticha* to an intolerance to eutrophication.

Of the species with gains, *Carex pendula* and *Typha latifolia* are often planted. All the others are tolerant of eutrophication.

Carex disticha, Brown Sedge Bob Ellis

Epilobium parviflorum, Hoary Willowherb Bob Ellis

Species	Broad Habitats	Native Status	WD	EN	G	L	R	Total	TF	RC	CF	90% Conf. Limits
Mentha arvensis	4, 11	N	n	6	44	55	44	143	48	-19	-26	23
Listera ovata	1, 11	N	n	5	24	31	25	80	27	-21	-25	26
Valeriana dioica	11	N	t	3	10	15	30	55	33	-19	-21	21
Carex disticha	11	N	t	4	17	21	24	62	32	-17	-19	27
Petasites hybridus	14	N	t	7	24	26	72	122	35	-10	-12	17
Solanum dulcamara	3, 11, 14	N	s	7	41	36	275	352	86	-5	-11	12
Salix purpurea	11, 14	N	t	5	16	16	13	45	27	-8	-9	36
Eupatorium cannabinum	11	N	t	7	33	29	101	163	49	-5	-6	16
Alisma plantago-aquatica	11, 13	N	w	7	51	46	98	195	56	-4	-6	19
Carex paniculata	1, 11	N	t	6	20	18	36	74	30	-5	-5	24
Equisetum telmateia	11	N	s	6	14	10	55	79	35	-2	-3	16
Galium uliginosum	11	N	n	4	28	24	38	90	41	-2	-3	24
Carex acutiformis	11	N	t	6	24	20	39	83	30	-2	-2	23
Glyceria notata	11, 14	N	t	7	47	42	29	118	50	-2	-2	28
Cardamine amara	1, 14	N	t	6	27	22	38	87	46	-1	-1	24
Persicaria amphibia	11, 13	N	n	6	37	26	107	170	44	0	0	17
Oenanthe crocata	11, 14	N	s	7	34	20	150	204	63	0	0	13
Barbarea vulgaris	3, 14	N	t	8	67	49	128	244	68	+2	+3	20
Juncus inflexus	6, 11	N	s	5	52	23	220	295	79	+4	+7	13
Epilobium hirsutum	11, 14	N	s	7	49	14	341	404	92	+3	+9	11
Rumex conglomeratus	11, 14	N	s	7	72	48	123	243	69	+5	+9	19
Apium nodiflorum	14	N	s	7	63	28	161	252	74	+9	+14	14
Lysimachia vulgaris	11	N	t	5	21	12	20	53	26	+14	+15	29
Lythrum salicaria	11	N	t	5	50	26	74	150	46	+12	+15	18
Scutellaria galericulata	11	N	n	5	30	13	40	83	28	+16	+19	21
Sparganium erectum	11, 13	N	t	7	83	41	132	256	59	+12	+21	17
Persicaria lapathifolia	4, 11	N	s	7	83	44	105	232	67	+13	+22	19
Lycopus europaeus	11	N	t	6	54	18	85	157	48	+18	+24	15
Typha latifolia	11	N	s	7	84	28	134	246	62	+19	+30	14
Carex pendula	1, 14	N	s	6	82	8	72	162	56	+41	+51	11
Epilobium parviflorum	11	N	t	5	142	45	102	289	75	+33	+59	17

WD: Wider Distribution   EN: Ellenberg N   G: Gains   L: Losses   R: Re-finds   TF: Tetrad Frequency   RC: Relative Change   CF: Change Factor (weighted)

Carex disticha
Brown Sedge

Mapped Change	- 9%	
Relative Change	-17%	±30%
Weighted CF	-19%	±27%
Tetrad Frequency	32%	

Epilobium parviflorum
Hoary Willowherb

Mapped Change	**+40%**	
Relative Change	**+33%**	±11%
Weighted CF	**+59%**	±17%
Tetrad Frequency	75%	

Carex disticha is such a frequent species in the Scottish Borders in even slightly base-rich wetlands that it is surprising how relatively infrequent it is elsewhere. It frequently does not flower in less-favourable habitats and this suggests a reason for the low proportion of re-finds between the two surveys. In these circumstances the indication of losses is only tentative.

Epilobium parviflorum is a species that thrives in eutrophic conditions as well as some much more infertile ones. It has spread throughout its range along with its relative, *Epilobium hirsutum*, but favouring shorter vegetation communities than that species, including seasonally wet vehicle ruts. In many areas it has spread from its previous wetland habitats to join other *Epilobium* species in set-aside fields or as a street weed.

Key to maps ● Loss ● Gain ○ Re-find
New Atlas distribution

Filipendula ulmaria group (1.2.1)

Species	37	Average tetrads	369	Mean CF	+ 3	Significance	0.89
		Widespread		No change			

This group includes many of the most characteristic plants of these habitats.

The species showing losses include plants that are almost ubiquitous at hectad scale. Nevertheless they are seen to be less frequent at tetrad scale and the apparent sharp declines may reflect a bias in this group towards plants more typical of fairly acid conditions and relatively open communities.

In contrast the increasing species include some of the most competitive species of these habitats such as *Phragmites australis* and *Phalaris arundinacea*. The apparent increase in *Carex remota* is intriguing and could partly be a response to climate change.

Caltha palustris, Marsh Marigold Bob Ellis

164

Species	Broad Habitats	Native Status	WD	EN	G	L	R	Total	TF	RC	CF	90% Conf. Limits
Caltha palustris	11	N	n	4	55	84	236	375	67	-15	-36	15
Equisetum palustre	11	N	n	3	52	79	128	259	54	-20	-34	16
Angelica sylvestris	11, 16	N	n	5	49	55	397	501	85	-7	-29	18
Cirsium palustre	11, 14	N	n	4	34	39	433	506	87	-6	-28	14
Myosotis scorpioides	11, 14	N	t	6	57	73	115	245	55	-16	-27	18
Callitriche stagnalis sens. lat.	11, 13, 14	N	t	6	83	91	160	334	64	-10	-23	22
Glyceria fluitans	11, 14	N	t	6	88	90	248	426	77	-7	-22	25
Cardamine pratensis	6, 11	N	n	4	70	62	394	526	90	-3	-21	30
Stellaria uliginosa	11, 14	N	t	5	62	59	298	419	81	-5	-15	18
Lotus pedunculatus	11	N	t	4	58	57	267	382	78	-6	-15	16
Veronica beccabunga	11, 14	N	t	6	59	55	294	408	84	-5	-14	17
Valeriana officinalis	11	N	n	5	46	38	222	306	64	-4	-7	13
Rorippa nasturtium-aquaticum agg.	11, 13, 14	N	s	7	84	74	165	323	70	-3	-6	22
Lychnis flos-cuculi	11	N	t	4	66	55	168	289	56	-2	-4	18
Persicaria hydropiper	11, 13, 14	N	t	6	69	58	127	254	67	-2	-3	20
Juncus conglomeratus	11	N	t	3	89	68	274	431	80	0	-1	24
Filipendula ulmaria	11	N	n	5	41	17	448	506	87	0	-1	17
Myosotis laxa	11	N	n	5	77	63	106	246	55	0	+1	24
Dactylorhiza fuchsii	11	N	t	3	65	51	96	212	50	+1	+2	22
Carex flacca	7, 11	N	s	2	103	80	234	417	75	+1	+2	29
Galium palustre	11	N	n	4	70	41	324	435	78	+2	+5	19
Mentha aquatica	11	N	t	5	76	45	255	376	73	+3	+8	18
Phalaris arundinacea	11, 14	N	n	7	77	39	257	373	73	+5	+13	16
Vicia cracca	3, 11	N	n	5	72	34	375	481	86	+3	+13	20
Stachys palustris	11, 14	N	n	7	81	50	118	249	56	+8	+15	20
Eleocharis palustris	11	N	w	4	77	46	113	236	46	+9	+15	19
Phragmites australis	11	N	w	6	50	20	113	183	42	+11	+15	14
Juncus bufonius sens. lat.	3, 1, 13, 14	N	w	5	102	65	329	496	85	+3	+16	32
Juncus articulatus	11	N	s	3	92	52	347	491	83	+4	+17	26
Hypericum tetrapterum	11	N	t	4	83	46	107	236	57	+12	+20	19
Carex remota	1, 14	N	t	6	65	20	134	219	59	+15	+23	13
Juncus acutiflorus	11	N	t	2	111	57	203	371	74	+11	+27	20
Iris pseudacorus	11	N	s	6	100	36	221	357	66	+14	+30	15
Calystegia sepium	11, 14	N	t	7	101	32	234	367	82	+14	+32	14
Salix cinerea	1, 11	N	n	5	94	34	371	499	91	+8	+33	21
Gnaphalium uliginosum	11, 13	N	n	5	119	55	170	344	73	+16	+35	19
Veronica serpyllifolia	3, 5, 11	N	n	5	106	48	361	515	92	+7	+36	27

WD: Wider Distribution EN: Ellenberg N G: Gains L: Losses R: Re-finds TF: Tetrad Frequency RC: Relative Change CF: Change Factor (weighted)

Caltha palustris
Marsh Marigold

Mapped Change	- 9%	
Relative Change	-15%	± 7%
Weighted CF	-36%	±15%
Tetrad Frequency	67%	

Carex remota
Remote Sedge

Mapped Change	+23%	
Relative Change	+15%	± 9%
Weighted CF	+23%	±13%
Tetrad Frequency	59%	

Caltha palustris is too frequent to have shown significant change at hectad scale in the *New Atlas*. However at tetrad scale the scarcity of this species in much of the south and east of England is evident and it is here that there is striking evidence of decline. *Caltha palustris* favours open mires rather than watersides and it is likely to be these communities that have continued to suffer losses in the south.

Carex remota appears to have been increasing within its range and possibly extending towards the east. A resurvey in 2004 after 25 years of a stretch of the River North Tyne in Northumberland showed a dramatic increase in this species and this may be in line with national trends rather than related to higher average river levels following construction of the Kielder reservoir. This example demonstrates the difficulty of linking observed changes with possible driving forces such as milder winters.

Key to maps   ● Loss   ● Gain   ○ Re-find
        ▨ *New Atlas* distribution

Phragmites australis
Common Reed

Mapped Change	+18%	
Relative Change	+11%	±10%
Weighted CF	+15%	±14%
Tetrad Frequency	42%	

Phragmites australis is not particularly frequent except in some parts of the south and east and is somewhat coastal in the north. It flourishes with eutrophication and its increase may relate to spread along ditches in the lowlands where it could be transported by ditch-cleaning machinery, though it is sometimes planted deliberately for game cover.

Key to maps   ● Loss   ● Gain   ○ Re-find
▨ *New Atlas* distribution

Bob Ellis

Ranunculus flammula group (1.2.2)

Species	25	Average tetrads	228	Mean CF	- 5	Significance	0.04
		Widespread		Significant decrease			

Most of the plants in this group occur predominantly in acid habitats in the north and west. They appear to be declining at the fringes of their ranges in the south and east. The decline is remarkably uniform and marked. The only two species showing increases are *Epilobium obscurum*, which is a plant of many habitats, including ruderal ones, and *Myosotis secunda* which may have been under-recorded in the first survey.

Pedicularis sylvatica, Lousewort Bob Ellis

Senecio aquaticus, Marsh Ragwort Bob Ellis

Species	Broad Habitats	Native Status	WD	EN	G	L	R	Total	TF	RC	CF	90% Conf. Limits
Hydrocotyle vulgaris	11	N	s	3	16	33	110	159	42	-20	-25	9
Ranunculus flammula	11	N	t	3	38	49	318	405	74	-9	-23	12
Pedicularis sylvatica	10, 12, 14	N	t	2	24	40	161	225	60	-15	-23	10
Senecio aquaticus	11, 14	N	t	5	40	52	96	188	46	-16	-22	17
Agrostis canina sens. lat.	8, 11	N	n	3	72	80	186	338	86	-10	-22	19
Triglochin palustre	11	N	n	2	39	49	94	182	51	-15	-21	17
Callitriche hamulata sens. lat.	11, 13, 14	N	w	5	28	32	19	79	32	-16	-20	30
Ranunculus hederaceus	11, 13	N	s	5	34	38	39	111	43	-13	-17	24
Carex viridula subsp. *oedocarpa*	14	N	n	2	48	47	199	294	69	-6	-12	14
Carex nigra	11	N	n	2	52	47	259	358	69	-5	-11	15
Achillea ptarmica	11	N	n	3	60	57	165	282	63	-6	-11	17
Carex panicea	11	N	n	2	45	40	245	330	67	-5	-10	13
Juncus bulbosus	14	N	n	2	58	52	201	311	71	-4	-9	16
Epilobium palustre	11, 14	N	n	3	56	46	227	329	72	-3	-6	15
Equisetum fluviatile	11	N	n	4	61	53	127	241	50	-3	-5	19
Potentilla palustris	11	N	n	3	32	26	76	134	46	-2	-3	18
Chrysosplenium oppositifolium	1, 14	N	t	5	42	26	213	281	68	-1	-1	12
Gymnadenia conopsea	7, 11	N	n	3	19	15	18	52	29	+2	+3	33
Montia fontana	11	N	n	3	66	45	168	279	68	+2	+4	18
Menyanthes trifoliata	11	N	n	3	32	17	89	138	41	+5	+6	16
Isolepis setacea	11, 14	N	t	3	59	47	39	145	43	+4	+6	28
Veronica scutellata	11, 13	N	n	3	52	36	45	133	47	+9	+12	24
Glyceria declinata	13, 14	N	t	6	82	59	60	201	62	+9	+15	26
Myosotis secunda	11	N	t	4	64	31	101	196	65	+13	+18	17
Epilobium obscurum	11, 14	N	t	5	130	55	136	321	78	+21	+44	19

WD: Wider Distribution   EN: Ellenberg N   G: Gains   L: Losses   R: Re-finds   TF: Tetrad Frequency   RC: Relative Change   CF: Change Factor (weighted)

Pedicularis sylvatica
Lousewort

Mapped Change	- 8%	
Relative Change	-15%	± 7%
Weighted CF	-23%	±10%
Tetrad Frequency	60%	

The decline of *Pedicularis sylvatica* has been more marked than that of the moorland with which it is largely associated. The losses are likely to be associated with the drying out of habitat fragments and with coniferisation.

Senecio aquaticus
Marsh Ragwort

Mapped Change	- 8%	
Relative Change	-16%	±14%
Weighted CF	-22%	±17%
Tetrad Frequency	46%	

The evidence of the decline of *Senecio aquaticus* is consistent with that in the *New Atlas*. It is more pronounced than would be expected from the general decline in wetland habitats, pointing to a link with a decline in the acid habitats favoured by this species as soil nutrient levels have risen across the country.

Key to maps   ● Loss   ● Gain   ○ Re-find
          New Atlas distribution

Viola palustris group (2.1)

Species	19	Average tetrads	29	Mean CF	- 8	Significance	0.01
		Moderately widespread		**Significant decrease**			

This group includes species of both base-rich and acid communities, including flushes and other small-scale habitats. The decline is very marked.

The two species show gains: *Rumex longifolius*, a plant of damp and dry waste places which has a very different ecology to the other species in the group, and *Carex dioica*, a small plant that is very easily overlooked and was probably under-recorded in the first survey.

Sagina nodosa, Knotted Pearlwort   Gillian Beckett

Species	Broad Habitats	Native Status	WD	EN	G	L	R	Total	TF	RC	CF	90% Conf. Limits
Sagina nodosa	11, 19	N	n	3	12	22	7	41	31	-43	-47	34
Carex viridula subsp. *brachyrrhyncha*	11,14	N	t	2	22	29	27	78	44	-21	-24	25
Carex curta	11	N	n	2	25	34	44	103	54	-20	-24	21
Potamogeton polygonifolius	11, 12, 13	N	t	2	31	40	139	210	61	-12	-18	13
Pedicularis palustris	11	N	n	2	21	26	64	111	44	-14	-16	17
Viola palustris .	11, 14	N	n	2	30	36	211	277	76	-9	-16	10
Pinguicula vulgaris	11, 12	N	n	2	9	15	155	179	67	-11	-15	5
Parnassia palustris	11	N	n	3	15	16	33	64	42	-10	-12	24
Littorella uniflora	11, 13	N	t	3	14	14	41	69	32	-8	-9	21
Crepis paludosa	11, 16	N	n	4	28	25	90	143	67	-5	-7	16
Carex echinata	11, 12, 14	N	n	2	41	30	207	278	72	-2	-4	12
Carex pulicaris	11, 16	N	t	2	40	31	132	203	63	-2	-3	15
Carum verticillatum	11, 14	N	s	2	4	3	11	18	33	-2	-2	36
Eleocharis quinqueflora	11	N	n	2	26	21	46	93	50	-1	-1	22
Dactylorhiza purpurella	11	N	n	2	26	21	35	82	39	0	0	24
Carex rostrata	11	N	n	2	43	27	126	196	58	+2	+3	16
Carex hostiana	11	N	t	2	35	23	83	141	54	+2	+3	18
Carex dioica	11	N	n	2	37	16	58	111	67	+14	+17	18
Rumex longifolius	3, 13	N	n	7	21	10	23	54	58	+17	+18	26

WD: Wider Distribution   EN: Ellenberg N   G: Gains   L: Losses   R: Re-finds   TF: Tetrad Frequency   RC: Relative Change   CF: Change Factor (weighted)

Carex curta
White Sedge

Mapped Change	-12%	
Relative Change	-20%	±21%
Weighted CF	-24%	±21%
Tetrad Frequency	54%	

Sagina nodosa
Knotted Pearlwort

Mapped Change	-34%	
Relative Change	-43%	±43%
Weighted CF	-47%	±34%
Tetrad Frequency	31%	

Carex curta showed no change in the *New Atlas* because better recording of the uplands countered probable losses in the lowlands. These surveys demonstrate that the loss of acid bogs in the lowlands is all too real, with coniferisation having been a likely driving force for much of the change.

Sagina nodosa is seen to be a scarce and highly elusive species at tetrad scale. It is late flowering, almost invisible when not in flower, and often confined to a few small flushes in a wide expanse of moorland. Its more predictable coastal habitats are little sampled by the survey. Although the *New Atlas* indicates great losses of this species since 1950, especially in SE England, the large decline indicated by the data table must be interpreted with caution given these uncertainties.

Key to maps ● Loss ● Gain ○ Re-find
       New Atlas distribution

Schoenus nigricans group (2.2)

Species	15	Average tetrads	42	Mean CF	+ 2	Significance	0.97
		Local		No change			

This is small group of northwestern species, including some Arctic-montane plants of flushes and streamsides at high altitude.

The tetrads sampled provide few records of these very local species thus a low confidence level in the trends shown. While the high losses of *Drosera intermedia*, *Sparganium natans* and *Trollius europaeus* are in line with the trends of the *Viola palustris* group (2.1) and may well be correct, the high apparent gains of *Eriophorum latifolium* and *Eleocharis multicaulis* are most unlikely to be real and probably relate to poor recording of these easily overlooked species in the first survey.

Species	Broad Habitats	Native Status	WD	EN	G	L	R	Total	TF	RC	CF	90% Conf. Limits
Drosera intermedia	12, 14	N	t	1	4	15	8	27	48	-56	-58	28
Trollius europaeus	11, 16	N	n	4	9	16	23	48	40	-26	-28	23
Saxifraga stellaris	11, 15, 16	N	n	3	7	8	32	47	63	-11	-12	19
Drosera anglica	11, 12	N	n	1	8	6	34	48	61	-4	-4	19
Saxifraga aizoides	7, 11, 15, 16	N	n	2	9	6	34	49	67	-1	-2	20
Carex limosa	11, 12	N	n	1	7	4	12	23	40	+7	+8	37
Selaginella selaginoides	7, 11	N	n	2	34	16	78	128	76	+8	+10	16
Thalictrum alpinum	7, 11, 15, 16	N	n	3	12	6	21	39	58	+10	+10	28
Epilobium anagallidifolium	11, 15	N	n	3	6	3	7	16	49	+14	+15	46
Salix phylicifolia	14, 16	N	n	4	8	5	5	18	31	+14	+15	51
Schoenus nigricans	11	N	s	2	15	4	32	51	44	+15	+16	19
Pinguicula lusitanica	10, 11	N	t	2	16	7	14	37	50	+22	+23	31
Eleocharis multicaulis	11, 12, 13	N	t	1	26	8	26	60	41	+26	+29	22
Eriophorum latifolium	11	N	n	2	17	3	9	29	41	+45	+47	29

WD: Wider Distribution   EN: Ellenberg N   G: Gains   L: Losses   R: Re-finds   TF: Tetrad Frequency   RC: Relative Change   CF: Change Factor (weighted)

Trollius europaeus
Globeflower

Mapped Change	-18%	
Relative Change	-26%	±25%
Weighted CF	-28%	±23%
Tetrad Frequency	40%	

Drosera intermedia
Oblong-leaved Sundew

Mapped Change	-48%	
Relative Change	-56%	±31%
Weighted CF	-58%	±28%
Tetrad Frequency	48%	

In the past losses of *Trollius europaeus* have been mainly reported in the lowlands where it is still a victim of agricultural improvement and the eutrophication of remnant wetlands. This map suggests decline across the whole range of the species and is a reminder that even in the Highlands many of the populations are low down on the hills.

Drosera intermedia is easily overlooked in the north-west of Scotland and it is here that the apparent change is concentrated. Nevertheless the apparent change is dramatic and this suggests a need for further survey.

Key to maps   ● Loss   ● Gain   ○ Re-find
       New Atlas distribution

Doubtfully native species and neophytes in Wetland habitats

Although there is only a small suite of doubtfully alien or neophyte species in wetlands, several of the neophytes are both frequent and conspicuous.

Species	Broad Habitats	Native Status	WD	EN	G	L	R	Total	TF	RC	CF	90% Conf. Limits
Doubtful Status												
Aconitum napellus sens. lat.	1, 3, 14, 17	NA	t	6	12	4	7	23	17	+34	+35	38
Ranunculus sardous	3, 6, 13	NA	t	7	8	7	9	24	35	-3	-3	42
Neophytes												
Acorus calamus	13, 14	AN		7	8	7	7	22	27	-2	-2	46
Crassula helmsii	13, 14	AN		7	33	2	3	38	30	+78	+81	24
Epilobium brunnescens	14, 15, 16	AN		3	66	11	69	146	65	+33	+41	13
Heracleum mantegazzianum	3, 14, 17	AN		8	17	14	17	48	27	0	0	34
Impatiens capensis	13, 14	AN		6	8	1	8	17	29	+35	+36	30
Impatiens glandulifera	14	AN		7	57	24	74	155	49	+17	+23	17
Juncus tenuis	1, 3, 13	AN		4	33	15	43	91	51	+16	+18	21
Mimulus agg.	13, 14	AN		5	23	28	60	111	39	-14	-17	18
Ribes nigrum	1, 3, 14	AN	n	6	51	44	38	133	44	0	0	26

WD: Wider Distribution   EN: Ellenberg N   G: Gains   L: Losses   R: Re-finds   TF: Tetrad Frequency   RC: Relative Change   CF: Change Factor (weighted)

Drosera intermedia, Oblong-leaved Sundew Simon Harrap

Gillian Beckett

Aquatic habitats (BH11, 13 & 14 in part)

Species	67	Average tetrads	102	Mean CF	+ 1	Significance	0.56
				No change			

The treatment of the plants of the wetland Broad Habitats is explained in the previous section. The aquatic plants are permanently submerged species, emergents rooted in more or less permanent water or plants which float on the water surface.

Aquatic plants are probably less well recorded than those in any of the other habitat groups. They share difficulties of access with the Montane habitats (BH15) and like them they are difficult to survey thoroughly. Recorders are often inadequately equipped to record open water where grapnels, chest waders or boats may be needed for satisfactory survey even if access is available, which it quite often is not. Additional complications come from the taxonomic complexity of some of the major genera. Aquatic plants therefore tend to be recorded thoroughly only by the more dedicated and experienced general recorders, or by specialists, and it is thus difficult to obtain adequate coverage of the tetrads in a 'snapshot' survey like Local Change.

Changes in aquatic habitats, 1950-2004

1950-1986

The wetland and aquatic habitats are clearly closely allied and similar changes have affected them both. The following relate specifically to the aquatic habitat.

- Eutrophication of both standing and flowing waters, both because of the general background increase in nutrients and because of pollution from 'point sources'.

- Canalisation of streams and rivers and protection of channel banks with artificial piling, reducing or eliminating the marginal emergent vegetation and the shallow water zone.

- The boom in canal traffic, saving canals which were once threatened by dewatering but having a very adverse effect on the submerged aquatic plants.

- Conversion of grazing marshes to arable land, with the loss of aquatic habitats in ditches which are no longer required as stock-proof barriers and thus are filled in, allowed to dry out or become overgrown with emergents.

- Falling water tables in highly populated areas, leading to the reduction in flow or seasonal drying out of springs, streams and the upper courses of rivers.

- Increase in the numbers of geese, including native and feral Greylag geese and Canada geese, leading to direct grazing of aquatics and eutrophication of the waters where they roost.

- Increase in gravel extraction in lowland river valleys, creating large areas of new aquatic habitat which may be left to colonise naturally or planted with both native and alien species; many of these pits are later filled in but others are retained for fishing or other amenity use.

- Planting of ornamental native aquatics in garden ponds, village ponds and around lakes, with the subsequent possibility of their escape or of the deliberate release of surplus material into 'wilder' habitats.

1987-2004

The changes discussed under Wetland habitats also apply to Aquatic plants. A particularly important factor affecting both wetland and aquatic species appears to be the great turnover of small ponds. This is documented by the results of the Countryside Survey (see Wetland habitats, p.153), and the effect at the tetrad scale is described by all the vice-county recorders who contributed accounts to the Local Assessment of Change (Chapter 7 p.307). The effect of new ponds on our flora is particularly marked as they are often planted with wetland and aquatic plants, including both species which are native to Britain and those which are not. Invasive aliens may also be introduced to them as contaminants with other plant material.

Earlier studies of changes in aquatic species

Many studies have grouped the true aquatics with other wetland species. Those which treat them separately present rather a mixed picture. In West Lancashire there has been an overall increase in aquatic habitats, with new wetlands developing, the construction of new reservoirs and the digging of gravel pits. Aquatic species (defined slightly more widely than here, with Ellenberg F=9-12) which have appeared in the county or are increasing slightly outnumber extinct or decreasing species (Greenwood 2003). Dony (1977) noted the increase in aquatic habitats brought about by mineral workings in Bedfordshire, and suggested that, in terms of species present in the county, "the limited purely aquatic flora has remained remarkably constant". However, a recent analysis of Bedfordshire and Northamptonshire has shown that the proportion of extinct freshwater species is greater than that in any other Broad Habitat except Bog and Dwarf shrub heath (Walker & Preston, in press). In other counties, including Cambridgeshire, Hertfordshire and Middlesex, the percentage of extinct and declining aquatic species is not very dissimilar to that for the flora as a whole (James 1997, Preston 2000).

Comparison of the two BSBI Atlas surveys is difficult. In Scotland a large-scale professional survey of lochs provided a far better coverage for the *New Atlas* than was available for the 1962 *Atlas*; in England and Wales the variation in recording effort, though less extreme, nevertheless hampers any comparison of the results.

There have been numerous site-based studies of aquatic and wetland plants, as water bodies provide well-defined localities for study. In the lowlands most studies indicate eutrophication, with the loss of species characteristic of less nutrient-rich waters. This has been documented, for instance, for the Norfolk Broads (George 1992), the Lancaster canal in West Lancashire (Greenwood 2005) and the River Cam and its floodplain in Cambridge (Preston *et al.* 2003a); occasionally the recovery of the flora has been noted once nutrient inputs have been reduced (Wade 1999).

The BSBI Local change surveys

In examining the results of the survey, it is clear that many species have not been refound consistently in the same places in the two surveys. This is illustrated by some of the species' accounts. Part of this is undoubtedly due to inefficiency in survey, described above. Nevertheless there is a probability that aquatic species are far more mobile than was once thought and that local extinctions and colonisations are commonplace both in response to changes in water quality and to physical factors, particularly the creation of new ponds, losses in rivers due to floods and losses from ditches when they are mechanically cleaned.

The few annual aquatics are small plants of shallow water or disturbed and periodically flooded sites. They have done less well than the perennials ($F_{1,65} = 7.96$, $p = 0.006$).

Perennation	No. species	Mean CF	Standard error
Annual	9	-17	5
Biennial	0		
Perennial	58	+4	3

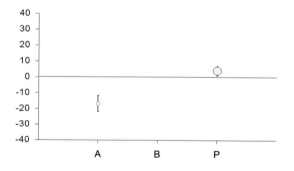

There is no marked trend in the changes of species with different geographical distributions ($F_{3,63} = 0.33$, $p = 0.80$).

Wider Distribution	No. species	Mean CF	Standard error
Northern	22	+1	4
Temperate	22	-1	5
Widespread	7	-2	5
Southern	16	+6	6

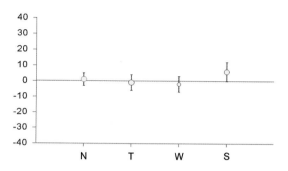

Similarly, pH requirements (as measured by Ellenberg R values) are poor predictors of performance ($r = -0.015$, $r = 0.90$).

Ellenberg R	No. species	Mean CF	Standard error
3 (acid)	1	+16	-
4	10	+8	6
5	7	-6	5
6	16	-9	6
7	31	+6	4
8 (basic)	2	-9	0.4

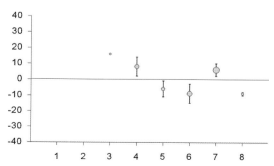

Much more surprisingly, the Ellenberg N values show no clear pattern of change in relation to fertility ($r = 0.056$, $p = 0.65$).

Ellenberg N	No. species	Mean CF	Standard error
1 (very infertile)	3	-5	6
2	8	+11	7
3	4	-12	10
4	8	-4	9
5	6	-10	9
6	17	+1	7
7	17	+7	4
8 (very fertile)	4	-2	4

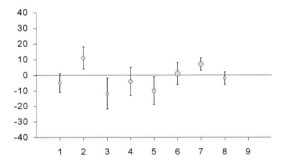

What environmental variables are driving the changes in Aquatic habitats?

The only variable tested above that correlated with Change Factor is perennation. For a model based on perennation alone, $R^2 = 10.9\%$, $p = 0.006$. Adding the other variables to this model tests for effects after allowing for differences in perennation, but none are detectable. The improvement in fit adding each of the variables in turn (together with their statistical significance) is as follows: Ellenberg R, $R^2 = 10.9\%$, $p = 0.92$; Ellenberg N, $R^2 = 11.9\%$, $p = 0.41$; Wider Distribution, $R^2 = 13.2\%$, $p = 0.66$; January temperature, $R^2 = 11.4$, $p = 0.53$; July temperature, $R^2 = 13.4\%$, $p = 0.18$; rainfall, $R^2 = 12.2\%$, $p = 0.33$).

The *New Atlas* failed to show meaningful change in many aquatic species because the survey had been very much more thorough for the *New Atlas* than for the 1962 *Atlas*. We expected that the Local Change survey would show the true patterns of change in this interesting group of species for the first time. This expectation has to a large measure been unfulfilled. The low proportion of refinds leads to wide confidence limits and this, coupled with the relative scarcity of aquatic habitats at tetrad scale, has limited the number of species with significant change. At group level there are often both increasing and decreasing species, their fortunes relating both to changes in water quality and to a net change in the number of water bodies, as more ponds have been dug in recent years than have been lost. All these factors have contributed to a picture of little overall change despite much suggestion of change at local scale.

Species groups

Four species groups are considered.

Aquatic plants (BH11, 13 & 14 in part): classification of species

Potamogeton crispus group (1.1)

Species	35	Average tetrads	46	Mean CF	+ 3	Significance	0.53
		Local		No change			

This is a group of largely southern species that are tolerant of eutrophication. There is little evidence of change except in a few species that are commonly introduced such as *Nymphoides peltata*, *Butomus umbellatus*, *Sagittaria sagittifolia* and *Nymphaea alba*.

Oenanthe aquatica, Fine-leaved Water-dropwort Gillian Beckett

Sagittaria sagittifolia, Arrowhead Bob Ellis

Species	Broad Habitats	Native Status	WD	EN	G	L	R	Total	TF	RC	CF	90% Conf. Limits
Oenanthe aquatica	11	N	t	6	4	9	3	16	25	-50	-52	48
Callitriche obtusangula	13, 14	N	s	6	7	12	4	23	23	-40	-42	45
Hippuris vulgaris	11, 13	N	n	4	7	13	11	31	18	-34	-35	32
Typha angustifolia	11	N	t	7	11	14	7	32	25	-23	-25	41
Ranunculus aquatilis sens. lat.	13, 14	N	w	5	36	41	30	107	63	-15	-20	26
Potamogeton perfoliatus	13, 14	N	n	5	10	12	10	32	21	-18	-19	38
Bolboschoenus maritimus	21	N	s	7	8	11	22	41	29	-18	-19	25
Lemna trisulca	11, 13	N	t	5	19	21	18	58	30	-14	-15	31
Ranunculus trichophyllus	11, 13	N	n	6	16	17	9	42	30	-12	-14	39
Veronica catenata	13, 14	N	t	8	21	22	25	68	42	-10	-12	28
Potamogeton crispus	13, 14	N	s	7	28	28	10	66	25	-8	-11	37
Zannichellia palustris	13, 14	N	s	7	13	13	3	29	18	-9	-10	50
Schoenoplectus tabernaemontani	11, 13	N	s	7	9	9	8	26	23	-9	-9	44
Nuphar lutea	13, 14	N	n	6	13	12	31	56	27	-6	-7	24
Rorippa amphibia	11, 13, 14	N	t	8	8	7	9	24	26	-3	-3	42
Veronica anagallis-aquatica	13, 14	N	s	7	27	24	21	72	38	-2	-2	29
Glyceria notata	11, 14	N	t	7	47	42	29	118	50	-2	-2	28
Schoenoplectus lacustris	13, 14	N	w	6	15	11	34	60	29	0	0	23
Glyceria maxima	11	N	t	8	26	18	76	120	45	0	0	16
Potamogeton pectinatus	13, 14	N	w	7	21	17	19	57	28	+2	+2	33
Lemna gibba	13	N	s	8	9	7	3	19	20	+8	+9	56
Myriophyllum spicatum	13, 14	N	t	7	25	18	15	58	26	+9	+10	33
Alisma lanceolatum	13	N	s	7	8	6	2	16	25	+11	+12	60
Berula erecta	11	N	t	7	19	11	15	45	25	+15	+16	32
Ranunculus lingua	11	N	t	7	10	7	2	19	14	+16	+18	54
Carex vesicaria	11	N	n	4	7	4	4	15	14	+19	+19	54
Ceratophyllum demersum	13	N	s	7	17	9	13	39	24	+18	+20	33
Rumex hydrolapathum	11	N	t	6	19	9	17	45	27	+19	+21	30
Nymphaea alba	13	N	t	4	31	13	31	75	27	+21	+24	23
Sparganium emersum	13, 14	N	n	6	28	12	17	57	27	+27	+30	27
Potamogeton berchtoldii	13, 14	N	n	5	22	14	2	38	18	+25	+34	45
Sagittaria sagittifolia	13, 14	N	n	6	16	3	14	33	30	+35	+36	25
Butomus umbellatus	13, 14	N	t	7	11	3	5	19	16	+41	+43	40
Nymphoides peltata	13, 14	N	t	6	14	4	5	23	23	+44	+46	38
Potamogeton pusillus	13	N	s	6	13	4	4	21	19	+44	+46	40

WD: Wider Distribution   EN: Ellenberg N   G: Gains   L: Losses   R: Re-finds   TF: Tetrad Frequency   RC: Relative Change   CF: Change Factor (weighted)

Oenanthe aquatica
Fine-leaved water-dropwort

Mapped Change	-42%	
Relative Change	-50%	±61%
Weighted CF	-52%	±48%
Tetrad Frequency	25%	

Hippurus vulgaris
Mare's-tail

Mapped Change	-25%	
Relative Change	-34%	±37%
Weighted CF	-35%	±32%
Tetrad Frequency	18%	

There is little consistency between the two surveys of *Oenanthe aquatica*, perhaps because it is inconspicuous when it is not flowering, and because populations vary in size from year to year in response to fluctuations in water levels. It is not possible to draw any conclusions on change.

There is little consistency between the two surveys of *Hippurus vulgaris* so it is not possible to draw any conclusions on change. This is a much more recognisable plant than *Oenanthe aquatica*, and the lack of correspondence between the two surveys is therefore more surprising, but it may be that inexperienced recorders have failed to recognise the submerged stems in those populations which fail to produce aerial stems every year.

Key to maps   ◐ Loss   ● Gain   ○ Re-find
▨ *New Atlas* distribution

Sparganium emersum
Unbranched Bur-reed

Mapped Change	+36%	
Relative Change	+27%	±29%
Weighted CF	+30%	±27%
Tetrad Frequency	27%	

Sagittaria sagittifolia
Arrowhead

Mapped Change	+43%	
Relative Change	+35%	±25%
Weighted CF	+36%	±25%
Tetrad Frequency	30%	

Sparganium emersum shows an extraordinary amount of change. It seems inescapable that it is under-recorded in ditches and streams where it does not always flower, and in water where in may grow as rather anonymous strap-shaped leaves in sites that are too deep to reach by wading in wellingtons. The evidence of increase must be treated with caution.

Sagittaria sagittifolia appears to have been increasing, possibly due to it having been planted in ponds. Some of these records may be misidentifications of the similar *Sagittaria latifolia*, a North American species which is now established in England.

Key to maps ⊙ Loss ● Gain ○ Re-find
▩ *New Atlas* distribution

Lemna minor group (1.2)

Species	14	Average tetrads	269	Mean CF	+ 1	Significance	0.78
		Widespread		**No change**			

This is much the most widespread subgroup and the most consistently recorded. The proportions of refinds are still fairly low for species as widespread as this. The three species showing increases are notably tolerant of eutrophication. *Callitriche* species, on the other hand, may be shaded out where dense waterside vegetation is encouraged and may be casualties of the fashion to fence off watersides from livestock.

Sparganium erectum, Branched Bur-reed Bob Ellis

Species	Broad Habitats	Native Status	WD	EN	G	L	R	Total	TF	RC	CF	90% Conf. Limits
Callitriche stagnalis sens. lat.	11, 13, 14	N	t	6	83	91	160	334	64	-10	-23	22
Glyceria fluitans	11, 14	N	t	6	88	90	248	426	77	-7	-22	25
Potamogeton natans	11, 13, 14	N	n	4	51	55	74	180	40	-11	-16	21
Veronica beccabunga	11, 14	N	t	6	59	55	294	408	84	-5	-14	17
Rorippa nasturtium-aquaticum agg.	11, 13, 14	N	s	7	84	74	165	323	70	-3	-6	22
Alisma plantago-aquatica	11, 13	N	w	7	51	46	98	195	56	-4	-6	19
Equisetum fluviatile	11	N	n	4	61	53	127	241	50	-3	-5	19
Persicaria amphibia	11, 13	N	n	6	37	26	107	170	44	0	0	17
Lemna minor	11, 13	N	s	6	83	53	174	310	69	+5	+10	19
Apium nodiflorum	14	N	s	7	63	28	161	252	74	+9	+14	14
Eleocharis palustris	11	N	w	4	77	46	113	236	46	+9	+15	19
Phragmites australis	11	N	w	6	50	20	113	183	42	+11	+15	14
Sparganium erectum	11, 13	N	t	7	83	41	132	256	59	+12	+21	17
Typha latifolia	11	N	s	7	84	28	134	246	62	+19	+30	14

WD: Wider Distribution   EN: Ellenberg N   G: Gains   L: Losses   R: Re-finds   TF: Tetrad Frequency   RC: Relative Change   CF: Change Factor (weighted)

Sparganium erectum
Branched Bur-reed

Mapped Change	+20%	
Relative Change	+12%	±11%
Weighted CF	+21%	±17%
Tetrad Frequency	59%	

The map of *Sparganium erectum* shows a considerable amount of apparent change for such a familiar and easily recorded bankside plant. While some local losses and recolonisation following ditch cleaning would be expected, this can hardly be the main explanation. It seems inescapable that *Sparganium erectum* is indeed increasing on balance, probably reflecting a fashion to fence off pond sides and river banks to protect livestock or for perceived conservation gains.

Key to maps ● Loss ● Gain ○ Re-find
■ *New Atlas* distribution

Typha latifolia
Bulrush

Mapped Change	+26%	
Relative Change	+19%	± 9%
Weighted CF	+30%	±14%
Tetrad Frequency	62%	

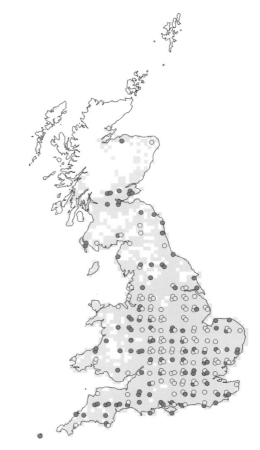

Typha latifolia has become dramatically more frequent in many areas of the north and west, where it was a scarce plant until recently. It has tended to colonise ponds, including informal ones such as those on quarry floors, rather than ditches and streamsides, and can quickly dominate shallow water. While it is available at tree nurseries as well as garden centres and has undoubtedly been introduced to some sites, there is every reason to think that the wind-dispersed seeds allow effective natural colonisation. It is favoured by eutrophication.

Juncus bulbosus group (2.1)

Species	9	Average tetrads	130	Mean CF	- 8	Significance	0.12
		Moderately widespread		**Decrease not significant**			

This group comprises plants of acid conditions of the north
and west and might be expected to be in decline. Their relative
resilience is encouraging. The species with the largest apparent
changes have small sample sizes and their trends should be
interpreted with caution.

Hypericum elodes, Marsh St John's-wort Bob Ellis

Species	Broad Habitats	Native Status	WD	EN	G	L	R	Total	TF	RC	CF	90% Conf. Limits
Apium inundatum	11, 13	N	t	4	3	7	7	17	18	-37	-38	37
Callitriche hamulata sens. lat.	11, 13, 14	N	w	5	28	32	19	79	32	-16	-20	30
Potamogeton polygonifolius	11, 12, 13	N	t	2	31	40	139	210	61	-12	-18	13
Ranunculus hederaceus	11, 13	N	s	5	34	38	39	111	43	-13	-17	24
Juncus bulbosus	14	N	n	2	58	52	201	311	71	-4	-9	16
Carex rostrata	11	N	n	2	43	27	126	196	58	+2	+3	16
Menyanthes trifoliata	11	N	n	3	32	17	89	138	41	+5	+6	16
Ranunculus omiophyllus	11	N	s	4	28	20	29	77	58	+6	+7	27
Hypericum elodes	11	N	t	2	10	3	19	32	39	+16	+16	25

WD: Wider Distribution   EN: Ellenberg N   G: Gains   L: Losses   R: Re-finds   TF: Tetrad Frequency   RC: Relative Change   CF: Change Factor (weighted)

Potamogeton polygonifolius
Bog Pondweed

Mapped Change	- 5%	
Relative Change	-12%	± 9%
Weighted CF	-18%	±13%
Tetrad Frequency	61%	

Potamogeton polygonifolius has been something of a problem species for recorders. At one time there was a perception that it was over-recorded for *P. natans* so it was then recorded with caution or avoided. More recently there has been an understanding that the fear of confusion had been overstated and some records have been reinstated. The apparent resurgence of this species in parts of the north and west may reflect this recording history. Meanwhile the species is now shown to have been decreasing at the edges of its distribution despite this uncertain recording history and there is every reason to think that this is a true trend due to such factors as falling water tables, coniferisation and eutrophication.

Key to maps ● Loss ● Gain ○ Re-find
░ *New Atlas* distribution

Bob Ellis

Sparganium angustifolium group (2.2)

Species	9	Average tetrads	35	Mean CF	0	Significance	0.82
		Local		No change			

This group comprises relatively scarce plants of acid waters in the northwest, though they may be locally frequent there. Some might reasonably have been expected to show decline so their apparent resilience is encouraging. However the relatively small sample sizes and the generally more thorough recording in the second survey in the northwest may conspire to conceal some less satisfactory trends.

Lobelia dortmanna, Water Lobelia Gillian Beckett (inset Bob Ellis)

Species	Broad Habitats	Native Status	WD	EN	G	L	R	Total	TF	RC	CF	90% Conf. Limits
Sparganium natans	13	N	n	3	5	8	2	15	29	-39	-40	57
Lobelia dortmanna	13	N	n	1	4	5	19	28	27	-13	-13	23
Littorella uniflora	11, 13	N	t	3	14	14	41	69	32	-8	-9	21
Isoetes lacustris	13	N	n	1	5	5	5	15	17	-9	-9	56
Myriophyllum alterniflorum	13, 14	N	n	3	19	17	37	73	33	-5	-5	23
Carex limosa	11, 12	N	n	1	7	4	12	23	40	+7	+8	37
Sparganium angustifolium	13	N	n	2	14	7	17	38	31	+14	+15	31
Utricularia minor	11, 12	N	n	2	9	4	11	24	31	+16	+17	36
Eleogiton fluitans	11	N	s	2	15	2	12	29	24	+40	+41	25

WD: Wider Distribution EN: Ellenberg NG: Gains L: Losses R: Re-finds TF: Tetrad Frequency RC: Relative Change CF: Change Factor (weighted)

Eleogiton fluitans
Floating Club-rush

Mapped Change	**+48%**	
Relative Change	**+40%**	±24%
Weighted CF	**+41%**	±25%
Tetrad Frequency	24%	

The apparent resurgence of *Eleogiton fluitans* is unexpected and should be interpreted with caution, as this can be a very elusive species. It favours shallow slow-moving acid water; a habitat thought to be in decline. It may be a species that is more evident in some seasons, and some years, than others, depending on rainfall patterns.

Doubtfully native species and neophytes in Aquatic habitats
There are only a few aquatic neophytes.

Species	Broad Habitats	Native Status	WD	EN	G	L	R	Total	TF	RC	CF	90% Conf. Limits
Neophytes												
Acorus calamus	13, 14	AN		7	8	7	7	22	27	-2	-2	46
Crassula helmsii	13, 14	AN		7	33	2	3	38	30	+78	+81	24
Elodea canadensis	13, 14	AN		6	26	42	27	95	31	-31	-38	24
Elodea nuttallii	13, 14	AN		7	32	8	15	55	32	+43	+47	24
Lemna minuta	13, 14	AN		7	49	2	1	52	43	+86	+92	20

WD: Wider Distribution   EN: Ellenberg N   G: Gains   L: Losses   R: Re-finds   TF: Tetrad Frequency   RC: Relative Change   CF: Change Factor (weighted)

A pond near Cwmbrwyno in tetrad SN78A, created since 1988. This added six species to the tetrad, *Eleogiton fluitans*, *Glyceria maxima*, *Lemna minor*, *Myriophyllum alterniflorum*, *Sparganium erectum* and *Typha latifolia*. Only the *Glyceria* appears to have been deliberately introduced. Arthur Chater

Paul Westley

Bog (BH12)

Species	28	Average tetrads	146	Mean CF	- 2	Significance	0.30
				No change			

Bogs are those wetland habitats which are dependent on rain water rather than ground water. They include both blanket and raised bogs, including their associated bog pools. We have also extended the definition to include the bog-like communities in very acidic lowland valley bogs. The ecological range of this habitat is much narrower than that of Fen, marsh and swamp (BH11), as conditions are usually acidic, nutrient-poor and conducive to peat formation.

The three habitats Acid grassland (BH8), Dwarf shrub heath (BH10) and Bog (BH12) form a series of increasingly wet habitats, all of them acidic, with overlapping species composition. The decline of many Bog species is similar to that of the plants of Dwarf shrub heath.

Changes in the Bog habitat, 1950-2004

1950-1986

This is a vulnerable Broad Habitat that has suffered from a variety of destructive or damaging changes. In some areas, notably the South Pennines, atmospheric pollution damaged many square miles of habitat in the 19th century, destroying the *Sphagnum* cover and thus exposing bog peat to severe erosion (Lee *et al.* 1988). In these areas the blanket bog "presents a depressing spectacle ... vegetation and peat are often coated with grime and even the sheep look grey" (Rodwell 1991b). In the lowlands bogs are uncommon habitats and suffered severe losses in recent centuries, so that in some counties this habitat had been completely lost by 1950.

Damaging influences which have affected British bogs in the past half-century include the following.

- Drainage, often followed by afforestation or agricultural improvement.

- Large-scale, mechanised peat cutting.

- Burning and grazing, especially of blanket bogs, favouring unpalatable species or plants which recover rapidly from grazing or fire (notably *Eriophorum vaginatum*).

- Desiccation as a result of falling water tables, leading to loss of species of wetter microhabitats or colonisation by trees and shrubs.

- Eutrophication from atmospheric nutrient inputs and other sources (including grazing animals).

1987-2004

The CEH Countryside Survey detected little overall change in the area of Bog in Great Britain between 1990 and 1998, although there were losses in Scotland in the lowlands and at intermediate altitudes, although not at high altitudes. An analysis of habitat quality showed an increase in moorland grass vegetation and a decrease in heath and bog vegetation within vegetation mosaics referred to this Broad Habitat, suggesting that soil fertility and grazing pressure had increased. Even the heath and bog species showed a trend in Scotland away from the species of the more extreme habitats to those of more fertile conditions (Haines-Young et al. 2000).

Earlier studies of changes in the species of Bogs

In S.E. England, where the historical record allows long-term changes in the flora to be detected more readily than elsewhere, the bog flora shows a marked decline in the historic period (Preston 2000, Walker & Preston in press). In many counties habitat destruction has resulted in the elimination of the more specialised species, sometimes as early as the 18th or 19th centuries. In lowland northern England there is also a disproportionately high rate of extinction in species of this habitat (Greenwood 1999, 2003). At the 10-km square scale, there is clear evidence from the Atlas surveys of the relative decline of Bog species in all regions except Highland Scotland during the 20th century (Preston et al. 2003b).

The BSBI Local change surveys

The relative homogeneity of the Bog habitat means that there is little to be learnt by splitting the species into groups of different ecological attributes. All species have northern or temperate distributions in the northern hemisphere, for example. It is, however, interesting that in contrast to many groups, there is a suggestion that northern species are more resistant to decline than the temperate ($F_{1,26} = 3.66$, $p = 0.067$). This may reflect the pressures on this habitat at its southerly margins.

Wider Distribution	No. species	Mean CF	Standard error
Northern	21	+2	3
Temperate	7	-13	10

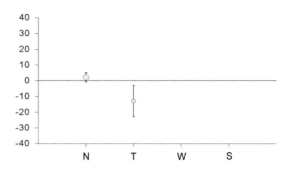

Almost all Bog species are calcifuges and there is little evidence of any pattern of change in relation to Ellenberg R values ($r = 0.036$, $p = 0.854$).

Ellenberg R	No. species	Mean CF	Standard error
1 (very acid)	2	+2	7
2	15	-3	6
3	4	-11	5
4	6	+8	8
5	0		
6 (weakly acid)	1	-15	-

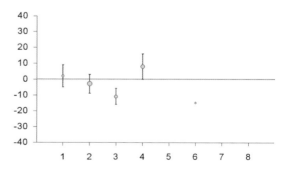

The range of Ellenberg N values is exceptionally narrow and there is no significant difference between the two values ($r = 0.058$, $p = 0.768$).

Ellenberg N	No. species	Mean CF	Standard error
1 (very infertile)	15	-3	5
2 (infertile)	13	-1	5

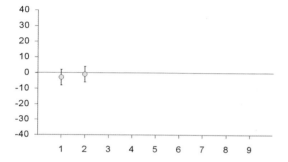

What environmental variables are driving the changes in Bogs?

Modelling the individual climatic variables provides a similar result to that obtained for Dwarf shrub heath (BH 10). The ecological variables Ellenberg R and N show no effects, in contrast to the individual climatic variables. Of the latter, rainfall accounts for most variation ($R^2 = 11.8\%$, $p = 0.074$) closely followed by July temperature ($R^2 = 11.6\%$, $p = 0.076$) and then January temperature ($R^2 = 5.7\%$, $p = 0.22$). For a model with both July temperature and rainfall, $R^2 = 12.1\%$ but neither July temperature ($p = 0.76$) nor rainfall ($p = 0.71$) is statistically significant. In other words, although there is a suggestion of a trend of Change Factor with July temperature and rainfall, the effects are statistically indistinguishable from these data. When Wider Distribution is included in the model with either July temperature or rainfall, none of the effects are statistically significant.

Species groups

Only two groups are recognised, one widespread and the other more northern. The more widespread group shows the greater decline, again a contrast to Broad Habitats such as Broadleaved woodland, Neutral grassland and Calcareous grassland where the more geographically restricted, northern groups show a greater decline than the more widespread groups.

Bog (BH12): classification of species

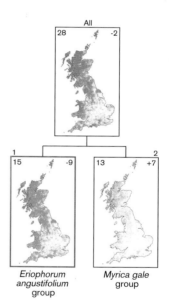

Eriophorum angustifolium group

Myrica gale group

Eriophorum angustifolium group (1)

Species	15	Average tetrads	237	Mean CF	- 9	Significance	0.00
		Widespread		Significant decrease			

This group includes the plants most characteristic of peatland. The trend of decline is very similar to that of dwarf shrub heath, suggesting losses at the fringes of the distributions of the individual species but with the caveat that for species that are so common within their range the adjustment for more thorough recording in the second survey is not accurate and the extent of the losses appears to be overstated.

Eriophorum vaginatum, Hare's-tail Cottongrass Richard Pryce

Species	Broad Habitats	Native Status	WD	EN	G	L	R	Total	TF	RC	CF	90% Conf. Limits
Pedicularis sylvatica	10, 12, 14	N	t	2	24	40	161	225	60	-15	-23	10
Potamogeton polygonifolius	11, 12, 13	N	t	2	31	40	139	210	61	-12	-18	13
Trichophorum cespitosum	10, 12	N	n	1	17	25	155	197	68	-12	-17	8
Calluna vulgaris	10, 12	N	n	2	23	26	301	350	70	-7	-15	7
Pinguicula vulgaris	11, 12	N	n	2	9	15	155	179	67	-11	-15	5
Erica tetralix	10, 12	N	t	1	27	28	203	258	68	-7	-12	10
Eriophorum angustifolium	12	N	n	1	24	23	206	253	65	-7	-11	9
Drosera rotundifolia	12	N	n	1	23	21	147	191	63	-6	-9	11
Polygala serpyllifolia	8, 10, 12	N	t	2	41	35	182	258	66	-4	-7	13
Narthecium ossifragum	12	N	n	1	20	15	172	207	67	-5	-7	8
Empetrum nigrum	10, 12, 15	N	n	1	24	18	121	163	63	-3	-5	12
Carex echinata	11, 12, 14	N	n	2	41	30	207	278	72	-2	-4	12
Juncus squarrosus	8, 12	N	t	2	29	17	220	266	74	-2	-3	10
Molinia caerulea	12	N	n	2	40	26	240	306	70	-2	-3	12
Eriophorum vaginatum	12	N	n	1	37	13	147	197	70	+6	+8	11

WD: Wider Distribution   EN: Ellenberg N   G: Gains   L: Losses   R: Re-finds   TF: Tetrad Frequency   RC: Relative Change   CF: Change Factor (weighted)

Eriophorum angustifolium
Common Cottongrass

Mapped Change	0%	
Relative Change	- 7%	± 6%
Weighted CF	-11%	± 9%
Tetrad Frequency	65%	

Eriophorum vaginatum
Hare's-tail Cottongrass

Mapped Change	+13%	
Relative Change	+ 6%	± 8%
Weighted CF	+ 8%	±11%
Tetrad Frequency	70%	

Although *Eriophorum angustifolium* is frequent over much of its range and is unchanged there, there have been losses in a few outlying stations on the fringe of its distribution.

Eriophorum vaginatum occupies a habitat that is very resilient to change, more so than that of *Eriophorum angustifolium*. At least towards the south of its range it is found mainly on hill tops or in extensive raised bogs, unlike *E. angustifolium* which is found in small mires at various altitudes. It is reasonable to think that it was overlooked on a few hilltops in Monitoring Scheme, as these are typically very species-poor habitats that may not have been selected for survey.

Key to maps ○ Loss ● Gain ○ Re-find
░ *New Atlas* distribution

Myrica gale group (2)

Species	13	Average tetrads	42	Mean CF	+ 7	Significance	0.50
		Local		**Increase not significant**			

These are local plants, some of which are elusive, and it is difficult to interpret the apparent trends with any confidence. *Drosera intermedia*, which shows a marked decrease, is a plant of peaty loch margins and it is not apparent whether or why it has declined. *Myrica gale* is a very resilient shrub that is likely to be well recorded and its losses are probably indicative of losses in the Broad Habitat as a whole.

The apparent marked increase in *Eleocharis multicaulis* is rather unlikely to be real: this is an elusive species that may well have been better recorded in the second survey.

Species	Broad Habitats	Native Status	WD	EN	G	L	R	Total	TF	RC	CF	90% Conf. Limits
Drosera intermedia	12, 14	N	t	1	4	15	8	27	48	-56	-58	28
Myrica gale	12	N	n	2	8	10	80	98	59	-10	-12	8
Rubus chamaemorus	10, 12	N	n	1	6	5	26	37	57	-5	-6	22
Drosera anglica	11, 12	N	n	1	8	6	34	48	61	-4	-4	19
Carex limosa	11, 12	N	n	1	7	4	12	23	40	+7	+8	37
Vaccinium uliginosum	12, 15, 16	N	n	2	5	2	13	20	52	+8	+8	31
Carex pauciflora	12	N	n	1	15	9	21	45	86	+8	+9	29
Vaccinium oxycoccos	12	N	n	1	14	4	31	49	42	+14	+15	19
Utricularia minor	11, 12	N	n	2	9	4	11	24	31	+16	+17	36
Rhynchospora alba	12	N	n	1	11	5	13	29	35	+16	+17	34
Utricularia intermedia sens. lat.	11, 12, 13	N	n	2	7	3	6	16	26	+22	+23	46
Eleocharis multicaulis	11, 12, 13	N	t	1	26	8	26	60	41	+26	+29	22
Listera cordata	2, 10, 12	N	n	2	38	11	17	66	65	+41	+46	24

WD: Wider Distribution   EN: Ellenberg N   G: Gains   L: Losses   R: Re-finds   TF: Tetrad Frequency   RC: Relative Change   CF: Change Factor (weighted)

Myrica gale
Bog-myrtle

Mapped Change	- 2%	
Relative Change	-10%	± 7%
Weighted CF	-12%	± 8%
Tetrad Frequency	59%	

Eleocharis multicaulis
Many-stalked Spike-rush

Mapped Change	+35%	
Relative Change	+26%	±22%
Weighted CF	+29%	±22%
Tetrad Frequency	41%	

Myrica gale is plentiful on the west coast of Scotland but is scarce to the east and south. Modest losses at the fringe of its distribution are much as would be expected from land drainage and afforestation

Eleocharis multicaulis is an inconspicuous species little known to many recorders. The *New Atlas* showed that it was more frequent in some areas than had been realised previously and it is reasonable to think that this knowledge has led to better recording in the resurvey.

Key to maps ● Loss ● Gain ○ Re-find
░ *New Atlas* distribution

Doubtfully native species and neophytes in Bogs

No neophytes attributed to this Broad Habitat have been found in 15 or more tetrads.

Eleocharis multicaulis, Many-stemmed Spike-rush Simon Harrap

Jim McIntosh

Montane habitats (BH15)

Species	27	Average tetrads	56	Mean CF	- 8	Significance	0.01
				Significant decrease			

These are the distinctive communities which are found above the tree-line, and are characterised by numerous Arctic-montane species. Montane willow-scrub, heathlands, acidic grasslands and snow-bed communities all belong here. The treatment of montane calcareous grassland is somewhat anomalous, as these communities are classified as Calcareous grassland (BH7) rather than Montane habitats.

Salix herbacea, Dwarf Willow Ron Payne

Changes in montane habitats, 1950-2004

1950-1986

Montane habitats are less affected than other Broad Habitats by land-use changes. There have been three main pressures in recent decades.

- Increased grazing by sheep and deer, both of which have been present in this period in historically large numbers – red deer numbers are thought to have doubled in Scotland between the mid 1960s and the mid 1990s (Harris *et al*. 1995). As well as its possible direct effect on palatable species, this has led to increased grass cover on some montane sites in the Lake District and Southern Uplands, and more locally in the Scottish Highlands.

- Aerial nitrogen deposition, which also leads (especially when combined with the effects of grazing) to the replacement of moss-dominated communities by swards dominated by grasses and sedges (van der Waal *et al*. 2003).

- Limited development for tourism, including skiing, often aided by public subsidy rather than simply a response to market demand.

Although these changes have not altered the general appearance of the vegetation in many areas, the characteristic montane species are often relict plants, which may be present as small populations. It is not inconceivable that they might be affected by small changes, or even by the continuing effects of unchanging pressures such as grazing, coupled with random events such as rock-falls. Increasing use of the mountains for hill-walking has had a visual impact on the landscape, particularly on the 284 peaks exceeding 3000 feet in Scotland ('Munros'), but a negligible impact on the montane flora.

1987-2004

Since 1987 there has been a reduction in sheep grazing pressure in some areas, both because of the effects of payments to sheep farmers and because of the (perhaps temporary) effects of Foot and Mouth disease. Red deer have continued to increase, although our knowledge of deer numbers is surprisingly vague and the extent of the increase is controversial (Clutton-Brock *et al*. 2004). Since 1987, however, there has been an increasing desire in Scotland to reverse the effects of centuries of high grazing levels and re-establish woodland at high altitude. In the Cairngorms a reduction on grazing has led to the spread of trees to higher altitudes and a natural subalpine scrubzone appears to be developing (French *et al*. 1997). There have, very locally, been deliberate attempts to re-establish montane willow scrub by planting shrubs in fenced areas.

Earlier studies of changes in the species of montane habitats

Assessing changes in Montane habitats poses difficulties. Rugged terrain is difficult to survey exhaustively, especially in remote sites where only a few hours are available for recording in the interval between a long walk to the site and the start of the return journey. This difficulty of survey is exacerbated if vegetation is close-grazed. The way in which plants can be overlooked in heavily grazed areas has been dramatically demonstrated in the Pennines recently, where the reduction of grazing after Foot and Mouth disease has led to the discovery in several sites of *Carex vaginata*, a Boreo-arctic Montane species not previously known in England (Corner 2004). In view of these uncertainties of recording it is usual to assume that Montane habitats are relatively immune to change, and to attribute any apparent changes to variations in recording, but this assumption needs critical examination.

There are few detailed studies of long-term trends in Montane species. Comparison of the two national Atlas surveys suggested a decline in all areas of Britain, though the species showed least decline in Highland Scotland. Clearly, in the lowlands this decline must refer to the other habitats of the more widespread Montane species.

The BSBI Local change surveys

All the Montane species analysed in this survey are perennials with a Northern distribution. They tend to be calcifuges (as many calcicole species of the mountains are excluded from this Broad Habitat) and they are all found in sites with low fertility. In view of this, it is not surprising that there is little indication in any trend in the Change Factor relation to either pH ($r = -0.21$, $p = 0.299$) or fertility ($r = -0.07$, $p = 0.736$).

Ellenberg R	No. species	Mean CF	Standard error
2 (very acid)	9	-2	5
3	3	-12	26
4	1	-18	-
5	3	-13	3
6	9	-6	5
7	0		
8 (basic)	2	-24	0.1

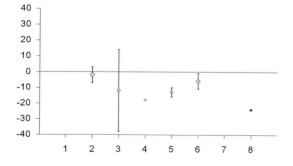

Ellenberg N	No. species	Mean CF	Standard error
1 (very infertile)	1	-5	-
2	13	-8	6
3	11	-6	4
4 (intermediate)	2	-16	13

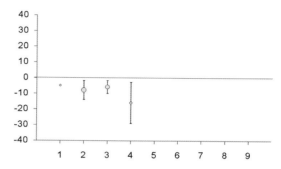

As none of the variables shows any correlation with the Change Factor, including the individual climatic variables, there is no scope for analysing the results of the survey by modelling in the usual way.

While there is a fairly consistent pattern of decline for the group overall, some comment is required before a more subjective interpretation can be attempted. The sharpest apparent losses are shown by two critical *Dryopteris* species, *D. expansa* and *D. oreades*, and, with low numbers of records, it would be wise to avoid placing too much reliance on trends for these species. The species sampled by Local Change are inevitably the more widespread montane species and therefore those which are also likely to grow in other upland habitats where they may be more vulnerable to change. In particular, two of the *Alchemilla* species, *A. filicaulis* and *A. glabra*, are found at much lower altitudes than many plants of this group and, as their losses are at the lower limits of their ranges, they suggest a decline in moorland-edge habitats rather than in montane communities as such.

Discounting these four species, the greatest declines are shown by *Persicaria vivipara*, *Oxyria digyna*, *Alchemilla alpina* and *Huperzia selago*. Taken together, the losses of these distinctive species are suggestive of some decline in the montane habitat as a whole and it is not unreasonable to think of them being out-competed by less montane species where the climate has ameliorated. *H. selago* is also vulnerable to burning in moorland habitats. However there are several similar species that show little change, such as *Saxifraga aizoides* and *Thalictrum alpinum*. One would not necessarily expect all species to behave in a similar manner, but the evidence for change in the Montane habitats remains weak. More thought needs to be given to ways in which change in the montane flora can be assessed.

Species	Broad Habitats	Native Status	WD	EN	G	L	R	Total	TF	RC	CF	90% Conf. Limits
Dryopteris expansa	1, 15, 16	N	n	2	5	14	4	23	62	-59	-61	39
Dryopteris oreades	15, 16	N	n	2	4	7	5	16	39	-34	-35	47
Alchemilla glabra	6, 15, 16	N	n	4	16	40	125	181	75	-22	-30	8
Asplenium viride	15, 16	N	n	3	4	7	14	25	37	-23	-24	27
Saxifraga oppositifolia	7, 15, 16	N	n	2	1	4	17	22	49	-23	-24	10
Alchemilla filicaulis	7, 15, 16	N	n	3	30	37	34	101	48	-18	-22	24
Persicaria vivipara	7, 15	N	n	2	6	9	21	36	55	-18	-20	24
Oxyria digyna	15, 16	N	n	3	4	6	17	27	57	-17	-18	25
Alchemilla alpina	7, 15, 16	N	n	3	6	10	40	56	82	-16	-18	14
Huperzia selago	15, 16	N	n	2	12	14	66	92	64	-11	-12	13
Saxifraga stellaris	11, 15, 16	N	n	3	7	8	32	47	63	-11	-12	19
Juniperus communis	7, 10, 15, 16	N	n	3	19	19	37	75	45	-8	-9	23
Empetrum nigrum	10, 12, 15	N	n	1	24	18	121	163	63	-3	-5	12
Plantago maritima	15, 21	N	n	4	18	13	76	107	42	-3	-3	14
Festuca vivipara	15, 16	N	n	2	11	5	100	116	73	-2	-3	8
Saxifraga aizoides	7, 11, 15, 16	N	n	2	9	6	34	49	67	-1	-2	20
Saxifraga hypnoides	7, 15, 16	N	n	3	8	7	5	20	29	-1	-1	50
Carex bigelowii	15	N	n	2	6	4	18	28	43	0	0	28
Arctostaphylos uva-ursi	10, 15	N	n	2	12	9	22	43	63	0	0	30
Sedum rosea	15, 16	N	n	3	7	4	22	33	36	+2	+2	27
Vaccinium vitis-idaea	2, 10, 15	N	n	2	20	9	72	101	63	+4	+5	15
Vaccinium uliginosum	12, 15, 16	N	n	2	5	2	13	20	52	+8	+8	31
Cryptogramma crispa	10, 15, 16	N	n	3	8	5	10	23	36	+8	+8	41
Thalictrum alpinum	7, 11, 15, 16	N	n	3	12	6	21	39	58	+10	+10	28
Epilobium anagallidifolium	11, 15	N	n	3	6	3	7	16	49	+14	+15	46
Diphasiastrum alpinum	15	N	n	2	14	6	21	41	52	+14	+15	27
Euphrasia scottica	10, 15	N	n	2	20	12	10	42	63	+18	+20	35
Salix herbacea	15	N	n	2	9	1	14	24	38	+26	+27	22

WD: Wider Distribution   EN: Ellenberg N   G: Gains   L: Losses   R: Re-finds   TF: Tetrad Frequency   RC: Relative Change   CF: Change Factor (weighted)

Alchemilla glabra
Smooth Lady's-mantle

Mapped Change	-15%	
Relative Change	-22%	± 6%
Weighted CF	-30%	± 8%
Tetrad Frequency	75%	

Alchemilla alpina
Alpine Lady's-mantle

Mapped Change	- 8%	
Relative Change	-16%	±13%
Weighted CF	-18%	±14%
Tetrad Frequency	82%	

Alchemilla glabra is very frequent by burnsides and in damp grassland in northern Britain, especially in the uplands. Its apparent sharp decline is somewhat unexpected and may relate to afforestation and to drainage and agricultural improvement of acid grassland.

Alchemilla alpina is one of the most widespread species of the montane element in the British flora and it is in general well recorded as it is found on open slopes rather than in rocky refugia. There is a suggestion of decline at the edges of its range but it is not known what factors are involved.

Key to maps   ● Loss   ● Gain   ○ Re-find
     New Atlas distribution

Asplenium viride
Green Spleenwort

Mapped Change	-14%	
Relative Change	-23%	±29%
Weighted CF	-24%	±27%
Tetrad Frequency	37%	

Salix herbacea
Dwarf Willow

Mapped Change	+35%	
Relative Change	+26%	±20%
Weighted CF	+27%	±22%
Tetrad Frequency	38%	

Asplenium viride is a widespread upland fern where basic rocks are found. While it has been quite well recorded for the surveys it is nevertheless easily overlooked and the number of records is rather too small for any definite pattern to emerge to support the suggestion of decline.

It is difficult to believe that *Salix herbacea* has been increasing. It is much more likely that the few apparent gains represent better recording of montane habitats where this species may be very sparse.

Key to maps   ● Loss   ● Gain   ○ Re-find
▨ *New Atlas* distribution

Doubtfully native species and neophytes in Montane habitats

Only a single neophyte occurring in this Broad Habitat was recorded in more than 15 tetrads.

Species	Broad Habitats	Native Status	WD	EN	G	L	R	Total	TF	RC	CF	90% Conf. Limits
Neophytes												
Epilobium brunnescens	14, 15, 16	AN		3	66	11	69	146	65	+33	+41	13

WD: Wider Distribution EN: Ellenberg N G: Gains L: Losses R: Re-finds TF: Tetrad Frequency RC: Relative Change CF: Change Factor (weighted)

Inland rock (BH16)

Species	105	Average tetrads	148	Mean CF	- 3	Significance	0.08
				Decrease marginally significant			

This Broad Habitat comprises all exposed rock surfaces, whether natural and artificial, and skeletal soils over rock. Inland cliffs, cliff ledges, caves, limestone pavements and screes are included here, as are quarries and quarry wastes (including mine spoil contaminated by heavy metals and lowland sand and gravel pits). This makes it a rather heterogeneous habitat, with consequent difficulties in interpreting the trends revealed by the Local Change surveys.

Over much of upland Britain rock outcrops act as refugia for species which have been eliminated from more accessible habitats by centuries of grazing pressure. By contrast, habitats in the lowlands such as sand and gravel workings, railway cuttings and quarries may be colonised by a range of opportunistic species, some of which might otherwise be absent from the region because of the lack of an equivalent natural habitat.

Changes in Inland rock habitats, 1950-2004

1950-1986

Obviously, many natural or semi-natural hard rock habitats are less likely to undergo change than habitats which are more actively managed. However, mines and quarries, particularly sand and gravel workings, often progress rapidly from the extractive phase to dereliction. In the active stages and in the first few years after they are abandoned they may offer islands of habitat characterised by low nutrient levels and little competition from perennial species. They might then be restored to agricultural use, allowed to flood or simply abandoned to the processes of vegetation succession. Some of the particular factors which have affected the Broad Habitat in recent decades are listed below.

- The increase in gravel extraction, especially in lowland river valleys, has created (at least temporarily) large new areas of quarried ground.

- Road cuttings have also given rise to new rock exposures, sometimes in areas where there are few natural rock outcrops.

- 'Landscaping' of waste tips and quarried ground and the use of gravel pits and quarries for 'landfill' has destroyed some of the available habitat.

- Mechanised removal of limestone pavement in the uplands has had a particular effect on this habitat, so that by 1975 only 61% of the total area was intact and only 3% undamaged.

- Species which find refugia from grazing animals on inland rocks may have been affected away from these sites, or on the more accessible rock outcrops and cliffs, by increasing grazing pressure from sheep and red deer.

1987-2004

Since 1987 there has been some reduction in grazing pressure in the uplands. The Wildlife and Countryside Act 1981 made special provision for the protection of limestone pavement by Limestone Pavement Orders and this, coupled with increasing public awareness of the value of the habitat, has halted the threat posed by quarrying. Many limestone pavements have been fenced under wildlife enhancement schemes.

Earlier studies of changes in the species of Inland rock

This varied habitat has not been identified specifically in many studies, and there is little systematic information on the species present. Analysis of the results of the two national Atlas surveys for species of this Broad Habitat indicated a slight relative decline in most northern and western areas, although not in some lowland areas such as the East Midlands and East Anglia.

Margules *et al.* (1994) reported a very high rate of species turnover in limestone pavements in the Ingleborough area of Yorkshire which were initially surveyed in 1974-75 and again, using the same methodology, in 1985. Most pavements lost more species than they gained in this period. The reasons for the high turnover were not at all clear, but might have included the failure of juvenile plants to become established and the effects of varying levels of sheep grazing.

The BSBI Local change surveys

The general trend in this Broad Habitat, as in many others, is for annual species to have done better than perennials ($F_{2,101} = 5.64$, $p = 0.005$).

Perennation	No. species	Mean CF	Standard error
Annual	19	+9	7
Biennial	4	+26	29
Perennial	81	-7	3

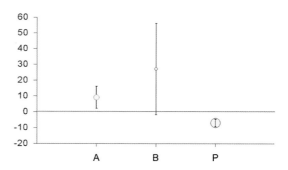

Species	Broad Habitats	Native Status	WD	EN	G	L	R	Total	TF	RC	CF	90% Conf. Limits
Clinopodium acinos	16	N	t	1	2	8	6	16	30	-51	-52	31
Inula conyzae	7, 16	N	t	3	8	13	17	38	25	-25	-27	28
Clinopodium ascendens	3, 16	N	t	6	9	10	3	22	22	-16	-18	53
Scleranthus annuus	4, 8, 10, 16	N	t	4	7	8	6	21	29	-16	-16	48
Myosotis ramosissima	8, 16	N	s	3	18	20	15	53	28	-14	-16	33
Thalictrum minus	16, 19	N	n	3	7	7	8	22	18	-9	-9	45
Mycelis muralis	1, 16	N	t	5	28	23	62	113	46	-2	-3	19
Origanum vulgare	7, 16	N	s	4	24	20	28	72	36	-1	-1	26
Hypericum maculatum	1, 3, 16	N	n	5	26	19	45	90	48	+2	+2	23
Filago minima	16	N	t	2	10	8	7	25	27	+3	+3	47
Artemisia absinthium	3, 16, 17	AR	t	9	15	11	16	42	34	+4	+5	34
Umbilicus rupestris	3, 16	N	s	4	15	4	66	85	54	+5	+6	13
Valerianella locusta	3, 16, 19	N	t	4	30	24	11	65	31	+6	+8	36
Erigeron acer	3, 16	N	n	3	20	12	21	53	31	+11	+12	29
Saxifraga tridactylites	16	N	s	2	17	10	14	41	27	+14	+15	34
Ceterach officinarum	3, 16	N	s	1	20	9	26	55	30	+16	+17	25
Parietaria judaica	16, 17	N	s	5	32	15	35	82	31	+17	+20	22
Sherardia arvensis	7, 16	N	s	4	64	19	51	134	51	+31	+39	17
Geranium lucidum	3, 16	N	s	6	69	19	55	143	52	+33	+41	17
Diplotaxis tenuifolia	3, 16, 17	AR	t	6	14	5	4	23	30	+41	+43	40
Verbena officinalis	3, 16	AR	s	6	22	3	15	40	33	+43	+45	22
Geranium sanguineum	7, 16	N	t	3	13	4	3	20	23	+48	+50	41
Foeniculum vulgare	3, 16, 17	AR	s	5	41	14	11	66	37	+44	+50	26
Geranium rotundifolium	3, 16, 17	N	s	6	32	5	7	44	44	+61	+65	25
Lactuca virosa	3, 16	N	s	7	36	5	8	49	42	+62	+66	23
Euphorbia lathyris	3, 16, 17	AR	s	5	56	7	9	72	42	+67	+74	20

WD: Wider Distribution   EN: Ellenberg N   G: Gains   L: Losses   R: Re-finds   TF: Tetrad Frequency   RC: Relative Change   CF: Change Factor (weighted)

Clinopodium acinos
Basil Thyme

Mapped Change	-43%	
Relative Change	-51%	±33%
Weighted CF	-52%	±31%
Tetrad Frequency	30%	

Clinopodium acinos is infrequent even within its limited distribution and is in sharp decline, perhaps following eutrophication of its calcareous but infertile grassland and arable habitats.

Lactuca virosa
Great Lettuce

Mapped Change	+70%	
Relative Change	+62%	±25%
Weighted CF	+66%	±23%
Tetrad Frequency	42%	

Lactuca virosa occurs as a native on rock outcrops and perhaps on coastal shingle, but it has spread on disturbed ground, especially on roadside embankments. It has probably been favoured by higher summer temperatures. Its expansion is similar to that of *Lactuca serriola* in the same roadside habitats (p.237), but it remains the scarcer of the two plants.

Key to maps   ● Loss   ● Gain   ○ Re-find
         ▨ *New Atlas* distribution

Tussilago farfara group (1.2)

Species	44	Average tetrads	272	Mean CF	- 3	Significance	0.16
		Moderately widespread		**Decrease not significant**			

This group of widespread species has a large overlap with other
Broad Habitats. As with the *Parietaria judaica* group, most of the
species which share this Broad Habitat with Calcareous (BH8) or
Acidic (BH7) grassland show a negative Change Factor, and most
of those occurring in Built-up areas and gardens (BH17) have a
positive value. This presumably suggests that to a large extent
the changes are taking place in the other habitats. The increase
of *Phyllitis scolopendrium*, an oceanic species which is rather
a special feature of the British flora, is a particularly interesting
result of the project and is discussed in the species account.

Phyllitis scolopendrium, Hart's-tongue Fern Bob Ellis

Species	Broad Habitats	Native Status	WD	EN	G	L	R	Total	TF	RC	CF	90% Conf. Limits
Rumex acetosella	8, 9, 16	N	w	3	47	87	346	480	83	-15	-51	15
Tussilago farfara	16	N	n	6	47	77	376	500	90	-12	-47	17
Trifolium campestre	3, 16, 19	N	s	4	45	65	87	197	52	-21	-31	18
Angelica sylvestris	11, 16	N	n	5	49	55	397	501	85	-7	-29	18
Orchis mascula	1, 7, 16	N	t	4	27	37	36	100	32	-22	-27	23
Viola riviniana	1, 7, 16	N	t	4	59	54	417	530	88	-4	-24	26
Alchemilla filicaulis	7, 15, 16	N	n	3	30	37	34	101	48	-18	-22	24
Solidago virgaurea	10, 16	N	n	3	30	41	121	192	53	-14	-20	13
Polystichum aculeatum	1, 16	N	t	5	27	33	43	103	38	-16	-19	22
Anemone nemorosa	1, 16	N	t	4	50	58	193	301	64	-10	-19	15
Arenaria serpyllifolia sens. lat.	16	N	s	5	53	59	101	213	55	-11	-18	19
Aira caryophyllea	10, 16	N	s	2	29	32	38	99	31	-12	-15	24
Aira praecox	8, 16	N	s	2	69	70	133	272	58	-8	-14	20
Salix aurita	1, 16	N	n	3	41	42	158	241	64	-8	-12	14
Lathyrus linifolius	8, 16	N	t	3	37	38	126	201	57	-8	-12	15
Teucrium scorodonia	1, 9, 16	N	s	3	33	32	237	302	64	-6	-12	11
Thymus polytrichus	7, 16	N	n	2	27	27	187	241	56	-7	-11	10
Oxalis acetosella	1, 2, 16	N	n	4	38	33	306	377	77	-5	-11	11
Vaccinium myrtillus	10, 16	N	n	2	27	25	237	289	77	-6	-11	9
Epilobium montanum	3, 16, 17	N	t	6	74	60	352	486	88	-2	-10	25
Geum rivale	1, 16	N	n	4	31	28	110	169	55	-6	-8	15
Athyrium filix-femina	1, 16	N	n	6	52	38	317	407	78	-2	-6	15
Blechnum spicant	1, 2, 10, 16	N	t	3	45	32	258	335	78	-2	-5	13
Carex pulicaris	11, 16	N	t	2	40	31	132	203	63	-2	-3	15
Hypericum pulchrum	10, 16	N	t	3	63	47	224	334	70	-1	-2	16
Asplenium trichomanes	3, 16, 17	N	s	2	51	39	143	233	54	-1	-2	16
Rosa pimpinellifolia	10, 16, 19	N	t	3	12	10	17	39	26	-2	-2	32
Sedum anglicum	16, 18	N	t	2	20	12	59	91	46	+2	+2	18
Sedum acre	16	N	t	2	65	50	95	210	51	+2	+3	22
Asplenium ruta-muraria	3, 16, 17	N	t	2	51	32	128	211	49	+3	+5	17
Luzula sylvatica	1, 16	N	t	4	52	23	159	234	58	+7	+10	13
Primula vulgaris	1, 16	N	t	4	77	40	306	423	76	+4	+12	18
Carex binervis	8, 10, 16	N	t	2	53	21	173	247	68	+7	+12	13
Carex laevigata	1, 16	N	t	4	20	13	15	48	31	+12	+13	33
Geranium robertianum	1, 16	N	t	6	55	18	453	526	96	+2	+13	20
Sedum telephium	1, 3, 16	N	t	5	31	20	23	74	42	+12	+14	28
Asplenium adiantum-nigrum sens. lat.	3, 16	N	s	5	55	29	73	157	41	+13	+17	19
Aphanes arvensis agg.	4, 8, 16	N	t	4	99	58	129	286	65	+11	+22	21
Cardamine hirsuta	16	N	s	6	116	65	279	460	89	+7	+27	26
Veronica arvensis	3, 4, 16	N	s	5	117	58	285	460	86	+9	+33	24
Arabidopsis thaliana	16, 17	N	t	2	101	42	127	270	63	+19	+33	17
Phyllitis scolopendrium	1, 16	N	t	5	84	16	163	263	62	+21	+33	11
Erophila verna sens. lat.	3, 16, 17	N	s	3	106	53	84	243	60	+21	+36	21
Dryopteris affinis	1, 16	N	t	5	114	29	190	333	71	+22	+42	13

WD: Wider Distribution EN: Ellenberg N G: Gains L: Losses R: Re-finds TF: Tetrad Frequency RC: Relative Change CF: Change Factor (weighted)

Phyllitis scolopendrium
Hart's-tongue Fern

Mapped Change	+28%	
Relative Change	+21%	± 7%
Weighted CF	+33%	±11%
Tetrad Frequency	62%	

Tussilago farfara
Colt's-foot

Mapped Change	- 7%	
Relative Change	-12%	± 4%
Weighted CF	-47%	±17%
Tetrad Frequency	90%	

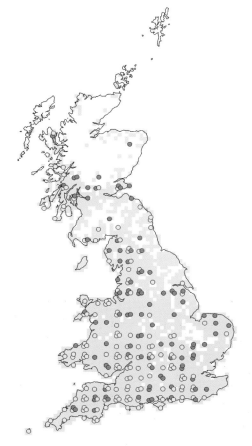

Phyllitis scolopendrium is a characteristic fern in the southwest where it is conspicuous in hedgebanks as well as woodland, but in the north and east it has been more demanding and found typically in ravines, wells and gardens. Recently, observers in southeast Scotland have noted that it is colonising walls and quite open woodland. This marked increase is confirmed by the survey results and could be a response to climate change, especially to a reduction in frosts, or to a more hardy variety of the fern being introduced as garden stock and naturalising.

Tussilago farfara is an almost ubiquitous plant at hectad and tetrad scale. Nevertheless it has become less plentiful in some areas and has suffered small losses which, when weighted for its wide distribution, become highly significant. The reasons for this decline are not apparent as this is a plant which thrives on disturbance.

Key to maps   ● Loss   ● Gain   ○ Re-find
░░ *New Atlas* distribution

Cystopteris fragilis group (2)

Species	33	Average tetrads	61	Mean CF	-14	Significance	0.00
		Moderately local		**Significant decrease**			

This northerly group is dominated by species with negative Change Factors, although many are represented in relatively few samples and confidence limits are therefore broad. The group is somewhat more ecologically coherent than the others, as most species are plants of natural rock habitats in the uplands. There is again a broad overlap with other Broad Habitats, mainly the Calcareous grassland and Montane habitats. *Cystopteris fragilis* is an example of a species showing a significant decrease.

Oreopteris limbosperma, Lemon-scented Fern Bob Ellis

Phegopteris connectilis, Beech Fern Bob Ellis

Species	Broad Habitats	Native Status	WD	EN	G	L	R	Total	TF	RC	CF	90% Conf. Limits
Dryopteris expansa	1, 15, 16	N	n	2	5	14	4	23	62	-59	-61	39
Viola lutea	7, 8, 16	N	n	2	3	18	13	34	46	-57	-59	16
Melica nutans	1, 7, 16	N	n	3	4	9	5	18	35	-44	-46	42
Dryopteris oreades	15, 16	N	n	2	4	7	5	16	39	-34	-35	47
Alchemilla glabra	6, 15, 16	N	n	4	16	40	125	181	75	-22	-30	8
Trollius europaeus	11, 16	N	n	4	9	16	23	48	40	-26	-28	23
Botrychium lunaria	7, 16	N	n	2	6	8	5	19	16	-24	-25	49
Asplenium viride	15, 16	N	n	3	4	7	14	25	37	-23	-24	27
Saxifraga oppositifolia	7, 15, 16	N	n	2	1	4	17	22	49	-23	-24	10
Cystopteris fragilis	16	N	n	4	16	23	37	76	46	-20	-23	21
Oxyria digyna	15, 16	N	n	3	4	6	17	27	57	-17	-18	25
Alchemilla alpina	7, 15, 16	N	n	3	6	10	40	56	82	-16	-18	14
Galium boreale	7, 16	N	n	3	13	16	24	53	62	-16	-17	26
Geranium sylvaticum	6, 16	N	n	5	14	18	42	74	63	-15	-17	19
Hymenophyllum wilsonii	1, 16	N	n	3	12	14	15	41	52	-15	-17	33
Gymnocarpium dryopteris	1, 16	N	n	4	19	21	39	79	55	-12	-13	22
Rubus saxatilis	1, 7, 16	N	n	4	12	13	16	41	36	-12	-13	33
Huperzia selago	15, 16	N	n	2	12	14	66	92	64	-11	-12	13
Saxifraga stellaris	11, 15, 16	N	n	3	7	8	32	47	63	-11	-12	19
Juniperus communis	7, 10, 15, 16	N	n	3	19	19	37	75	45	-8	-9	23
Cirsium heterophyllum	6, 16	N	n	5	18	17	27	62	53	-6	-7	27
Crepis paludosa	11, 16	N	n	4	28	25	90	143	67	-5	-7	16
Oreopteris limbosperma	1, 16	N	t	3	37	31	130	198	72	-4	-6	14
Festuca vivipara	15, 16	N	n	2	11	5	100	116	73	-2	-3	8
Saxifraga aizoides	7, 11, 15, 16	N	n	2	9	6	34	49	67	-1	-2	20
Saxifraga hypnoides	7, 15, 16	N	n	3	8	7	5	20	29	-1	-1	50
Phegopteris connectilis	1, 16	N	n	4	19	10	78	107	63	+1	+2	15
Sedum rosea	15, 16	N	n	3	7	4	22	33	36	+2	+2	27
Equisetum sylvaticum	1, 16	N	n	5	45	32	74	151	59	+3	+4	20
Vaccinium uliginosum	12, 15, 16	N	n	2	5	2	13	20	52	+8	+8	31
Cryptogramma crispa	10, 15, 16	N	n	3	8	5	10	23	36	+8	+8	41
Thalictrum alpinum	7, 11, 15, 16	N	n	3	12	6	21	39	58	+10	+10	28
Salix phylicifolia	14, 16	N	n	4	8	5	5	18	31	+14	+15	51

WD: Wider Distribution   EN: Ellenberg N   G: Gains   L: Losses   R: Re-finds   TF: Tetrad Frequency   RC: Relative Change   CF: Change Factor (weighted)

Cystopteris fragilis
Brittle Bladder-fern

Mapped Change	-12%	
Relative Change	-20%	±21%
Weighted CF	-23%	±21%
Tetrad Frequency	46%	

Cystopteris fragilis is a predominantly northern fern that may colonise mortared walls in lowland areas where these are sufficiently damp and sheltered. It is these lowland sites that appear to have suffered and climate change could have been a factor.

Key to maps   ● Loss   ● Gain   ○ Re-find
       ▨ *New Atlas* distribution

Simon Harrap

Doubtfully native species and neophytes of Inland rocks

Several neophytes occurring in this Broad Habitat are sufficiently frequent to be listed here.

Species	Broad Habitats	Native Status	WD	EN	G	L	R	Total	TF	RC	CF	90% Conf. Limits
Neophytes												
Centranthus ruber	3, 16, 17, 18	AN		5	83	9	40	132	49	+52	+62	14
Cotoneaster horizontalis	3, 16, 17	AN		4	57	13	11	81	46	+57	+66	21
Cotoneaster simonsii	3, 10, 16, 17	AN		4	50	17	11	78	42	+46	+56	24
Cymbalaria muralis	3, 16, 17, 19	AN		6	66	40	126	232	56	+6	+10	18
Diplotaxis muralis	3, 4, 16, 17	AN		6	19	9	18	46	34	+19	+20	29
Epilobium brunnescens	14, 15, 16	AN		3	66	11	69	146	65	+33	+41	13
Leucanthemum x superbum	3, 16, 17	AN		5	29	7	9	45	28	+49	+53	27
Linaria purpurea	3, 16, 17	AN		6	85	17	42	144	50	+46	+57	16
Oenothera agg.	3, 16, 17, 19	AN		4	38	16	19	73	33	+30	+35	25
Rhododendron ponticum	1, 10, 16	AN		3	55	28	111	194	49	+9	+13	16
Sedum rupestre	3, 16	AN		4	46	19	14	79	36	+37	+44	26

WD: Wider Distribution   EN: Ellenberg N   G: Gains   L: Losses   R: Re-finds   TF: Tetrad Frequency   RC: Relative Change   CF: Change Factor (weighted)

Richard Pryce

Built-up areas and gardens (BH17)

Species	53	Average tetrads	211	Mean CF	+23	Significance	0.00
				Significant increase			

Habitats of towns and villages are included here, including buildings, farmsteads, industrial and post-industrial 'brown-field' sites, parks in towns, gardens, and urban walls, pavements and transport networks.

Changes in Built-up areas and gardens, 1950-2004

1950-1986

The main changes in this Broad Habitat probably result from its increase in area rather than major changes in quality within the habitat. Some of the major changes are listed below.

- Expansion of towns, villages and industrial estates, often accompanied by building of new roads or by road improvement works.

- Large-scale transfers of topsoil and turf in association with housing development and road construction, and the seeding of roadside verges with commercial seed mixes.

- Increased salting of roads in winter.

- Differing changes in the fortune of urban land: some areas (especially industrial areas close to city centres) have become run-down, or have been abandoned as post-industrial 'brown-field' sites; others have been redeveloped by 'landscaping' and new building. Many residential areas have been cleaned up as they undergo 'gentrification'.

- Replacement of manual weeding by chemical control, especially in municipally-managed streets, gardens and amenity grassland but also to a lesser extent in private gardens.

- Increasing popularity of 'low maintenance' gardening, with a reduction in the areas of annually dug land such as vegetable plots and allotments.

- Growth of garden centres, with garden plants normally obtained by commercial purchase rather than (as one suspects was often the case in the past) by exchange with neighbours, and thus an increase in the possibility of weed dispersal though the horticulture trade.

- The use of an increased range of garden plants in the planting schemes of municipal authorities and other corporate bodies (e.g. supermarkets), leading to a greater chance of species escaping and colonising urban areas and transport corridors.

All the above changes, including the spread of built-up areas and their associated transport networks, have continued in recent years. The warmer weather in this period has clearly affected all Broad Habitats but large towns are 'heat islands' and experience warmer, drier conditions than the adjacent countryside.

Earlier studies of changes in the species of Built-up areas and gardens

Studies of the flora of urban areas have often concentrated on the spread of neophytes; there have been relatively few studies of changes in native species and archaeophytes. A detailed study of the botanical history of Glasgow (Dickson *et al.* 2000), however, identifies successive expansions of plants which are native to Britain, and in some cases occurred as natives in the Glasgow area itself, along canals in the late 18th century, railways in the 19th and salt-treated roads in the late 20th century. Most of the extinctions from the area are of species which were associated with other Broad Habitats which have now been lost or degraded as the city has expanded; a few garden plants which were formerly cultivated no longer occur as escapes but very few plants of urban habitats have been lost. In the English Midlands (Bedfordshire and Northamptonshire) the situation is similar: the proportion of extinctions in the flora of Built-up areas and gardens is lower than that in any other Broad Habitat (Walker & Preston in press).

At a 10-km square scale the species of Built-up areas and gardens showed a greater relative increase in Britain between the two BSBI Atlas surveys than that of any other Broad Habitat. The increase was apparent in all areas other than the regions of Scotland, where these species declined or remained stable.

Fine-scale changes in the street flora of Aberystwyth were detected when 54 streets, initially surveyed in 1970-73, were resurveyed in 1998-9 (Chater *et al.* 2000). The townscape did not change greatly between the two surveys but the turnover of species was substantial. There was a marked increase in the proportion of species associated with drier, warmer and lighter conditions.

The BSBI Local change surveys

This Broad Habitat, like Arable and horticultural land (BH4) but unlike many of the semi-natural habitats, includes a majority of archaeophytes (species introduced before AD 1500). Both natives and archaeophytes show a substantial increase, with little difference in the performance of the two groups ($F_{1,51} = 0.04$, $p = 0.84$).

History	No. species	Mean CF	Standard error
Native	20	+24	6
Archaeophyte	33	+22	5

Annuals and perennials have also been equally successful ($F_{2,50} = 0.28$, $p = 0.76$).

Perennation	No. species	Mean CF	Standard error
Annual	31	+22	5
Biennial	3	+34	23
Perennial	19	+22	6

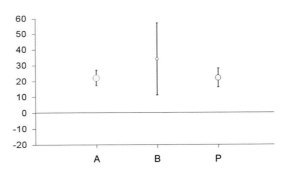

Southern species have been even more successful than temperate species in the period between the surveys ($F_{3,49} = 4.55$, $p = 0.007$). The single northern species is the Boreo-temperate *Lamium album*. The mean Change Factor for the two widespread species, *Capsella bursa-pastoris* and *Polygonum aviculare* agg., is misleadingly low, as explained in the account of the *C. bursa-pastoris* species group (1.1).

Wider Distribution	No. species	Mean CF	Standard error
Northern	1	-8	-
Temperate	23	+14	6
Widespread	2	-6	11
Southern	27	+34	4

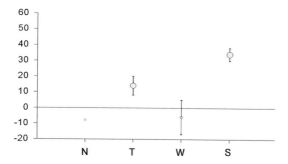

Ellenberg R	No. species	Mean CF	Standard error
4 (acid)	1	+47	-
5	2	+52	7
6	14	+29	7
7	27	+16	5
8 (basic)	9	+25	7

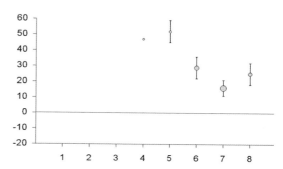

The plants of this Broad Habitat show, unusually, a significant trend in relation to Ellenberg L value, with those of open habitats being the most successful ($r = 0.32$, $p = 0.022$).

There is a significant trend with respect to fertility preferences, but for the species of this Broad Habitat the trend is for plants of infertile soils to have higher Change Factors than those of fertile soils ($r = -0.32$, $p = 0.019$).

Ellenberg L	No. species	Mean CF	Standard error
5 (semi-shade)	1	-2	-
6	9	+14	11
7	23	+20	5
8	18	+29	7
9 (full light)	2	+53	3

Ellenberg N	No. species	Mean CF	Standard error
2 (very infertile)	5	+22	9
3	3	+49	6
4	3	+12	27
5	8	+47	6
6	14	+27	6
7	16	+11	6
8	3	-8	5
9 (very fertile)	1	+5	-

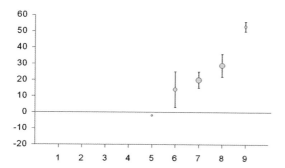

The species in this group have a range of pH preferences but there is not a statistically significant trend ($r = -0.22$, $p = 0.12$).

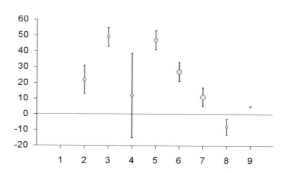

This most unusual trend is explained, at least in part, by the success of a suite of species which in urban areas characteristically grow in chinks in pavements and in other virtually soil-free habitats, and which therefore have very low Ellenberg N values. These species include *Arabidopsis thaliana*, *Catapodium rigidum*, *Erophila verna* sens. lat., *Sagina apetala* and *Vulpia myuros*.

The overall picture for this Broad Habitat is of species which have done well in recent years, almost irrespective of their detailed ecological requirements. There is, however, a tendency for Southern species and plants of open habitats with skeletal soils to have done particularly well.

What environmental variables are driving the changes in Built-up areas and gardens?

For a model including perennation and both Ellenberg N and L, $R^2 = 19.6\%$ with significant effects for both N ($p = 0.040$) and L ($p = 0.039$), but not perennation ($p = 0.40$). When Wider Distribution is added to a model with N and L, R^2 increases to 29.8%, and the effect of the Distribution term is statistically significant ($p = 0.042$) but there is a reduction in the statistical significance for N ($p = 0.19$) and L ($p = 0.12$). Adding the individual climate variables to a model based on N, L and Wider Distribution reduces the statistical significance of Wider Distribution but shows effects of January temperature ($R^2 = 35.4\%$, $p = 0.051$), July temperature ($R^2 = 51.6\%$, $p < 0.001$) and rainfall ($R^2 = 52.1\%$, $p < 0.001$).

Dropping Wider Distribution increases the statistical significance of N (but not L) and shows effects of January temperature ($R^2 = 29.2\%$, $p = 0.005$), July temperature ($R^2 = 45.6\%$, $p < 0.001$) and rainfall ($R^2 = 45.5\%$, $p < 0.001$). For a model including both January temperature and July temperature, the effect of January temperature is reduced ($p = 0.64$), but not July temperature ($p < 0.001$). Similarly for January temperature ($p = 0.57$) and rainfall ($p < 0.001$). For a model including N, L, July temperature and rainfall, $R^2 = 46.1\%$ with an effect for N ($p = 0.006$), but not L ($p = 0.67$), July temperature ($p = 0.45$) or rainfall ($p = 0.48$).

The absence of an effect of either July temperature or rainfall when both are included in the model reflects the high correlation between them ($r = -0.96$).

In summary, the analysis shows good evidence for an effect of Ellenberg N (after allowing for either January temperature, July temperature or rainfall), an effect of July temperature after allowing for N and an effect of rainfall after allowing for N. However, for these data the effects of July temperature and rainfall are statistically indistinguishable. For a model with N and July temperature $R^2 = 45.0\%$, whereas for a model with N and rainfall $R^2 = 45.3$, with both terms being statistically significant in each case. By comparison for a model with N and both July temperature and rainfall $R^2 = 46.0\%$, with neither July temperature nor rainfall statistically significant.

Thus, plants with low fertility requirements and those of climates characterised by low rainfall and warm summers have done especially well in Built-up areas and gardens.

Species groups

3 groups of species are considered, one widespread and the other two showing an increasing restriction to the lowlands. The more southern the group the higher the mean Change Factor, supporting the conclusions reached by the analysis of the broad phytogeographical groups.

Built-up areas and gardens (BH17):
classification of species

Capsella bursa-pastoris group (1.1)

Species	9	Average tetrads	429	Mean CF	- 6	Significance	0.02
		Very Widespread		**Significant decrease**			

These are very widespread species for which no change would
be expected at tetrad scale. Two species, *Capsella bursa-pastoris*
and *Galium aparine* show apparently significant losses. As the
account of *Galium aparine* explains this is almost certainly
an artefact relating to the fact that these species have been
exceptionally well recorded.

Capsella bursa-pastoris, Shepherd's Purse Gillian Beckett

Species	Broad Habitats	Native Status	WD	EN	G	L	R	Total	TF	RC	CF	90% Conf. Limits
Capsella bursa-pastoris	4, 17	AR	w	7	39	33	426	498	91	-4	-17	15
Galium aparine	3, 4, 17	N	t	8	15	6	495	516	90	-3	-16	16
Epilobium montanum	3, 16, 17	N	t	6	74	60	352	486	88	-2	-10	25
Senecio vulgaris	3, 4, 17	N	s	7	47	33	400	480	89	-2	-9	17
Aegopodium podagraria	3, 17	AR	t	7	52	38	336	426	80	-2	-7	15
Sambucus nigra	3, 17	N	t	7	28	8	451	487	91	-1	-4	10
Asplenium trichomanes	3, 16, 17	N	s	2	51	39	143	233	54	-1	-2	16
Polygonum aviculare agg.	3, 4, 17	N	w	6	52	23	450	525	94	+1	+5	22
Asplenium ruta-muraria	3, 16, 17	N	t	2	51	32	128	211	49	+3	+5	17

WD: Wider Distribution   EN: Ellenberg N   G: Gains   L: Losses   R: Re-finds   TF: Tetrad Frequency   RC: Relative Change   CF: Change Factor (weighted)

Galium aparine
Cleavers

Mapped Change	+ 2%	
Relative Change	- 3%	± 1%
Weighted CF	-16%	±16%
Tetrad Frequency	63%	

Galium aparine is very widespread throughout lowland Britain and is thought to be increasing in abundance in response to rising soil nutrient levels, though no change is evident at the tetrad scale. This species has been so well recorded in both surveys, as evidenced by the high proportion of re-finds, that the over-recording adjustment is largely inappropriate and the relative loss reported is almost certainly false. The weighting applied to calculate CF accentuates this problem. The exceptionally narrow confidence limits of ± 1% for relative change reflect the near-certainty of this species being recorded where present.

Key to maps ● Loss ● Gain ○ Re-find
▨ *New Atlas* distribution

Gillian Beckett

Sagina apetala group (1.2)

Species	15	Average tetrads	318	Mean CF	+19	Significance	0.00
		Widespread		**Significant increase**			

Several of the species with large increases are most commonly, but not exclusively, found in the urban environment and their success may be due not only to urban sprawl but to climate change favouring species of habitats that are prone to drought. *Sagina apetala*, *Tanacetum parthenium*, *Arabidopsis thaliana* and *Artemisia vulgaris* fall into this category. Other species are both weeds of arable ground and gardens and it is not possible to comment on the change in the two habitats separately.

Species	Broad Habitats	Native Status	WD	EN	G	L	R	Total	TF	RC	CF	90% Conf. Limits
Lamium album	3, 17	AR	n	8	34	27	263	324	86	-4	-8	10
Sinapis arvensis	3, 4, 17	AR	t	7	68	55	204	327	77	-2	-4	18
Lamium purpureum	3, 4, 17	AR	t	7	62	42	311	415	87	-1	-2	17
Sisymbrium officinale	3, 4, 17	AR	s	7	57	27	281	365	84	+3	+6	14
Medicago lupulina	7, 17	N	t	4	53	20	284	357	85	+4	+8	12
Anisantha sterilis	3, 4, 17	AR	s	7	50	16	281	347	91	+4	+9	11
Tripleurospermum inodorum	4, 17	AR	t	6	82	49	286	417	94	+3	+9	20
Artemisia vulgaris	3, 17	AR	t	7	59	20	247	326	78	+6	+13	12
Veronica hederifolia	1, 3, 4, 17	AR	s	6	94	42	207	343	88	+11	+23	17
Euphorbia helioscopia	4, 17	AR	s	6	90	39	162	291	74	+13	+25	16
Arabidopsis thaliana	16, 17	N	t	2	101	42	127	270	63	+19	+33	17
Euphorbia peplus	4, 17	AR	s	6	100	32	153	285	76	+20	+35	15
Erophila verna sens. lat.	3, 16, 17	N	s	3	106	53	84	243	60	+21	+36	21
Tanacetum parthenium	3, 17	AR	s	6	121	46	102	269	66	+27	+47	18
Sagina apetala	17	N	s	3	104	27	59	190	53	+40	+55	16

WD: Wider Distribution   EN: Ellenberg N   G: Gains   L: Losses   R: Re-finds   TF: Tetrad Frequency   RC: Relative Change   CF: Change Factor (weighted)

Arabidopsis thaliana
Thale Cress

Mapped Change	+26%	
Relative Change	+19%	±11%
Weighted CF	+33%	±17%
Tetrad Frequency	63%	

Sagina apetala
Annual Pearlwort

Mapped Change	+47%	
Relative Change	+40%	±13%
Weighted CF	+55%	±16%
Tetrad Frequency	53%	

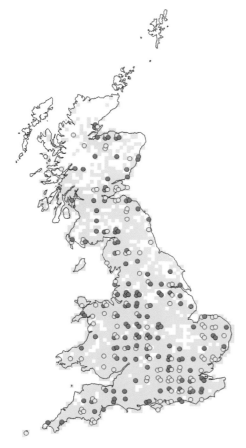

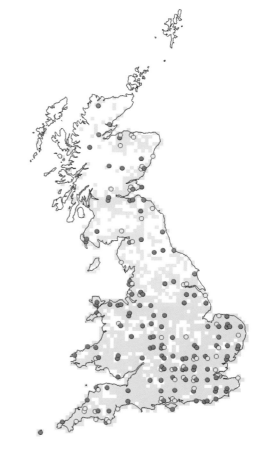

In many areas *Arabidopsis thaliana* is such a familiar weed of gardens and urban areas that it is perhaps surprising that it is still relatively localised. It may sometimes have colonised ruderal habitats from local native sites rather than being distributed by the rail and road network. The data table gives evidence of continuing spread, but the map shows little evidence of recent long-distance dispersal.

Sagina apetala is an easily overlooked species but the scale of the increase recorded can hardly be other than real. It has spread along roadsides and in other disturbed habitats. Along roads salted in winter it is usually found further from the tarmac than roadside halophytes including its relative, *Sagina maritima*, with which it might sometimes be confused.

Key to maps ● Loss ● Gain ○ Re-find
▨ *New Atlas* distribution

Hordeum murinum group (2)

Species	29	Average tetrads	88	Mean CF	+34	Significance	0.00
		Moderately local		**Significant increase**			

As with the *Sagina apetala* group, a large proportion of these species are archaeophytes, many of which also occur in Boundary and linear features (BH3) and to a lesser extent Arable and horticultural land (BH4).

The consistent trend of marked increase in this group is most striking. While the species are not specific to the urban habitat many are strongly associated with habitation. These include *Euphorbia lathyris*, *Lactuca serriola*, *Geranium rotundifolium*, *Vulpia myuros*, *Trifolium micranthum*, *Diplotaxis tenuifolia*, *Mercurialis annua*, *Reseda luteola*, *Malva sylvestris*, *Catapodium rigidum*, *Parietaria judaica* and *Hordeum murinum*. While some of these species, such as *Trifolium micranthum* and *Mercurialis annua*, are associated with fairly nutrient-rich habitats, the majority are associated with nutrient-poor habitats and once again their success may be due not only to urban sprawl but to climate change favouring species of habitats that are prone to drought. Other species are again weeds of both arable ground and gardens and it is not possible to comment on the change in the two habitats separately.

Mercurialis annua, Annual Mercury Bob Ellis

Lactuca serriola, Prickly Lettuce Richard Pryce

Species	Broad Habitats	Native Status	WD	EN	G	L	R	Total	TF	RC	CF	90% Conf. Limits
Chaenorhinum minus	3, 4, 17	AR	t	4	27	37	20	84	39	-26	-31	28
Melilotus altissimus	3, 17	AR	t	7	26	24	30	80	42	-5	-6	26
Urtica urens	4, 17	AR	s	8	54	43	83	180	56	0	+1	22
Lepidium campestre	3, 4, 17	AR	t	6	11	9	8	28	29	+2	+2	45
Artemisia absinthium	3, 16, 17	AR	t	9	15	11	16	42	34	+4	+5	34
Epilobium roseum	1, 3, 14, 17	N	t	7	20	16	6	42	38	+7	+8	42
Veronica agrestis	3, 4, 17	AR	t	7	54	39	26	119	51	+11	+15	29
Hordeum murinum	3, 17	AR	s	6	57	19	130	206	68	+13	+19	13
Parietaria judaica	16, 17	N	s	5	32	15	35	82	31	+17	+20	22
Saponaria officinalis	3, 17	AR	t	6	25	16	9	50	26	+18	+21	35
Medicago arabica	3, 17	N	s	5	34	7	52	93	57	+23	+27	15
Catapodium rigidum	7, 17	N	s	2	32	14	24	70	32	+24	+27	25
Malva sylvestris	3, 17	AR	s	7	77	12	172	261	73	+19	+31	10
Reseda luteola	3, 17	AR	s	6	77	28	79	184	55	+24	+34	17
Mercurialis annua	3, 4, 17	AR	s	7	30	9	24	63	45	+31	+34	23
Mentha spicata	3, 17	AR	s	7	42	19	14	75	30	+33	+39	27
Viscum album	3, 17	N	t	5	21	5	13	39	28	+39	+41	27
Diplotaxis tenuifolia	3, 16, 17	AR	t	6	14	5	4	23	30	+41	+43	40
Trifolium micranthum	8, 17	N	s	5	32	11	11	54	34	+40	+45	27
Spergularia rubra	8, 17	N	s	2	44	15	16	75	37	+40	+47	24
Foeniculum vulgare	3, 16, 17	AR	s	5	41	14	11	66	37	+44	+50	26
Vulpia myuros	3, 17	AR	s	3	46	13	13	72	37	+48	+55	23
Epilobium tetragonum	3, 17	N	t	5	108	32	50	190	85	+41	+58	18
Valerianella carinata	3, 17	AR	s	4	30	6	7	43	42	+56	+61	27
Centaurea cyanus	3, 4, 17	AR	t	5	11	2	2	15	17	+61	+62	42
Geranium rotundifolium	3, 16, 17	N	s	6	32	5	7	44	44	+61	+65	25
Lactuca serriola	3, 17	AR	s	6	104	2	63	169	80	+54	+65	8
Euphorbia lathyris	3, 16, 17	AR	s	5	56	7	9	72	42	+67	+74	20
Onopordum acanthium	3, 17	AR	t	7	21	4	1	26	23	+69	+75	30

WD: Wider Distribution   EN: Ellenberg N   G: Gains   L: Losses   R: Re-finds   TF: Tetrad Frequency   RC: Relative Change   CF: Change Factor (weighted)

Hordeum murinum
Wall Barley

Mapped Change	+20%	
Relative Change	+13%	± 9%
Weighted CF	+19%	±13%
Tetrad Frequency	68%	

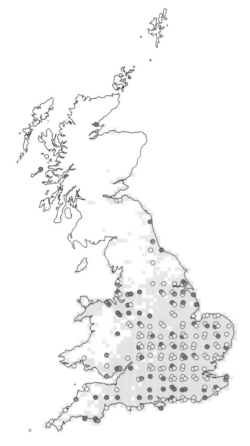

Hordeum murinum shows an increase in frequency within its range. It has spread more within the built-up landscape than in the countryside and could have been favoured by climate change as no parallel increase has occurred in the north.

Mercurialis annua
Annual Mercury

Mapped Change	+39%	
Relative Change	+31%	±22%
Weighted CF	+34%	±23%
Tetrad Frequency	45%	

Mercurialis annua is a southern species that is favoured by milder winters and by eutrophication. Both these factors appear to have contributed to its spread.

Key to maps   ● Loss   ● Gain   ○ Re-find
▨ *New Atlas* distribution

Lactuca serriola
Prickly Lettuce

Mapped Change	+61%	
Relative Change	+54%	± 6%
Weighted CF	+65%	± 8%
Tetrad Frequency	80%	

Euphorbia lathyris
Caper Spurge

Mapped Change	+75%	
Relative Change	+67%	±21%
Weighted CF	+74%	±20%
Tetrad Frequency	42%	

The spread of *Lactuca serriola* has been dramatic with almost three times as many records made for the Local Change survey as for the Monitoring Scheme. *Lactuca serriola* colonises disturbed ground and is favoured by hot summers; it is known to have increased in abundance immediately after the hot summer of 1976 (Prince *et al.* 1985). Climate change seems likely to be a factor in its spread.

Although *Euphorbia lathyris* is an archaeophyte in Britain, many of its stations relate to much more recent introductions as garden outcasts and from bird seed. The species has increased strongly across and beyond its previous range but remains southern. As an introduction it may well have been occurring over a wider range than that in which it is naturalised. Climate change could have been a factor in the observed spread.

Key to maps   ● Loss   ● Gain   ○ Re-find
    ▨ *New Atlas* distribution

Doubtfully native species and neophytes in Built-up areas and gardens

In addition to its native plants, this Broad Habitat supports a large suite of neophytes, many of which have increased in frequency in recent years.

Species	Broad Habitats	Native Status	WD	EN	G	L	R	Total	TF	RC	CF	90% Conf. Limits
Doubtful Status												
Aconitum napellus sens. lat.	1, 3, 14, 17	NA	t	6	12	4	7	23	17	+34	+35	38
Aethusa cynapium	3, 4, 17	NA	t	6	53	40	124	217	69	0	0	17
Brassica oleracea	17, 18	NA	s	8	11	4	0	15	29	+55	-	-
Dipsacus fullonum sens. lat.	3, 6, 17	NA	t	7	87	26	123	236	70	+22	+34	14
Lapsana communis	3, 17	NA	t	7	42	15	428	485	94	+1	+2	15
Neophytes												
Alchemilla mollis	3, 17	AN		6	94	2	7	103	60	+83	+89	14
Amaranthus retroflexus	3, 4, 17	AN		7	18	2	0	20	30	+80	-	-
Antirrhinum majus	3, 17	AN		5	40	6	6	52	27	+66	+71	23
Aster agg.	3, 17, 21	AN		6	25	26	24	75	33	-10	-12	29
Buddleja davidii	3, 17	AN		5	119	7	58	184	60	+56	+70	10
Calendula officinalis	3, 17	AN		7	23	8	2	33	25	+51	+59	33
Calystegia pulchra	3, 17	AN		7	16	13	3	32	32	+7	+9	49
Calystegia silvatica	3, 17	AN		6	74	29	130	233	68	+15	+23	15
Campanula portenschlagiana	3, 17	AN		6	14	1	0	15	20	+84	-	-
Campanula poscharskyana	3, 17	AN		6	31		3	34	35	+83	+84	12
Centranthus ruber	3, 16, 17, 18	AN		5	83	9	40	132	49	+52	+62	14
Cerastium tomentosum	3, 17, 19	AN		5	48	26	22	96	39	+23	+29	26
Cicerbita macrophylla	3, 17	AN		6	13	6	10	29	25	+22	+23	36
Claytonia perfoliata	4, 17, 19	AN		5	14	10	12	36	32	+7	+7	38
Conyza canadensis	3, 4, 17, 19	AN		6	78	6	38	122	57	+54	+63	13
Coronopus didymus	4, 17	AN		7	80	18	63	161	64	+36	+46	15
Cotoneaster horizontalis	3, 16, 17	AN		4	57	13	11	81	46	+57	+66	21
Cotoneaster integrifolius	3, 17	AN		4	6	8	4	18	19	-25	-26	52
Cotoneaster simonsii	3, 10, 16, 17	AN		4	50	17	11	78	42	+46	+56	24
Crepis vesicaria	3, 5, 6, 17	AN		7	54	35	94	183	72	+5	+8	19
Crocosmia x crocosmiiflora	1, 3, 17	AN		4	86	7	42	135	48	+54	+64	12
Cymbalaria muralis	3, 16, 17, 19	AN		6	66	40	126	232	56	+6	+10	18
Diplotaxis muralis	3, 4, 16, 17	AN		6	19	9	18	46	34	+19	+20	29
Echinochloa crus-galli	17	AN		8	17	1	0	18	36	+86	-	-
Epilobium ciliatum	3, 4, 17	AN		6	128	54	183	365	86	+17	+41	19
Eranthis hyemalis	1, 3, 17	AN		6	21	7	5	33	34	+45	+49	34
Fragaria ananassa	3, 17	AN		7	15	9	1	25	26	+29	+37	50
Galanthus nivalis	1, 3, 17	AN	s	7	123	36	71	230	65	+38	+58	17

WD: Wider Distribution   EN: Ellenberg N   G: Gains   L: Losses   R: Re-finds   TF: Tetrad Frequency   RC: Relative Change   CF: Change Factor (weighted)

Species	Broad Habitats	Native Status	WD	EN	G	L	R	Total	TF	RC	CF	90% Conf. Limits
Neophytes *continued*												
Galega officinalis	3, 17	AN	t	8	16	4	6	26	49	+46	+48	34
Galinsoga parviflora	4, 17	AN		7	12	3	1	16	26	+61	+64	41
Galinsoga quadriradiata	3, 4, 17	AN		6	18	6	2	26	33	+51	+56	36
Geranium endressii	3, 17	AN		6	14	2	2	18	22	+66	+68	37
Geranium pyrenaicum	3, 17	AN	t	6	62	11	45	118	49	+40	+47	15
Heracleum mantegazzianum	3, 14, 17	AN		8	17	14	17	48	27	0	0	34
Hesperis matronalis	3, 17	AN		7	38	37	28	103	35	-7	-9	28
Hirschfeldia incana	3, 17	AN		5	19	1	5	25	33	+66	+68	26
Hyacinthoides hispanica	1, 3, 17	AN		6	65	27	18	110	65	+38	+50	24
Lamium maculatum	3, 17	AN	t	8	43	21	4	68	45	+38	+59	34
Leucanthemum x superbum	3, 16, 17	AN		5	29	7	9	45	28	+49	+53	27
Linaria purpurea	3, 16, 17	AN		6	85	17	42	144	50	+46	+57	16
Lysimachia punctata	1, 3, 17	AN		5	48	9	27	84	38	+44	+50	18
Melilotus officinalis	3, 17	AN		5	24	30	23	77	42	-20	-23	27
Melissa officinalis	3, 17	AN		6	40	4	6	50	44	+70	+74	22
Myrrhis odorata	3, 17	AN		7	10	21	57	88	44	-22	-25	12
Oenothera agg.	3, 16, 17, 19	AN		4	38	16	19	73	33	+30	+35	25
Oxalis articulata	3, 17, 19	AN		2	33	2	3	38	35	+78	+81	24
Oxalis corniculata	3, 17	AN		5	48	5	10	63	38	+66	+71	20
Oxalis exilis	3, 17	AN		4	20	1	0	21	31	+86	-	-
Oxalis stricta	3, 17	AN		5	11	6	0	17	41	+37	-	-
Pentaglottis sempervirens	1, 3, 17	AN		7	99	17	77	193	56	+39	+53	13
Phalaris canariensis	3, 17	AN		6	19	17	1	37	27	+1	+3	90
Pilosella aurantiaca	3, 17	AN	n	2	73	11	11	95	38	+66	+77	18
Pseudofumaria lutea	3, 17	AN		5	43	8	36	87	35	+36	+41	17
Pulmonaria officinalis	1, 3, 17	AN	t	6	18	8	7	33	34	+31	+34	36
Sempervivum tectorum	3, 17	AN		1	10	4	2	16	34	+41	+43	48
Senecio squalidus	3, 17	AN		7	26	48	51	125	45	-30	-37	18
Senecio viscosus	3, 17, 19	AN	t	6	43	38	46	127	41	-2	-3	24
Sisymbrium orientale	3, 17	AN		5	12	8	7	27	23	+12	+13	44
Soleirolia soleirolii	3, 17	AN	s	6	28	6	16	50	33	+42	+45	24
Solidago canadensis	3, 17	AN		6	28	22	17	67	37	+5	+6	33
Solidago gigantea	3, 17	AN		6	27	9	5	41	34	+48	+53	31
Tellima grandiflora	1, 3, 17	AN		4	22	4	1	27	48	+70	+77	29
Veronica filiformis	3, 17	AN		7	69	51	115	235	58	+2	+4	21
Veronica persica	3, 4, 17	AN		7	76	34	275	385	88	+6	+15	16
Veronica polita	4, 17	AN	s	5	42	28	22	92	52	+14	+17	28
Vinca major	1, 3, 17	AN		6	93	12	42	147	56	+52	+64	14

WD: Wider Distribution   EN: Ellenberg N   G: Gains   L: Losses   R: Re-finds   TF: Tetrad Frequency   RC: Relative Change   CF: Change Factor (weighted)

Paul Westley

Coastal habitats (BH18, 19, 21)

Species	56	Average tetrads	70	Mean CF	+ 9	Significance	0.07
					Increase marginally significant		

The regular grid of tetrads sampled for the BSBI surveys provides a rather small sample of coastal squares. For this reason the following three coastal Broad Habitats have been amalgamated for this analysis.

Broad Habitat 18, Supralittoral rock, includes those habitats on coastal rock which are above the high water mark, but still within range of wavesplash and sea-spray. They comprise plant communities in crevices and on ledges of both hard and soft cliffs, including cliffs where sea-birds nest, and those on shallow, drought-prone, cliff-top soils. The latter include both annual-dominated swards and the most maritime grasslands.

Broad Habitat 19, Supralittoral sediment, comprises the plant communities which colonise vegetation of coastal sediments (rather than rocks) above the high water mark. The main habitats are strandlines, shingle beaches and coastal sand dunes (including machair and dune heath). *Broad Habitat 21, Littoral sediment*, covers sediments below the high water mark. From a botanical perspective the only important plant communities are those of salt marshes on mud or muddy sand, as other sediments (such as pure sands and gravels) are usually unvegetated.

There are no relevant species in the remaining coastal Broad Habitats, Littoral rock (BH20) and Inshore sublittoral sediment (BH23).

Changes in coastal habitats, 1950-2004

1950-1986

Their terrain protects the more rugged coastal habitats from the effects of major land-use change. The main influences on coastal habitats in this period are listed below.

- Recognition of the need to protect the coastal zone from the sprawling developments which characterised the more populous areas in the inter-war years, and in particular the campaign by the National Trust ('Operation Neptune') to safeguard scenically important stretches of coast.

- Increasing public affluence and mobility leading to increased pressure on coastal sites, a notable development being the establishment of long-distance coastal footpaths. Public pressure often has a detrimental effect on the strand-line flora but footpaths and associated seats and view-points may also preserve islands of open habitat on otherwise overgrown cliff-tops, as well as providing possibilities for plant dispersal. Since the 1960s the increasing ability of people to visit the coast has been offset by the inexorable growth in the number of foreign holidays.

- Loss of grazing from the coastal fringe, with cliff slopes fenced off and becoming overgrown by scrub in sites which are not severely exposed, although grazing on west-coast salt marshes remains heavy.

- Increasing stability of sand-dune areas, with the loss of the natural mobility of these systems and thus of early successional stages of dune vegetation.

- Increase in the construction of sea defences, which has changed patterns of accretion and erosion and often reduced the width of the intertidal zone.

The salting of inland roadside verges has also had a dramatic effect on the distribution of a minority of coastal species.

1987-2004

There has been little change to the factors affecting coastal habitats in this period. The number of holidays taken in Britain (which may reflect pressures on coastal habitats) was approximately stable, whereas the number of foreign holidays continued to rise (Matheson & Summerfield 2000). Rising sea levels in S.E. England have led to the acceptance that sea defences can no longer be maintained in some areas, leading to the creation of new saltmarshes in coastal areas in a strategy which has been called 'managed retreat' or, more euphemistically, 'managed realignment'. It is unlikely that this has yet had an appreciable effect in plant distribution.

Earlier studies of changes in the species of coastal habitats

Few detailed studies of floristic change are available for coastal counties. In West Lancashire the coastal flora prospered in the 20th century, with new and increasing species greatly outnumbering extinct and declining species (Greenwood 2003), despite the loss of semi-natural sand dunes to golf courses or building development. A rather different study of Berwickshire, a county with a steep and often inaccessible coastline with few sand or shingle beaches, showed that the survival of scarce coastal taxa has been better than that of plants in any other habitat (Braithwaite 2004).

Comparison of the two BSBI Atlas surveys (Preston *et al.* 2003b) showed relatively little overall change in coastal habitats. In most regions plants of coastal rocks were doing at least as well as most species, and often better. There was considerable more regional variation in the plants of soft coasts.

Unfortunately, the Countryside Survey sample squares are insufficiently representative of coastal habitats to provide data on change at the scale of that survey.

The BSBI Local change surveys

The coastal species include a small group of halophytes that have been spreading inland along roadsides and the dramatic gains for these species bias the overall measure of change. For this reason the statistical analyses in this section exclude the 5 roadside colonists with the highest change factors (*Atriplex littoralis*, *A. prostrata*, *Cochlearia danica*, *Puccinellia distans*, *Spergularia marina*). Even so, the change factors for the remaining species may relate in part to the less dramatic spread along roadsides of other plants such as *Plantago coronopus*, *Sagina maritima* and *Spergularia media*).

Annual and biennial species appear to show higher mean change factors than the perennials, but the difference is not statistically significant ($F_{2,48} = 1.26$, $p = 0.29$).

Perennation	No. species	Mean CF	Standard error
Annual	15	+9	7
Biennial	3	+14	4
Perennial	33	0	3

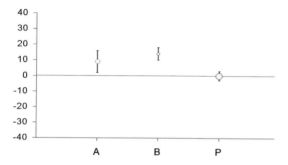

Similarly, there is no significant correlation with Wider Distribution.

Wider Distribution	No. species	Mean CF	Standard error
Northern	16	-4	4
Temperate	10	-2	6
Widespread	4	+7	5
Southern	21	+11	5

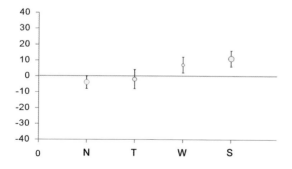

Not unexpectedly, there is no clear trend with respect to pH ($r = -0.14$, $p = 0.31$).

Ellenberg R	No. species	Mean CF	Standard error
4 (acid)	2	+42	40
5	4	-6	16
6	15	+1	4
7	22	+4	4
8 (basic)	8	+1	6

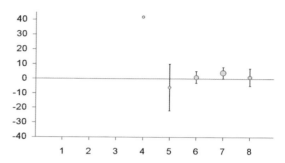

Nor is there a significant correlation with nutrient requirements ($r = -0.026$, $p = 0.86$).

Ellenberg N	No. species	Mean CF	Standard error
2 (very infertile)	2	+5	3
3	11	-5	7
4	10	+13	10
5	10	+14	6
6	13	-4	3
7	3	+1	11
8 (fertile)	2	-1	8

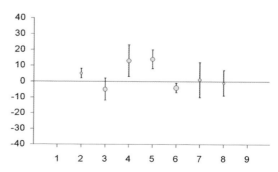

What environmental variables are driving the changes in Aquatic habitats?

In the absence of good evidence of an effect of any individual variable tested above, and of the individual climatic variables, there is little to be gained in extending the analysis to models including combinations of variables.

For the coastal specialists, sample sizes are often small and at the level of individual species the changes may not be real. At the current level of sampling, the BSBI Surveys provide little evidence for change in coastal habitats at the tetrad scale. However, it would be worth considering an extension of the tetrad network to include further coastal squares, and thus increase the sample size for coastal species.

Species groups

Three species groups are considered.

Coastal habitats (BH18, 19, 21): classification of species

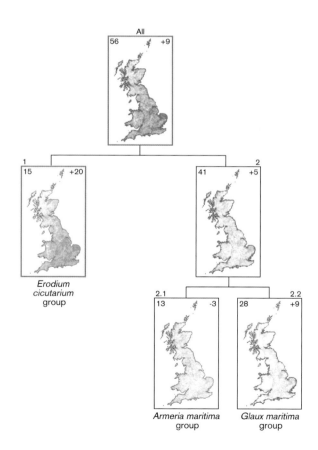

Erodium cicutarium group (1)

Species	15	Average tetrads	148	Mean CF	+20	Significance	0.07
		Moderately widespread		Increase marginally significant			

The majority of the species in this group occur inland in other
Broad Habitats. The group includes three of the commonest
halophytes which have spread inland along roadsides in recent
years, *Cochlearia danica*, *Puccinellia distans* and *Atriplex
prostrata*, though the last of these has always been widespread
inland in the south and is restricted to salt-treated roadsides only
in the north. The mean Change Factor refers in large measure to
the massive change in these three species in the period between
the two surveys. This clearly relates to the ubiquitous practice of
salting roads in winter, which creates a saline habitat in a narrow
band at the roadside that is unsuitable for most plants and has
been colonised by these annual species. It is possible that the
spread of the winter annual *Cochlearia danica*, at least, has also
been assisted by warmer winter weather.

Species	Broad Habitats	Native Status	WD	EN	G	L	R	Total	TF	RC	CF	90% Conf. Limits
Trifolium campestre	3, 16, 19	N	s	4	45	65	87	197	52	-21	-31	18
Cynoglossum officinale	7, 19	N	t	6	3	5	14	22	24	-19	-20	25
Thalictrum minus	16, 19	N	n	3	7	7	8	22	18	-9	-9	45
Rumex crispus	3, 6, 19	N	s	6	56	40	409	505	88	-2	-9	22
Elytrigia repens	3, 4, 19	N	w	7	62	34	357	453	87	+1	+4	19
Centaurium pulchellum	21	N	s	3	10	8	5	23	34	+5	+5	51
Valerianella locusta	3, 16, 19	N	t	4	30	24	11	65	31	+6	+8	36
Centaurium erythraea	7, 19	N	s	3	63	41	84	188	52	+7	+11	20
Viola tricolor	4, 8, 19	N	t	4	38	26	27	91	43	+10	+13	27
Cerastium semidecandrum	8, 18, 19	N	t	3	24	16	10	50	29	+15	+17	35
Erodium cicutarium agg.	19	N	s	4	49	18	50	117	40	+23	+29	19
Atriplex prostrata	3, 4, 19, 21	N	w	7	130	38	115	283	80	+31	+53	16
Puccinellia distans	3, 21	N	n	7	63	7	12	82	44	+67	+74	18
Cochlearia danica	3, 18	N	t	5	73	5	15	93	35	+69	+76	16
Stellaria pallida	3, 19	N	s	4	24	1	2	27	28	+80	+82	28

WD: Wider Distribution   EN: Ellenberg N   G: Gains   L: Losses   R: Re-finds   TF: Tetrad Frequency   RC: Relative Change   CF: Change Factor (weighted)

Puccinellia distans
Reflexed Saltmarsh-grass

Mapped Change	+75%	
Relative Change	+67%	±18%
Weighted CF	+74%	±18%
Tetrad Frequency	44%	

Cochlearia danica
Danish Scurvygrass

Mapped Change	+77%	
Relative Change	+69%	±14%
Weighted CF	+76%	±16%
Tetrad Frequency	35%	

Puccinellia distans has, as reported in the *New Atlas*, spread rapidly in recent years along inland roadsides. The roads colonised by this annual species include minor roads as well as main ones and extend into the uplands. In many areas it has arrived a few years after *Spergularia marina* and occurs as a narrow 'comb' along the verge. Its distribution is more eastern than that of *Cochlearia danica*.

The dramatic spread of *Cochlearia danica* along motorways and other main roads reported in the *New Atlas* is confirmed as a recent phenomenon. It is notable that the roads colonised are lowland. It seems that this winter annual does not have the same cold-tolerance as the perennial *Cochlearia* species found in the uplands.

Key to maps   ● Loss   ● Gain   ○ Re-find
        ▓ *New Atlas* distribution

Armeria maritima group (2.1)

Species	13	Average tetrads	68	Mean CF	- 3	Significance	0.34
		Moderately local		**No change**			

These species are predominantly coastal; those which extend inland often do so in the north and west. *Sagina nodosa* is the only species showing unequivocal change and its losses appear to relate to inland rather than coastal habitats. The apparent gains of *Asplenium marinum* could be in part real and climate-related but this is a species that often occupies highly inaccessible sites on coastal rocks and more information is desirable before a firm conclusion is reached. *Plantago coronopus* also shows an increase which may be related to its spread inland.

Species	Broad Habitats	Native Status	WD	EN	G	L	R	Total	TF	RC	CF	90% Conf. Limits
Sagina nodosa	11, 19	N	n	3	12	22	7	41	31	-43	-47	34
Silene uniflora	18	N	n	4	8	10	28	46	27	-14	-15	22
Tripleurospermum maritimum	18, 19	N	n	6	15	15	34	64	41	-8	-9	24
Armeria maritima	18, 21	N	n	5	8	8	60	76	33	-8	-9	12
Salix repens	10, 19	N	n	3	24	23	69	116	45	-7	-9	17
Plantago maritima	15, 21	N	n	4	18	13	76	107	42	-3	-3	14
Cerastium diffusum	18, 19	N	t	3	19	16	27	62	32	-2	-2	27
Ligusticum scoticum	18	N	n	5	4	3	11	18	30	-2	-2	36
Rosa pimpinellifolia	10, 16, 19	N	t	3	12	10	17	39	26	-2	-2	32
Sedum anglicum	16, 18	N	t	2	20	12	59	91	46	+2	+2	18
Cochlearia officinalis sens. lat.	18	N	n	4	17	5	57	79	34	+8	+9	14
Plantago coronopus	3, 6, 18	N	s	4	42	14	65	121	42	+18	+22	16
Asplenium marinum	18	N	s	5	10	3	10	23	24	+26	+27	34

WD: Wider Distribution   EN: Ellenberg N   G: Gains   L: Losses   R: Re-finds   TF: Tetrad Frequency   RC: Relative Change   CF: Change Factor (weighted)

Silene uniflora
Sea Campion

Mapped Change	- 5%	
Relative Change	-14%	±23%
Weighted CF	-15%	±22%
Tetrad Frequency	27%	

Although *Silene uniflora* is thought of as a familiar species round much of the British coast the Local Change coverage is poor, indicating not only the limitations of the sampled tetrads when it comes to coastal habitats but also a real scarcity of this species except where the coasts are rocky. The change recorded is not significant.

Asplenium marinum
Sea Spleenwort

Mapped Change	+35%	
Relative Change	+26%	±34%
Weighted CF	+27%	±34%
Tetrad Frequency	24%	

Although *Asplenium marinum* was only recorded from 23 tetrads over the two surveys the apparent gains are so marked as to require comment. This fern frequents sea cliffs that may be highly inaccessible and it is likely that more thorough recording has played the greatest part in the observed change. Nevertheless milder winters could have been favouring this species by opening up new sites for colonisation by this frost-sensitive plant.

Key to maps ● Loss ● Gain ○ Re-find
            ▨ *New Atlas* distribution

Glaux maritima group (2.2)

Species	28	Average tetrads	29	Mean CF	+ 9	Significance	0.16
		Local		**Increase not significant**			

Most of the species in this group are exclusively coastal. Overall they show little change, the few that do show apparent change having data samples that are too small for high confidence in the trends at individual species level. *Vicia lathyroides* is the only species showing unequivocal losses and these appear to relate to inland grassland rather than coastal habitats. *Spergularia marina* and *Atriplex littoralis* show the greatest increases but these relate to inland roadsides.

Atriplex littoralis, Grass-leaved Orache Richard Pryce

Species	Broad Habitats	Native Status	WD	EN	G	L	R	Total	TF	RC	CF	90% Conf. Limits
Vicia lathyroides	8, 19	N	t	3	3	8	5	16	25	-47	-48	41
Elytrigia juncea	19	N	s	6	4	6	9	19	20	-22	-23	38
Bolboschoenus maritimus	21	N	s	7	8	11	22	41	29	-18	-19	25
Atriplex glabriuscula	19	N	n	8	8	8	11	27	27	-9	-9	40
Elytrigia atherica	19, 21	N	s	6	6	6	16	28	38	-9	-9	31
Glaux maritima	21	N	n	5	6	4	37	47	27	-4	-4	16
Juncus gerardii	21	N	w	6	7	5	35	47	27	-4	-4	18
Triglochin maritimum	21	N	n	5	10	8	27	45	30	-3	-3	24
Suaeda maritima	21	N	s	6	4	3	12	19	22	-2	-2	34
Atriplex portulacoides	21	N	s	6	2	1	12	15	24	-1	-1	26
Puccinellia maritima	21	N	n	6	10	8	16	34	26	-1	-1	33
Ammophila arenaria	19	N	s	3	4	2	22	28	27	-1	-1	21
Honckenya peploides	19	N	n	6	5	3	16	24	20	+1	+1	31
Juncus maritimus	21	N	s	5	2		13	15	23	+5	+5	13
Beta vulgaris subsp. *maritima*	18, 19	N	s	8	8	4	17	29	28	7	+8	30
Carex arenaria	19	N	t	2	9	4	22	35	26	+8	+8	26
Aster tripolium	21	N	t	6	10	5	21	36	29	+8	+8	27
Salicornia agg.	21	N	w	6	4	1	12	17	22	+10	+10	28
Sagina maritima	18, 19	N	s	4	10	7	5	22	24	+11	+12	49
Leymus arenarius	19	N	n	6	5	2	9	16	21	+13	+13	38
Cakile maritima	19	N	w	7	10	5	9	24	25	+18	+19	40
Hippophae rhamnoides	19	N	n	5	9	3	8	20	22	+27	+28	38
Catapodium marinum	18	N	s	3	10	4	7	21	24	+27	+28	41
Spergularia media	21	N	s	5	12	3	13	28	25	+27	+29	29
Carex distans	21	N	s	5	10	3	8	21	19	+30	+31	37
Carex extensa	21	N	s	5	8	2	5	15	23	+38	+38	42
Atriplex littoralis	19	N	t	6	28	2	6	36	31	+68	+71	24
Spergularia marina	3, 21	N	s	6	68	13	12	93	46	+61	+72	20

WD: Wider Distribution   EN: Ellenberg N   G: Gains   L: Losses   R: Re-finds   TF: Tetrad Frequency   RC: Relative Change   CF: Change Factor (weighted)

Atriplex littoralis
Grass-leaved Orache

Mapped Change	+76%	
Relative Change	+68%	±23%
Weighted CF	+71%	±24%
Tetrad Frequency	31%	

Spergularia marina
Lesser Sea-spurrey

Mapped Change	+69%	
Relative Change	+61%	±21%
Weighted CF	+72%	±20%
Tetrad Frequency	46%	

The spread of *Atriplex littoralis* along roadsides in eastern England was demonstrated in the *New Atlas*. These results underline what a very recent phenomenon this has been. It is too early to predict the likely distribution when this colonisation has run its course.

There are differences in the distributions of the coastal species colonising inland roadsides. *Spergularia marina* is the most northerly and seems set to become ubiquitous in Scotland both on low and high ground, though it is as yet frequent only in the east. It can form a continuous strip along the road verge, and is apparently able to colonise ground which is so highly compacted that *Cochlearia danica* and *Puccinellia distans* are excluded, but it is much discouraged where a concrete kerb is in place.

Key to maps   ● Loss   ● Gain   ○ Re-find
               New Atlas distribution

Bolboschoenus maritimus
Sea Club-rush

Mapped Change	- 9%	
Relative Change	-18%	±27%
Weighted CF	-19%	±25%
Tetrad Frequency	29%	

Bolboschoenus maritimus is a very persistent perennial of brackish places and has generally been well recorded in the surveys. The suggestion of decline evident from the clusters of apparent losses in southeast England may relate to coastal development.

Key to maps   ● Loss   ● Gain   ○ Re-find
         ▦ *New Atlas* distribution

Gillian Beckett

Doubtfully native species and neophytes in Coastal habitats

There is a small group of coastal neophytes.

Species	Broad Habitats	Native Status	WD	EN	G	L	R	Total	TF	RC	CF	90% Conf. Limits
Neophytes												
Anisantha diandra	3, 4, 19	AN	s	4	23		4	27	50	+77	+78	12
Aster agg.	3, 17, 21	AN		6	25	26	24	75	33	-10	-12	29
Centranthus ruber	3, 16, 17, 18	AN		5	83	9	40	132	49	+52	+62	14
Cerastium tomentosum	3, 17, 19	AN		5	48	26	22	96	39	+23	+29	26
Claytonia perfoliata	4, 17, 19	AN		5	14	10	12	36	32	+7	+7	38
Conyza canadensis	3, 4, 17, 19	AN		6	78	6	38	122	57	+54	+63	13
Cymbalaria muralis	3, 16, 17, 19	AN		6	66	40	126	232	56	+6	+10	18
Lathyrus latifolius	3, 18	AN	s	3	23	8	9	40	29	+38	+41	31
Lepidium draba	3, 19, 21	AN		6	31	16	30	77	39	+16	+19	24
Lobularia maritima	18, 19	AN	s	4	19	9	5	33	26	+33	+36	37
Oenothera agg.	3, 16, 17, 19	AN		4	38	16	19	73	33	+30	+35	25
Oxalis articulata	3, 17, 19	AN		2	33	2	3	38	35	+78	+81	24
Senecio viscosus	3, 17, 19	AN	t	6	43	38	46	127	41	-2	-3	24
Doubtful Status												
Brassica oleracea	17, 18	NA	s	8	11	4	0	15	29	+55	-	-

WD: Wider Distribution   EN: Ellenberg N   G: Gains   L: Losses   R: Re-finds   TF: Tetrad Frequency   RC: Relative Change   CF: Change Factor (weighted)

Bob Ellis

Summary of change in Broad Habitats

The results for the Broad Habitats are summarised in Table 4.5. The Overall performance column is drawn from the analysis of the overall mean Change Factor, with 'possible' indicating a marginally significant effect. In 'Regional variation' we attempt to summarise the results of the TWINSPAN analysis of species groups. The remaining columns summarise the results of the statistical analysis.

Overall patterns of change

There is statistically significant evidence for a decrease in the species of three Broad Habitats, Calcareous grassland, Dwarf shrub heath and Montane habitats, with a possible decrease in the species of Broadleaved woodland. The decline of the species of Calcareous grassland and Dwarf shrub heath has been identified by other studies, including the Atlas surveys, and comes as no surprise. The montane species analysed are the more widespread ones and the evidence suggests that it is their more lowland outliers that have suffered losses. The situation in the true montane communities is uncertain, because of the rarity of many of their characteristic species and the difficulties of surveying these habitats effectively.

There is robust evidence for the increase of species in only one Broad Habitat, Built-up areas and gardens, but increases in the species of Arable and horticultural land, Improved grassland and Coastal habitats are also indicated. The apparent increase in Arable

plants is a major reversal of earlier trends. The other results are less surprising, that of Coastal habitats being in large part attributable to the well-documented spread of some coastal plants on salted roadsides. Within the coastal zone itself there is little evidence of change.

There are a number of reasons why change has not been detected in the other Broad Habitats. In some, the lack of overall change represents a balance between groups of increasing and of decreasing species. Inland rock, with decreasing northern species and increasing southern species, is a particularly clear example. Other Broad Habitats are too poorly represented in the sample, or contain too few vascular plants, to provide adequate data for study.

It is interesting to note that the habitats in which species are in decline are characterised by very few neophytes, whereas the habitat in which species are thriving, Built-up areas and gardens, is the one with much the largest number of associated neophytes.

Regional patterns of change

This provides a more informative, and perhaps more novel, series of results than those of the overall performance in Broad Habitats. The general, and surprisingly consistent, pattern is that southerly species have been more successful than northerly species. We have wondered whether this could be caused by less effective recording in the north in the repeat survey, but detailed analyses of the pattern of recording fail to reveal any such disparity (see chapter 3).

Two of the three Broad Habitats which are most strongly concentrated in the north and west, Dwarf shrub heath and Bog, show a contrasting pattern. The more widespread species in these groups show greater losses than the more northerly plants. This presumably reflects the pressures on these species at the southern limits of their range, where the available habitats are more restricted than in the northern heartlands. The third predominantly northern habitat, Montane, cannot be subdivided regionally.

Other exceptions to the general trend are provided by Calcareous grassland, where both northerly and southerly groups have declined, Coastal habitats, where the plants which have increased are those that also occur in, or have recently invaded, inland localities, and Arable and horticultural land and Aquatic habitats, where no clear-cut regional trends are apparent.

Possible drivers of change

Limitations of the analysis

There are two major reasons why the 'Possible drivers of change' must be taken as suggestions rather than firm conclusions. The first is, of course, that the statistical analysis on which it is based relies on correlations of trends with ecological and climatic factors. Climatic and ecological factors, land-use changes and other pressures are often inter-correlated, and this is particularly true in Britain where warmer areas tend to have softer rocks and less rugged relief, and have thus become the most densely populated regions. It is not only theoretically possible but actually quite likely that some factors which correlate with change are not themselves the causal factors.

The second reason for caution is that the statistical analysis is limited to climatic and other ecological factors for which data are available for all British species. It is possible to test for the possible effects of eutrophication, for example, or climate change, but we lack indices to measure the extent of other potentially important influences on plant distribution. Habitat destruction is one important omission. Regional variations in the extent of habitat destruction might well lead to misleading correlations with other environmental factors. We also lack measures of the extent to which species respond to habitat disturbance. The C-S-R system of Grime (1979) might be a very useful tool in such an analysis, but only selected species rather than all British species have been characterised.

Drivers of change

Rather few ecological and environmental factors correlate with change. In general, perennation, Ellenberg N values, Wider Distribution and the specific climatic factors, particularly the species' mean January and July temperature preferences, are the only factors examined which will help explain the observed changes. Other factors, including pH, shade and salinity preferences and plant height (not all dealt with in this report) either fail to correlate with the patterns of change or, if they do, prove to be redundant when other factors are included in the analysis.

A positive correlation between Ellenberg N values and the Change Factor can be interpreted with some confidence as an indication that eutrophication is a factor driving change in the Broad Habitat. The evidence for this is particularly strong in the grassland Broad habitats, with Neutral, Calcareous and Acidic grasslands all showing this correlation (and Improved grassland, which is by nature eutrophic, showing a possible overall increase). This interpretation is supported by our recorders who have rather seldom reported major habitat loss as the perceived reason for losses of the species of these habitats. Inland rock and Wetland habitats also show evidence of eutrophication but, surprisingly, not Aquatic habitats. The Aquatic habitats include lowland ponds which appear to have undergone an extraordinary amount of physical change with new ponds being dug and others lost. While the overall number of water bodies may have increased only a little, the mixture of gains and losses coupled with uneven recording and small sample sizes limits the scope for effective analysis of the results by ecological and climatic factors. The increase of species with low Ellenberg N values in Built-up areas and gardens is a rare exception to one of the most frequently reported trends not only in this but in many other studies of floristic change.

The direct climatic variables suggest an effect of climate change. The increase in winter temperatures has been a particular feature of the period between the two surveys, and January temperature correlates best with the observed changes in Broadleaved woodland, Boundary and linear features and Calcareous grassland. By contrast, the analysis suggests that increasing summer temperatures may be responsible for the increase of some species of Built-up areas and gardens. Changes in Neutral grassland and, less certainly, Inland rock habitats also appear to correlate with climatic factors, but it is impossible to disentangle which of the inter-correlated factors may be responsible. One should not, perhaps, totally rule out a direct effect of climate change on some Dwarf shrub heath and Bog species, but for these two Broad Habitats the correlation seems least likely to indicate a causal connection, and more likely to reflect the areas where residual fragments of these habitats are particularly threatened.

It is impossible to say, from just a single resurvey, the extent to which the apparent effects of climate change represent a long-term trend or simply a response to the weather of the survey seasons. The main reason for caution here is that 2003 was a very dry year, and this might have had a short-term effect on the vegetation in this and the following year.

The explanatory power of the Wider Distribution term in the analyses of several Broad Habitats (Arable and horticultural, Neutral, Calcareous and Acidic grasslands and Inland rock) is a surprising result. In general, the wider distribution of a species reflects its climatic preferences, and one would expect that the direct climatic variables would replace the very general phytogeographical term in these analyses. In the case of Neutral

grassland the Wider Distribution effect cannot be disentangled from those of the direct climatic factors, so the latter might indeed be responsible for the observed changes. However, in the other Broad Habitats the effects of Wider Distribution cannot be accounted for by the climatic variables alone. As the Wider Distribution of species is reflected in their British distributions, the most likely explanation is perhaps that Wider Distribution is acting as a surrogate for some other regional effect. Further consideration of these results is clearly needed.

The relative success of annuals in relation to perennials is a feature of Boundary and linear features, and both Neutral and Calcareous grassland. Plants clearly do not succeed just because they are annuals; annuals succeed because ecological conditions favour them. In these three Broad Habitats the other variables we have tested do not account for the success for the annuals, suggesting that some other factor may be responsible. Disturbance is one obvious candidate. Natural disturbance through summer drought might be expected to be reflected by the July temperature variable, but human disturbance must be a strong possibility, particularly in view of the strong apparent correlation between change and disturbance reported by many recorders, especially those in central and southern England. Hodgson (1986) has drawn attention to the importance of the combination of eutrophication and increased disturbance as a driver of change in the modern landscape. In Wetland habitats annuals have done badly, and here a reduction in disturbance seems very likely to be the cause.

Interestingly such indirect evidence as there is from recorders suggests that species loss is little correlated with substantial loss of semi-natural habitats. We cannot offer even indirect evidence of whether or not such habitat loss has been occurring without leading to immediate species loss, as species are so often able to survive for extended periods in small populations in remaining fragments of the habitat.

The probable increase in arable species is thought to relate to the effects of agri-environment options and to increased disturbance of non-agricultural habitats, but we are unable to investigate such factors statistically as it only ecological and climatic factors for which suitable data are available to us.

Conclusion

Inevitably, any conclusions on the drivers of change in the British flora which can be drawn from a single repeat of the BSBI Survey must be tentative and uncertain. The changes in the native flora which the resurvey has detected are substantial but seldom dramatic. The nature of the changes is surprisingly consistent between Broad Habitats. Eutrophication and climate change (especially warmer winters) have been the most important of the potential causal factors we have investigated in this analysis. There is a strong possibility that agri-environment options and human disturbance have also been important in enabling species to increase, but we have not been able to investigate these factors statistically.

Broad Habitat number	Broad Habitat name	Overall performance	Regional variation	Plants doing relatively well	Plants doing relatively badly	Possible drivers of change
1	Broadleaved, mixed and yew woodland	Possible decrease	Decrease of northernmost and widespread groups	Plants preferring higher temperatures	Plants preferring lower temperatures	Climate change (warmer winters)
2	Coniferous woodland	No change detected	Not analysed	Not analysed	Not analysed	
3	Boundary and linear features	No change detected	Increase of most southerly group; decrease of most widespread group	Annuals; plants preferring higher temperatures	Perennials; plants preferring lower temperatures	Climate change (warmer winters)
4	Arable and horticultural	Possible increase	Variation in species groups shows no clear regional pattern	Temperate, southern and widespread species	Northern species	Agri-environment policies; increased disturbance
5	Improved grassland	Possible increase	Not analysed	Not analysed	Not analysed	
6	Neutral grassland	No change detected	Decrease of more northerly groups	Annuals; species of nutrient-rich habitats; southern species	Perennials; species of nutrient-poor habitats; northern species	Eutrophication; climate change
7	Calcareous grassland	Decrease	Decrease of more specialised northern and southern groups	Annuals; species of nutrient-rich habitats; southern species	Perennials; species of nutrient-poor habitats; northern and temperate species	Eutrophication; climate change (warmer winters)

Table 4.5 Summary of results for Broad Habitats.

Broad Habitat number	Broad Habitat name	Overall performance	Regional variation	Plants doing relatively well	Plants doing relatively badly	Possible drivers of change
8	Acid grassland	No change detected	Decrease of northern/western group; no change in southern group	Species of nutrient-rich habitats; temperate and southern species	Species of nutrient-poor habitats; northern species	Eutrophication
9	Bracken	No change detected	Not analysed	Not analysed	Not analysed	
10	Dwarf shrub heath	Decrease	Decrease of western and widespread groups; no change in northernmost group	Species of cooler, moister areas	Species of warmer, drier areas	Perhaps land-use change rather than climate change?
12	Bog	No change detected	Decrease of more widespread group	Species of cooler, moister areas	Species of warmer, drier areas	Perhaps land-use change rather than climate change?
15	Montane habitats	Decrease	Not analysed	-	-	Loss of outlying populations away from mountains
16	Inland rock	No change detected	Increase of southerly group; decrease of northerly group	Species of nutrient-rich habitats; southern species	Species of nutrient-poor habitats; northern species	Eutrophication; perhaps climate change
17	Built-up areas and gardens	Increase	Increase of southerly groups; decrease of widespread group	Species of nutrient-poor habitats and of warmer, drier areas	Species of nutrient-rich habitats and of colder, wetter areas	Climate change (warmer summers?)
11,13,14 (in part)	Wetland habitats	No change detected	Decrease of groups with widespread, predominantly northerly distributions	Species of nutrient-rich habitats	Species of nutrient-poor habitats	Eutrophication
11,13,14 (in part)	Aquatic habitats	No change detected	Change not detected in any regional groups	Perennials	Annuals	Fencing of water bodies eliminating poached margins
18,19,21	Coastal habitats	Possible increase	Increase of species occurring inland as well as by coast	-	-	Salting of roadside verges

Table 4.5 continued Summary of results for Broad Habitats.

5. Neophytes

Bob Ellis

Introduction

The spread of neophytes is a major element in the changes currently taking place in the British flora. Mechanisms for this spread include the following.

- The deliberate planting of non-native species in the countryside, including new ponds.

- Fly-tipping of garden waste.

- Movement of topsoil during housing development and road-building.

- The disposal of aquatic plants from aquaria and garden ponds into the countryside.

- The introduction of non-native seed with game-cover crops and wild bird food both as intentional and unintentional constituents.

- The introduction of non-native seed with imported crop seed (rare in post-war years with effective seed cleaning, but perhaps becoming frequent again as unintentional constituents of landscaping and conservation headland mixes etc.).

- Bird-sown fruits from garden and amenity plantings.

- Continuing and increasing spread of established ruderals by both natural means (e.g. wind-blown seed and water-borne propagules) and human activity (e.g. increasing traffic, both farm vehicles carrying soil on their tyres and eddies and water "splash and run-off" along trunk roads.).

- Increasing "suburbanisation" – where the distinction between traditionally "wild" countryside and more "domesticated" suburban places such as parks, gardens and amenity green spaces becomes increasingly vague.

The analysis of change in neophyte distributions is affected by differences in recording practice between the two surveys. The first survey did not have the benefit of what is now the standard work for identification, Stace's *New Flora of the British Isles*, which was first published in 1991. This has popularised the recording of alien plants and has brought the means of identifying a much wider range of species to the recording community.

The BSBI Monitoring Scheme report (Rich and Woodruff 1990) noted that in 1987-1988 it was more widely accepted to record garden escapes and introductions than it was for the 1962 *Atlas*. This trend has continued and accelerated, but it is difficult to assess to what extent. Different attitudes amongst botanical recorders remain and there are regional differences apparent in the recording of garden escapes for the *New Atlas* (see Figure 5.1). A further consideration is that planted trees, shrubs and crops were excluded from the scope of the first survey.

It is probable that both this change in attitude and the availability of '*Stace*' has led to increased recording of garden escapes and throw-outs and also, possibly, of weed species such as *Galinsoga parviflora* that show a preference for gardens, allotments and other habitats associated with housing.

In the following analysis only species with a total of 15 or more tetrads across the two surveys are considered.

Species	1962 Atlas	First Record	G	L	R	Total	TF	RC	CF	90% Conf. (CF)
Acorus calamus	y	1668	8	7	7	22	27	-2	-2	46
Ribes nigrum	y	1660	51	44	38	133	44	0	+0	26
Heracleum mantegazzianum	y	1828	17	14	17	48	27	0	+0	35
Fallopia japonica	y	1886	58	41	123	222	53	+2	+3	19
Veronica filiformis	y	1838	69	51	115	235	58	+2	+4	21
Crepis vesicaria	y	1713	54	35	94	183	72	+5	+8	19
Impatiens parviflora	y	1851	8	6	6	20	29	+6	+6	51
Barbarea intermedia	y	1836	19	15	9	43	41	+6	+7	39
Veronica persica	y	1825	76	34	275	385	88	+6	+15	16
Cymbalaria muralis	y	1640	66	40	126	232	56	+6	+10	18
Claytonia perfoliata	y	1849	14	10	12	36	32	+7	+7	38
Calystegia pulchra	y	1850	16	13	3	32	32	+7	+9	49
Barbarea verna	y	1803	9	7	3	19	27	+8	+9	56
Rhododendron ponticum	y	1894	55	28	111	194	49	+9	+13	16
Claytonia sibirica	y	1837	31	17	37	85	40	+12	+14	23
Sisymbrium orientale	y	1832	12	8	7	27	23	+12	+13	44
Veronica polita	y	1777	42	28	22	92	52	+14	+17	28
Calystegia silvatica	y	1863	74	29	130	233	68	+15	+23	15
Juncus tenuis	y	1796	33	15	43	91	51	+16	+18	21
Lepidium draba	y	1802	31	16	30	77	39	+16	+19	24
Epilobium ciliatum	y	1891	128	54	183	365	86	+17	+41	19
Impatiens glandulifera	y	1855	57	24	74	155	49	+17	+23	17
Symphytum x uplandicum		1864	89	38	116	243	63	+18	+29	17
Diplotaxis muralis	y	1778	19	9	18	46	34	+19	+20	29
Cicerbita macrophylla		1915	13	6	10	29	25	+22	+23	36
Epilobium brunnescens	y	1904	66	11	69	146	65	+33	+41	13
Impatiens capensis	y	1822	8	1	8	17	29	+35	+36	30
Coronopus didymus	y	1778	80	18	63	161	64	+36	+46	15
Pentaglottis sempervirens	y	1724	99	17	77	193	56	+39	+53	13
Geranium pyrenaicum	y	1762	62	11	45	118	49	+40	+47	15
Elodea nuttallii	y	1966	32	8	15	55	32	+43	+47	24
Cotoneaster simonsii	y	1910	50	17	11	78	42	+46	+56	25
Amsinckia micrantha		1910	13	2	6	21	33	+49	+51	33
Allium paradoxum	y	1849	10	3	2	15	26	+50	+51	46
Galinsoga quadriradiata	y	1909	18	6	2	26	33	+51	+56	36
Conyza canadensis	y	1690	78	6	38	122	57	+54	+63	13
Galinsoga parviflora	y	1860	12	3	1	16	26	+61	+64	41
Hirschfeldia incana		1837	19	1	5	25	33	+66	+68	26
Symphytum orientale	y	1849	23		7	30	39	+68	+70	11
Allium triquetrum	y	1847	24	2	4	30	45	+70	+72	27
Anisantha diandra	y	1835	23		4	27	50	+77	+78	12
Lemna minuta		1977	49	2	1	52	43	+86	+92	20
Conyza sumatrensis		1961	20		1	21	58	+87	+88	18

G: Gains   L: Losses   R: Re-finds   TF: Tetrad Frequency   RC: Relative Change   CF: Change Factor (weighted)

Senecio squalidus
Oxford Ragwort

Mapped Change	-22%	
Relative Change	-30%	±17%
Weighted CF	-37%	±18%
Tetrad Frequency	45%	

Myrrhis odorata
Sweet Cicely

Mapped Change	-14%	
Relative Change	-22%	±11%
Weighted CF	-25%	±12%
Tetrad Frequency	44%	

Senecio squalidus is the only common ruderal neophyte showing a significant decline between the two surveys. The decline comes as something of a surprise. This species spread rapidly with the railways in the late 19th century, colonising ballast, and latterly appeared widely in towns amongst rubble and in pavement cracks. It has been lost from some urban locations though redevelopment of brown field sites and from some railway ballast following line closures and effective weed control.

Myrrhis odorata is most commonly found on roadsides near habitation and, although very persistent there, is probably decreasing in such places following development and road maintenance. It also colonises riverbanks but is restricted to sandy alluvium, not the commonest of habitats by the northern rivers where it is found, and little new colonisation appears to have taken place.

Key to maps ● Loss ● Gain ○ Re-find
▨ *New Atlas* distribution

Elodea canadensis
Canadian Waterweed

Mapped Change	-23%	
Relative Change	-31%	±25%
Weighted CF	-38%	±24%
Tetrad Frequency	31%	

Elodea nuttallii
Nuttall's Waterweed

Mapped Change	+51%	
Relative Change	+43%	±25%
Weighted CF	+47%	±24%
Tetrad Frequency	32%	

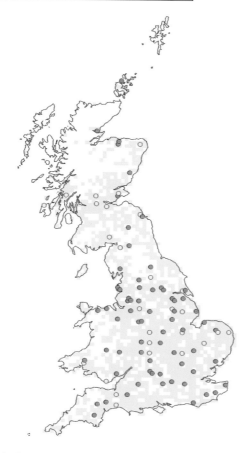

Elodea canadensis, in common with many aquatic plants, has been re-found relatively infrequently in the same tetrads as in MS but, despite some apparent gains, there is strong evidence of a steady real decline throughout its range. This plant is now rarely seen in great abundance, and certainly not in the quantities that attracted so much attention when it first colonised Britain in the 19th century. Its decline has coincided with an increase in *E. nuttallii* in some areas, but this does not explain the overall pattern of decline.

Elodea nuttallii was first recorded in Britain as recently as 1966. It was probably some time after this that the majority of botanists became aware of its presence and for this reason it may have been somewhat under-recorded in the first survey (and it is possible that it was sometimes mistakenly recorded as *E. canadensis*).
In some localities it seems to be displacing *E. canadensis*, which is found in similar habitats.

Key to maps ● Loss ● Gain ○ Re-find
New Atlas distribution

Lemna minuta
Least Duckweed

Mapped Change	+94%	
Relative Change	+86%	±24%
Weighted CF	+92%	±20%
Tetrad Frequency	43%	

First recorded in 1977, *Lemna minuta* is currently the most rapidly expanding alien species in Britain. It has been shown to be more competitive than the other duckweeds (Leslie & Walters 1983). Reproducing vegetatively, it is presumably spread over distances by water birds and locally by flooding and other surface water movements.

Hirschfeldia incana
Hoary Mustard

Mapped Change	+75%	
Relative Change	+66%	±24%
Weighted CF	+68%	±26%
Tetrad Frequency	33%	

A plant of waste places, often in urban areas, *Hirschfeldia incana* has markedly increased its range over the period between the two surveys. It is a native of southern Europe and its spread and continuing establishment may be assisted by climatic changes.

Key to maps ● Loss ● Gain ○ Re-find
▨ *New Atlas* distribution

Conyza sumatrensis
Guernsey Fleabane

Mapped Change	+95%	
Relative Change	+87%	± 6%
Weighted CF	+88%	±18%
Tetrad Frequency	58%	

Conyza canadensis
Canadian Fleabane

Mapped Change	+62%	
Relative Change	+54%	±11%
Weighted CF	+63%	±13%
Tetrad Frequency	57%	

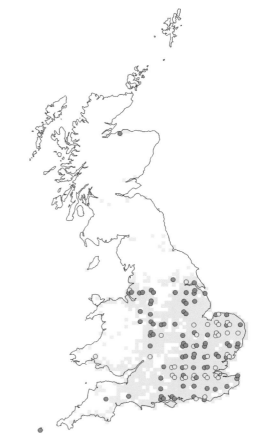

Originating in South America, *Conyza sumatrensis* is now a common plant of waste ground in the London area and is beginning to increase in similar habitats in other parts of the country.

Conyza canadensis was first recorded from the wild in Britain as early as 1690. By 1905, Dunn in his *Alien Flora of Britain* considered it to be a common weed in the south and east. More recently, it would appear to be spreading north and west but there is an intriguing hint of a few losses in its heartland in the London area where its relative *Conyza sumatrensis* is now frequent.

Key to maps   ● Loss   ● Gain   ○ Re-find
       ▦ *New Atlas* distribution

Galinsoga parviflora
Gallant Soldier

Mapped Change	+69%	
Relative Change	+61%	±62%
Weighted CF	+64%	±41%
Tetrad Frequency	26%	

Galinsoga quadriradiata
Shaggy Soldier

Mapped Change	+60%	
Relative Change	+51%	±53%
Weighted CF	+56%	±36%
Tetrad Frequency	33%	

Both *Galinsoga parviflora* and
G. quadriradiata are annual weeds of
disturbed ground on light soils and share a
similar distribution in Britain. *G. parviflora*
is particularly associated with nurseries,
garden centres, gardens and allotments.
A marked increase in range was indicated in
the *New Atlas* and this is corroborated here.

Galinsoga quadriradiata is probably more
often associated with urban waste ground
and pavement cracks than its horticulturally
inclined cousin *G. parviflora*, but it too occurs
in gardens and as an arable weed. Again, the
increase in range indicated in the *New Atlas*
is supported.

Key to maps   ● Loss   ● Gain   ○ Re-find
       ▪ *New Atlas* distribution

Amsinckia micrantha
Common Fiddleneck

Mapped Change	+58%	
Relative Change	+49%	±34%
Weighted CF	+51%	±33%
Tetrad Frequency	33%	

Anisantha diandra
Great Brome

Mapped Change	+85%	
Relative Change	+77%	± 7%
Weighted CF	+78%	±12%
Tetrad Frequency	50%	

Amsinckia micrantha is an increasing colonist of arable land in eastern Britain, particularly on lighter soils, where it is occasionally a pernicious weed. However, it is only beginning to reach any great frequency at tetrad scale in very limited areas.

Anisantha diandra has been established as a persistent arable weed in East Anglia for some years. It also occurs in waste ground and on roadsides. There is evidence that it is increasing its range.

Key to maps ● Loss ● Gain ○ Re-find
▨ *New Atlas* distribution

Coronopus didymus
Lesser Swine-cress

Mapped Change	+43%	
Relative Change	+36%	±12%
Weighted CF	+46%	±15%
Tetrad Frequency	63%	

Geranium pyrenaicum
Hedgerow Crane's-bill

Mapped Change	+48%	
Relative Change	+40%	±13%
Weighted CF	+47%	±15%
Tetrad Frequency	49%	

Coronopus didymus has a much more western distribution than *Coronopus squamatus* and is reported to be more of an urban cousin to that largely rural species. However, in the southwest it is common in arable fields and is still increasing rapidly there. It favours sites that are damp in winter but has not succeeded in the north. Its increase may relate as much to gradual expansion following introduction as to other factors.

Geranium pyrenaicum has been established in the wild in many parts of Britain for over two centuries but was still rare by 1900. However, it is still a little surprising that it seems to have been increasing so much of late. The temptation is to point to climate change as this is a southern species but the evidence is not overwhelming.

Key to maps   ● Loss   ● Gain   ○ Re-find
    ▢ *New Atlas* distribution

Epilobium ciliatum
American Willowherb

Mapped Change	+24%	
Relative Change	+17%	± 9%
Weighted CF	+41%	±19%
Tetrad Frequency	86%	

Epilobium brunnescens
New Zealand Willowherb

Mapped Change	+41%	
Relative Change	+33%	±11%
Weighted CF	+41%	±13%
Tetrad Frequency	65%	

The *New Atlas* demonstrated a rapid spread of *Epilobium ciliatum* between 1962 and 1999. In the Local Change survey, there is a concentration of re-finds in the longer-established southern, lowland parts of its range; elsewhere there is a mixture of gains and losses. In many ways this is a mirror image of the next species, *Epilobium brunnescens*.

Epilobium brunnescens was shown by the *New Atlas* to have increased markedly and some of this change is now shown to be quite recent. The tetrad pattern shows that this species has now achieved a mature distribution in which it is almost ubiquitous in its favoured upland habitats.

Key to maps ● Loss ● Gain ○ Re-find
▨ *New Atlas* distribution

Impatiens glandulifera
Himalayan Balsam

Mapped Change	+25%	
Relative Change	+17%	±14%
Weighted CF	+23%	±17%
Tetrad Frequency	49%	

Impatiens capensis
Orange Balsam

Mapped Change	+44%	
Relative Change	+35%	±28%
Weighted CF	+36%	±30%
Tetrad Frequency	29%	

An invasive colonist, particularly of riverbanks, *Impatiens glandulifera* is showing less of an increase than might be expected. The *New Atlas* demonstrated a significant increase, but there are signs that its spread has slowed in some parts of the country whilst it has increased its range in others, such as west Wales.

First recorded from the wild in 1822, *Impatiens capensis* is now well established, particularly beside rivers and in fens where its seeds are dispersed by water. It is less competitive and invasive than *I. glandulifera*. There is evidence that it is very slowly continuing to expand its range.

Key to maps ● Loss ● Gain ○ Re-find
▨ *New Atlas* distribution

Allium paradoxum
Few-flowered leek

Mapped Change	+58%	
Relative Change	+50%	±62%
Weighted CF	+51%	±46%
Tetrad Frequency	26%	

Allium triquetrum
Three-cornered Leek

Mapped Change	+79%	
Relative Change	+70%	±28%
Weighted CF	+72%	±27%
Tetrad Frequency	45%	

The survey data suggests that the spread of *Allium paradoxum* is a recent phenomenon. Curiously the gains are not strongly correlated with those areas with the most *New Atlas* records. This is evidence that it is still quite a scarce species at tetrad scale as it is dependent on a mechanism for the dispersal of its bulbils that has most often been provided by rivers and is only now being supplemented by dispersal along roads.

Allium triquetrum, unlike *A. paradoxum*, is dispersed by seed and has continued to colonise roadsides and other grassland habitats in recent years, expanding beyond its initial southwestern stronghold. Its tetrad frequency is about twice that of *A. paradoxum* and its gains are strongly correlated with those areas with the most *New Atlas* records, where it is fast becoming ubiquitous.

Key to maps ● Loss ● Gain ○ Re-find
▨ *New Atlas* distribution

Symphytum orientale
White Comfrey

Mapped Change	+77%	
Relative Change	+68%	± 7%
Weighted CF	+70%	±10%
Tetrad Frequency	38%	

Symphytum orientale was first recorded in the wild in 1832 and is now widespread on roadsides, in woodland, in waste places and as a garden weed. The data is, perhaps, partly affected by better recording of this species since 1988 and this is a plant that may well be tolerated, if not encouraged, by some gardeners. However, the increase in range is probably genuine.

Pentaglottis sempervirens
Green Alkanet

Mapped Change	+47%	
Relative Change	+39%	±10%
Weighted CF	+53%	±13%
Tetrad Frequency	56%	

Pentaglottis sempervirens has been grown for centuries (it was first recorded from the wild in 1724) and is still most often found near habitation where it is well established in a wide variety of shaded habitats. Like *Geranium pyrenaicum*, it is slightly odd that it appears to have spread so much recently when one would have expected a more stable distribution.

Key to maps ● Loss ● Gain ○ Re-find
▨ *New Atlas* distribution

Neophytes Group 2
Widely naturalised species significantly affected by continuing introductions

This group includes a number of species that are usually associated with gardens and habitation but which are probably as much tolerated as attractive weeds as deliberately grown. Such species include *Campanula poscharskyana*, *Centranthus ruber*, *Linaria purpurea*, *Lunaria annua*, *Oxalis exilis* and *Pseudofumaria lutea*, which all spread very easily by seed or bulbils.

As with group 1, there is a relationship between date of first record and relative change but the overall mean relative change is twice as high.

Relative change between the two surveys for group 2 neophytes first recorded in the wild before and after 1830:

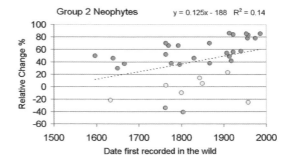

Figure 5.3 Graph of relative change between the two surveys for group 2 neophytes against date first recorded in the wild.

Date of first known record in the wild	No. of species	Mean RC
Before 1830	15	+25.7
1830 or later	19	+53.1

Species	1962 Atlas	First Record	G	L	R	Total	TF	RC	CF	90% Conf. (CF)
Medicago sativa subsp. *sativa*	y	1804	11	25	18	54	37	-41	-45	24
Trifolium hybridum	y	1762	45	78	49	172	56	-34	-49	21
Cotoneaster integrifolius		1957	6	8	4	18	19	-25	-26	52
Doronicum pardalianches	y	1633	6	9	13	28	21	-22	-23	32
Aster agg.		1800	25	26	24	75	33	-10	-12	29
Ribes uva-crispa	y	1763	77	58	142	277	66	+2	+3	21
Solidago canadensis		1849	28	22	17	67	37	+5	+6	33
Petasites albus	y	1843	5	2	8	15	32	+14	+15	41
Cerastium tomentosum	y	1909	48	26	22	96	39	+23	+29	26
Oenothera agg.	y	1650	38	16	19	73	33	+30	+35	25
Pseudofumaria lutea	y	1796	43	8	36	87	35	+36	+41	17
Sedum rupestre	y	1666	46	19	14	79	36	+37	+44	26
Galanthus nivalis	y	1776	123	36	71	230	65	+38	+58	17
Ribes sanguineum		1867	52	21	15	88	46	+38	+47	25
Soleirolia soleirolii		1917	28	6	16	50	33	+42	+45	24
Linaria purpurea	y	1830	85	17	42	144	50	+46	+57	16
Galega officinalis		1640	16	4	6	26	49	+46	+48	35
Leucanthemum x *superbum*		1913	29	7	9	45	28	+49	+53	27
Lunaria annua		1597	115	25	41	181	58	+50	+68	16
Centranthus ruber	y	1763	83	9	40	132	49	+52	+62	14
Crocosmia x *crocosmiiflora*	y	1907	86	7	42	135	48	+54	+64	12
Buddleja davidii	y	1922	119	7	58	184	60	+56	+70	10
Cotoneaster horizontalis		1940	57	13	11	81	46	+57	+66	21
Pilosella aurantiaca		1793	73	11	11	95	38	+66	+77	18
Oxalis corniculata	y	1770	48	5	10	63	38	+66	+71	20
Tellima grandiflora		1866	22	4	1	27	48	+70	+77	29
Melissa officinalis	y	1763	40	4	6	50	44	+70	+74	22
Crassula helmsii		1956	33	2	3	38	30	+78	+81	24
Lamiastrum galeobdolon subsp. *argentatum*		1974	117	3	14	134	58	+79	+88	12
Campanula poscharskyana		1957	31		3	34	35	+83	+84	12
Campanula portenschlagiana		1922	14	1		15	20	+84		
Hyacinthoides x *massartiana*		1953	165	5	8	178	80	+85	+97	12
Cotoneaster rehderi		1986	15		1	16	58	+85	+86	19
Oxalis exilis		1913	20	1		21	31	+86		

G: Gains   L: Losses   R: Re-finds   TF: Tetrad Frequency   RC: Relative Change   CF: Change Factor (weighted)

Trifolium hybridum
Alsike Clover

Mapped Change	-26%	
Relative Change	-34%	±18%
Weighted CF	-49%	±21%
Tetrad Frequency	56%	

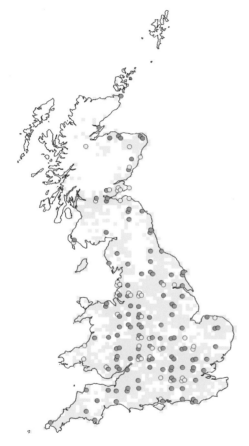

Medicago sativa subsp. *sativa*
Lucerne

Mapped Change	-33%	
Relative Change	-41%	±27%
Weighted CF	-45%	±24%
Tetrad Frequency	37%	

Trifolium hybridum probably relies on re-introductions to a large extent and it is grown less frequently than it was in the past. The *New Atlas* suggested its distribution was stable but there is evidence here of a decline.

Previously cultivated as a fodder crop or as green manure but only poorly naturalised, *Medicago sativa* subsp. *sativa* has fallen out of fashion. It showed a decline in the *New Atlas* and an even greater one is indicated here.

Key to maps   ● Loss   ● Gain   ○ Re-find
         New Atlas distribution

Lunaria annua
Honesty

Mapped Change	+58%	
Relative Change	+50%	±14%
Weighted CF	+68%	±16%
Tetrad Frequency	58%	

Lunaria annua is most often found naturalised close to habitation. It is possible that the increase in range shown here is at least partly the result of differences in recording practice between the two surveys.

Crassula helmsii
New Zealand Pigmyweed

Mapped Change	+86%	
Relative Change	+78%	±25%
Weighted CF	+81%	±24%
Tetrad Frequency	30%	

Crassula helmsii is a notoriously aggressive colonist, which was only recorded for the first time in 1956. Most of the spread has occurred since 1980 and due to the publicity about its threat to natural vegetation, the records are well documented and the map will accurately reflect its distribution.

Key to maps   ● Loss   ● Gain   ○ Re-find
        ▦ *New Atlas* distribution

Campanula poscharskyana
Trailing Bellflower

Mapped Change	+91%	
Relative Change	+83%	± 6%
Weighted CF	+84%	±12%
Tetrad Frequency	34%	

Hyacinthoides x *massartiana*
(*H. non-scripta* x *hispanica*) Hybrid Bluebell

Mapped Change	+92%	
Relative Change	+85%	±11%
Weighted CF	+97%	±12%
Tetrad Frequency	80%	

Campanula poscharskyana is increasingly becoming established on banks, on walls and in paving cracks, and once established, is ineradicable. However, as with many other species in this group, interpretation of the increase shown must take into account differences in recording practice, both better resources for the identification of garden species and the possibility of a greater tendency to record garden escapes near their source.

Hyacinthoides × *massartiana* has only become understood by recorders since the time of the first survey, so, while this hybrid is undoubtedly increasing, the extent of the increase is conjectural. Nevertheless this map does demonstrate that this garden plant is now very well established across much of lowland Britain where it is most often found on roadsides or with other introductions in woodland managed for amenity.

Key to maps   ● Loss   ● Gain   ○ Re-find
      New Atlas distribution

Neophytes Group 3
Locally naturalised species

These are garden plants that may be found in the countryside as escapes, throw-outs or deliberate plantings. They include a larger proportion of modern introductions than the other groups.

This group is the most strongly affected by differences in recording practice between the two surveys, and the reported change should be considered with this in mind.

These species, by and large, are still spreading from repeated introductions and have not achieved a stable distribution in Britain so they show much less relationship to date of first record than the widely-naturalised species.

Relative change between the two surveys for group 3 neophytes first recorded in the wild before and after 1830:

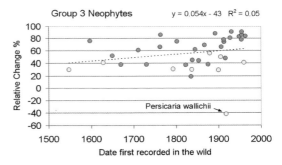

Figure 5.4 Graph of relative change between the two surveys for group 3 neophytes against date first recorded in the wild.

Date of first known record in the wild	No. of species	Mean RC
Before 1830	12	+52.6
1830 or later	24	+57.9

Species	1962 Atlas	First Record	G	L	R	Total	TF	RC	CF	90% Conf. (CF)
Persicaria wallichii	y	1917	4	8	4	16	30	-42	-43	48
Petasites fragrans	y	1835	28	10	39	77	31	+19	+21	20
Fragaria ananassa	y	1900	15	9	1	25	26	+29	+37	50
Saxifraga x urbium		1837	14	6	7	27	27	+30	+31	38
Ornithogalum angustifolium	y	1548	42	22	10	74	42	+30	+38	30
Pulmonaria officinalis	y	1793	18	8	7	33	34	+31	+34	36
Oxalis stricta	y	1823	11	6		17	41	+37		
Hyacinthoides hispanica		1875	65	27	18	110	65	+38	+50	24
Lathyrus latifolius		1670	23	8	9	40	29	+38	+41	31
Lamium maculatum		1730	43	21	4	68	45	+38	+59	35
Sempervivum tectorum		1629	10	4	2	16	34	+41	+43	48
Rheum x hybridum		1960	20	9	2	31	42	+41	+48	38
Lysimachia punctata	y	1853	48	9	27	84	38	+44	+50	19
Eranthis hyemalis	y	1838	21	7	5	33	34	+45	+49	34
Solidago gigantea		1916	27	9	5	41	34	+48	+53	31
Sedum spurium	y	1905	16	6	1	23	23	+50	+58	39
Vinca major	y	1650	93	12	42	147	56	+52	+64	14
Lychnis coronaria		1879	16	5	1	22	30	+56	+62	37
Narcissus agg.		1711	188	17	65	270	82	+61	+85	11
Centaurea montana		1845	37	8	4	49	32	+62	+70	25
Antirrhinum majus	y	1762	40	6	6	52	27	+66	+71	23
Geranium endressii	y	1906	14	2	2	18	22	+66	+68	37
Polygonatum x hybridum		1867	20	3	2	25	29	+69	+72	32
Aubrieta deltoidea		1913	16	2	1	19	22	+74	+77	34
Campanula persicifolia	y	1802	16	1	2	19	30	+75	+76	34
Cyclamen hederifolium	y	1597	13	2		15	27	+76		
Oxalis articulata		1912	33	2	3	38	35	+78	+81	24
Geranium x oxonianum		1954	34	3	2	39	64	+78	+83	24
Viola x wittrockiana		1927	27	2	1	30	41	+81	+85	26
Alchemilla mollis		1948	94	2	7	103	60	+83	+89	14
Crocus tommasinianus		1963	14	1		15	42	+84		
Lupinus x regalis		1955	19	1		20	31	+86		
Crocus vernus	y	1763	20	1		21	35	+86		
Muscari armeniacum		1892	60	1	1	62	53	+88	+93	21
Sedum spectabile		1930	15			15	44	+91		
Tulipa gesneriana		1955	16			16	49	+91		

G: Gains   L: Losses   R: Re-finds   TF: Tetrad Frequency   RC: Relative Change   CF: Change Factor (weighted)

Hyacinthoides hispanica
Spanish Bluebell

Mapped Change	+46%	
Relative Change	+38%	±25%
Weighted CF	+50%	±24%
Tetrad Frequency	65%	

It is notoriously difficult to tell whether a variable population of *Hyacinthoides* plants contains *H. hispanica* or not. Our experience suggests that pure *H. hispanica* is considerably scarcer than these records suggest. The evidence of spread is not based on a firm baseline and should be discounted as unsafe.

Narcissus agg.
Garden Daffodil

Mapped Change	+68%	
Relative Change	+61%	± 8%
Weighted CF	+85%	±11%
Tetrad Frequency	82%	

Any changes in the distribution of garden daffodils are thoroughly masked by the changes in recording practice between the two surveys. The abundance of garden cultivars planted along roadside verges and in open spaces typifies the trend of "suburbanisation" in the countryside.

Key to maps   ● Loss   ● Gain   ○ Re-find
▨ *New Atlas* distribution

Neophytes Group 4
Rarely naturalised species

Very few true casuals occur frequently enough to be considered in this analysis. Most are annual species grown in gardens, though *Borago officinalis* is now often found as a field crop, which may persist as a casual for a few years. Planted trees and shrubs and field crops are presented in Chapter 6.

Relative Change between the two surveys for group 4 neophytes first recoded in the wild before and after 1830:

Date of first known record in the wild	No. of species	Mean RC
Before 1830	4	+43.5
1830 or later	7	+78.7

Species	1962 Atlas	First Record	G	L	R	Total	TF	RC	CF	90% Conf. (CF)
Phalaris canariensis	y	1632	19	17	1	37	27	+1	+3	90
Lobularia maritima	y	1804	19	9	5	33	26	+33	+36	37
Calendula officinalis		1868	23	8	2	33	25	+51	+59	33
Borago officinalis		1777	23	6	4	33	24	+54	+58	31
Tropaeolum majus		1904	44	1	1	16	31	+78	+80	37
Lobelia erinus		1905	16	1	1	18	25	+80	+81	35
Amaranthus retroflexus		1853	18	2		20	30	+80		
Alcea rosea		1905	30	1	1	32	48	+85	+88	27
Echinochloa crus-galli	y	1690	17	1		18	36	+86		
Eschscholzia californica		1864	18	1		19	29	+86		
Nigella damascena		1832	17			17	30	+91		

G: Gains   L: Losses   R: Re-finds   TF: Tetrad Frequency   RC: Relative Change   CF: Change Factor (weighted)

Amaranthus retroflexus
Common amaranth

Mapped Change	+89%	
Relative Change	+80%	
Weighted CF	N/A	
Tetrad Frequency	30%	

Echinochloa crus-galli
Cockspur

Mapped Change	+94%	
Relative Change	+86%	
Weighted CF	N/A	
Tetrad Frequency	36%	

Amaranthus retroflexus is the most frequently recorded of this genus of late-flowering American weeds. In part, this increase may be due to seed contamination in game-cover crops and from wild bird food. Of the species in this group, this is one of the least likely to be affected by differences in recording practice as it is not cultivated in gardens.

Known in the wild since 1690, the distribution of *Echinochloa crus-galli* has probably fluctuated over the years. It currently appears to be undergoing a resurgence which we initially thought related to introductions as a contaminant in game-cover maize and wild bird food. However, S J Leach (*pers. comm.*) has now demonstrated that this species is spreading rapidly along roadsides and appears to be salt-tolerant. Of the species in this group, this is the least likely to be affected by changes in recording practice.

Lobularia maritima
Sweet Alison

Mapped Change	+42%	
Relative Change	+33%	±48%
Weighted CF	+36%	±37%
Tetrad Frequency	26%	

Known in the wild since 1802 and although it has been a popular garden plant for many years, there is no obvious reason why *Lobularia maritima* should be any more frequent in 2004 than in 1987 other than as a result of better recording of neophytes. However, although it is mostly sown as an annual, it does occasionally perennate and perhaps milder winters are allowing it to survive better, particularly inland.

Key to maps   ● Loss   ● Gain   ○ Re-find
          ■ *New Atlas* distribution

Richard Pryce

Summary of change in Neophytes

Neophyte species are analysed separately from native and archaeophyte species because they show quite different patterns of change. Many of the native and archaeophyte species analysed in this report have very stable distributions and those that are changing may include roughly as many that are increasing as those that are in decline (though we cannot be sure of this as we can only measure relative change). In contrast the neophytes analysed in this section show a great preponderance of increasing species.

Neophyte species as a class are much less numerous than native and archaeophyte species. Thus while the Broad Habitat section analyses 725 of the 1473 native and archaeophyte species mapped in the *New Atlas*, or 49%, we only analyse in this section 134 of the 545 neophyte and casual species mapped in the *New Atlas*, or 25%. To put it another way the neophytes are 16% of the species analysed. While the exclusion of trees and shrubs from the analysis of both sections does bias these figures, the relatively small number of neophytes that are frequent at tetrad scale is itself an interesting finding. As shown in the *New Atlas*, neophytes have nevertheless become an integral element in the British flora and those that are widespread are just as frequent at tetrad scale as typical native species with the same range.

The great preponderance of increasing species amongst the neophytes should not be thought of as unexpected or alarming. It is unsurprising that neophytes that, by definition, have become naturalised in Britain since 1500 are taking a considerable period to achieve a stable distribution. Some species are dispersed much more freely than others but even the most freely dispersed, such as *Epilobium ciliatum*, first recorded in the wild in 1891, and *E. brunnescens*, first recorded in 1904, have yet to reach a stable distribution after a century, though they are now approaching stability, and less freely dispersed species may take much longer.

The general pattern of naturalisation of a neophyte often becomes apparent quite early in its colonisation, both with regard to the habitats colonised and to its geographical preferences. Many of the maps of aliens in this report show pronounced regional patterns and this is true even for some quite scarce species. Similarly the pattern of change is as much of increasing frequency within an existing range as of notable extension of range. While the less pronounced geographical preferences may relate simply to the incidence of urban areas, the more pronounced preferences presumably relate mainly to climatic factors, as a relation to geology or to a single point of introduction is seldom evident. Nevertheless it is seldom possible to postulate a link between the spread of neophytes and climate change as it is difficult to separate the spread that follows from a relatively recent date of introduction from any increase in the rate of spread that may be due to recent climatic factors.

There are a few species that were introduced at relatively early dates that do seem to have increased much more rapidly in recent years and these are of particular interest. Three such species selected for the species accounts are *Echinochloa crus-galli*, *Geranium pyrenaicum* and *Pentaglottis sempervirens*. The first seems to have joined the group of species colonising salted roadsides while the other two are found in a variety of habitats including hedgebanks where an ability to thrive in relatively nutrient-rich soils may be as important as any climatic factors. These are not species that we would have anticipated having interesting results to report on. *Coronopus didymus* might be a fourth example that has more in common with those native species whose increase seems to be linked to climate change, but its recent expansion may owe as much to the acceleration of a long-term pattern of colonisation following increased disturbance linked to urban and suburban development.

Many neophytes have come to Britain as garden plants. As one of the criteria that plants must satisfy before they can be promoted for cultivation is that they do not become too invasive, it is only to be expected that most garden plants are either annuals whose seed does not survive our winters in the soil or clump-forming perennials that do not readily self-seed. Inevitably a few introductions have been ill-chosen and equally inevitably it is just these that are most often found as cast-outs. Nevertheless it is few indeed of this class that have spread to a significant extent in the countryside. Our Group 3 species are largely of this type and represent the most frequent of a larger class. They are here to stay but have little impact on our flora as a whole.

The most apparent impact of neophytes on our landscape has undoubtedly come from planted trees and shrubs, some of which may naturalise to a degree. As explained elsewhere, inconsistency in recording between the two surveys has prevented us presenting trends for such species.

Many of the most successful neophytes colonise disturbed ruderal habitats rather than established native vegetation. Again

this is unsurprising. Species that can colonise disturbed habitats have enhanced prospects of dispersion along our transport networks and their success is what brings them within the scope of this survey. Other neophytes may find a place in native vegetation but are often unable to disperse effectively; they remain therefore among the very large cohort of scarce neophyte species that do not come within the scope of this study.

This survey has not identified many species as increasing which had not already been so identified in the *New Atlas*. This reflects both the recent date of the *New Atlas* and the fact that hectad recording is even more effective than tetrad recording in picking up the presence of new colonists.

Conclusion

These surveys have done much to clarify the frequency with which neophytes occur in the countryside by extending our knowledge of their distribution from the hectad scale of the *New Atlas* to tetrad scale. It is a comparatively small class of neophyte species that have become both widely naturalised and frequent within their range. These neophytes offer many opportunities for interesting study, not least with regard to the wide range of strategies with which they achieve remarkable success in an environment which is increasingly hostile to wild plants. Most such species have found a place within our vegetation where they compete on equal terms with native species and are largely unproblematic; it is only a very few species that are so competitive as to threaten native plant communities, albeit locally.

With only a few exceptions these widely naturalised species continue to spread strongly, but to a large extent this is an unsurprising consequence of their earlier introduction and establishment. It reflects the considerable period, often a century or several centuries, which can be expected to elapse before even a successful naturalised plant can disperse and reach a mature distribution across Britain.

6. Species excluded from the preceding sections

Bob Ellis

Several groups of species are excluded from the Broad Habitat and neophyte chapters in this report (Chapters 4 and 5). This chapter provides some details of these.

Native and archaeophyte species which are widespread as recent introductions

A few species were excluded from the analysis by Broad Habitat because, although the plants occur as natives or archaeophytes in some parts of the country, we considered that the majority of records in the survey were for garden escapes or other introductions and that the change related to this neophyte part of their distribution.

Roses

Due to difficulties with identification, the main groups of native wild roses were recorded unevenly in both surveys. The data is only comparable when the species are aggregated, but because the species within the aggregates have such different distributions, it has been thought best to exclude roses entirely from the analysis by Broad Habitat. None of the aggregates showed a significant change.

Very widespread species

The most widespread species were eliminated from the analysis by Broad Habitat as the estimate of the Change Factor is invalid (see Chapter 3 and Appendix 2). For these species we show the position in a 'league table' of the number of tetrads in which a species was recorded. They are presented in order of LC frequency; the equivalent position in the MS 'league table' is shown in the column pMS. These species are not only very widespread but are also more or less ubiquitous within their wide ranges at tetrad scale, with Tetrad Frequencies ranging from 89% to 100%. There is little change in 'league table' position between the two surveys; apart from *Agrostis stolonifera* no species moved more than 5 places.

Matricaria discoidea, which is included in Chapter 5, is the only neophyte that falls into this category.

Native and archaeophyte species which are widespread as recent introductions	Broad Habitats	NS	G	L	R	Total	TF	RC	CF	90% Conf. (CF)
Aquilegia vulgaris	1, 3, 16	N	53	14	23	90	34	+43	+50	21
Arum italicum	1, 3	N	13	1	2	16	23	+71	+73	37
Erysimum cheiri	3, 16, 17	AR	23	8	5	36	24	+45	+49	33
Meconopsis cambrica	1	N	88	18	38	144	53	+48	+60	16
Papaver somniferum	3, 4, 17	AR	133	13	50	196	62	+58	+75	12
Sedum album	3, 16, 17	AR	63	26	44	133	44	+27	+35	20
Vinca minor	1, 3, 17	AR	57	21	29	107	47	+34	+42	21

NS: Native Status   G: Gains   L: Losses   R: Re-finds   TF: Tetrad Frequency   RC: Relative Change   CF: Change Factor (weighted)

Roses	Broad Habitats	NS	G	L	R	Total	RC	CF	90% Conf. (CF)
Rosa canina agg.	1, 3	N	51	39	394	484	-3	-11	18
Rosa mollis agg.	1, 3, 16	N	51	51	88	190	-8	-11	20
Rosa rubiginosa agg.	3, 7	N	28	15	13	56	+23	+26	31

NS: Native Status   G: Gains   L: Losses   R: Re-finds   RC: Relative Change   CF: Change Factor (weighted)

pLC	Very widespread species	Broad Habitats	NS	G	L	R	Total	TF	RC	pMS
1	*Plantago lanceolata*	6, 7	N	14	7	600	621	100	-3	2
2	*Cerastium fontanum*	6	N	15	7	599	621	100	-3	3
3	*Trifolium repens*	6	N	13	10	599	622	100	-4	1
4	*Holcus lanatus*	3, 6	N	27	10	579	616	100	-1	7
5	*Ranunculus repens*	3, 6	N	10	3	595	608	100	-3	4
6	*Taraxacum agg.*	3, 5, 17	N	24	15	581	620	100	-3	5
7	*Rumex acetosa*	6	N	40	16	555	611	99	0	12
8	*Bellis perennis*	6	N	28	15	562	605	98	-2	10
9	*Poa annua*	3, 4, 5, 6	N	18	20	570	608	100	-5	6
10	*Ranunculus acris*	6	N	30	22	556	608	100	-3	9
11	*Achillea millefolium*	6	N	20	19	565	604	99	-4	8
12	*Urtica dioica*	3, 14, 17	N	18	6	565	589	97	-2	13
13	*Prunella vulgaris*	6, 7	N	45	12	534	591	97	+1	17
14	*Cirsium vulgare*	3, 5, 6, 7	N	17	14	561	592	97	-4	11
15	*Festuca rubra agg.*	3, 5, 6, 21	N	62	31	512	605	99	+1	18
16	*Lotus corniculatus*	6, 7	N	53	24	519	596	97	+1	19
17	*Juncus effusus*	8, 11	N	32	20	538	590	97	-2	14
18	*Plantago major*	3, 5	N	21	12	544	577	96	-3	15
19	*Cirsium arvense*	3, 4, 6	N	11	10	545	566	95	-4	16
20	*Rumex obtusifolius*	3, 5, 17	N	31	11	524	566	96	-1	22
21	*Agrostis stolonifera*	4, 6	N	101	41	450	592	97	+6	32
22	*Stellaria media*	3, 4	N	22	21	522	565	95	-4	20
23	*Dactylis glomerata*	6	N	21	11	518	550	93	-3	23
24	*Anthoxanthum odoratum*	6	N	32	39	503	574	94	-6	21
25	*Veronica chamaedrys*	1, 3, 6	N	48	17	487	552	97	+1	27
26	*Lolium perenne*	3, 6	N	27	11	505	543	92	-2	25
27	*Senecio jacobaea*	3, 6, 7, 8	N	49	21	482	552	93	+1	28
28	*Trifolium pratense*	6, 7	N	43	21	487	551	93	-1	26
29	*Heracleum sphondylium*	3, 6	N	13	11	512	536	92	-4	24
30	*Hypochaeris radicata*	6	N	74	41	445	560	93	+2	34
31	*Agrostis capillaris*	8	N	93	46	426	565	95	+4	36
32	*Arrhenatherum elatius*	3, 6	N	40	17	478	535	93	0	30
33	*Leontodon autumnalis*	6	N	107	70	399	576	96	+2	37
34	*Deschampsia cespitosa*	1, 6	N	44	41	460	545	95	-4	29
35	*Chamerion angustifolium*	3, 17	N	45	34	458	537	97	-3	31
36	*Poa pratensis sens. lat.*	3, 5, 6, 7	N	71	62	429	562	95	-3	33
37	*Poa trivialis*	1, 3, 6	N	75	53	421	549	96	-1	35
38	*Sagina procumbens*	6, 16, 17	N	81	43	414	538	89	+3	38

pLC: Position, Local Change   NS: Native Status   G: Gains   L: Losses   R: Re-finds   TF: Tetrad Frequency   RC: Relative Change   pMS: Position, Monitoring Scheme

Crops

With crop species, it was not possible to determine the proportions that were recorded as field crops or casual occurrences from spillage and the like. The following species were recorded in 15 or more tetrads across both surveys. The list includes a number of agricultural and horticultural species that may be more often recorded as casual occurrences than as field crops.

Brassica rapa is an archaeophyte and *Brassica oleracea* is of doubtful status, but they are included here rather than in the Broad Habitats section as most records were considered to have been as crops or as recent introductions.

Trees and shrubs

Native and archaeophyte trees and shrubs

The data for native and archaeophyte trees are shown opposite. As well as spreading naturally, many of these are widely planted in both woods and hedges as they have been for centuries. Thus apparent gains may be affected

by the changes in the survey methodology. Note that *Crataegus monogyna* and *Fraxinus excelsior* would also have been excluded because they are very widespread (and near ubiquitous within their range). The data is tabulated in descending order of total records.

Neophyte trees and shrubs

The woody neophyte species *Buddleja davidii*, *Ribes sanguineum*, *Rhododendron ponticum* and *Cotoneaster* species are omitted from this table (p.300) as they are treated in the main neophyte section (Chapter 5). The remainder are tabulated in descending order of total records.

Unsurprisingly, because of the change in survey protocol, the majority of these neophyte trees and shrubs show large increases. The exceptions are *Acer pseudoplatanus*, which is widespread and almost ubiquitous within its range, and *Mahonia aquifolium*, which was frequently planted for game cover on estates and may have gone out of fashion.

Crops	Broad Habitats	NS	G	L	R	Total	TF	RC	CF	90% Conf. (CF)
Avena sativa	4	AC	58	3	5	66	46	+79	+84	19
Beta vulgaris subsp. *vulgaris*			10	3	3	16	31	+45	+47	45
Brassica napus	3, 4, 17	AN	117	18	61	196	59	+48	+64	13
Brassica oleracea	17, 18	NA	11	4	0	15	29	+55		
Brassica rapa	4	AR	44	36	21	101	46	+4	+6	32
Fagopyrum esculentum	4	AN	10	5	0	15	35	+41		
Helianthus annuus	3, 17	AN	35	2	2	39	63	+81	+84	24
Hordeum distichon sens. lat.	3, 4	AC	89	3	0	92	64	+89		
Linum usitatissimum	3, 4, 17	AN	30	3	2	35	22	+76	+80	26
Lolium multiflorum	5	AN	75	61	69	205	65	+2	+4	26
Lycopersicon esculentum	17	AN	28	2	0	30	32	+84		
Panicum miliaceum	1, 4, 17	AC	21	0	0	21	35	+91		
Phacelia tanacetifolia			17	0	0	17	46	+91		
Solanum tuberosum	4	AN	70	5	2	77	63	+82	+94	17
Triticum aestivum	3, 4	AC	133	0	1	134	85	+92	+96	14
Vicia faba	4, 17	AN	38	2	1	41	54	+84	+89	23
Zea mays	4, 17	AC	15	1	0	16	-	+85		

NS: Native Status   G: Gains   L: Losses   R: Re-finds   TF: Tetrad Frequency   RC: Relative Change   CF: Change Factor (weighted)

Trees and shrubs (native and archaeophyte)	Broad Habitats	NS	G	L	R	Total	TF	RC	CF	90% Conf. (CF)
Crataegus monogyna	1, 3	N	21	9	492	522	98	-3	-13	11
Fraxinus excelsior	1	N	23	10	484	517	95	-2	-12	9
Sorbus aucuparia	1, 2, 16	N	83	22	353	458	84	+9	+28	15
Corylus avellana	1, 3	N	64	18	372	454	86	+5	+17	14
Ilex aquifolium	1	N	64	23	356	443	90	+4	+14	15
Quercus robur	1, 3	N	37	27	368	432	91	-3	-10	12
Alnus glutinosa	1, 14	N	80	37	308	425	79	+5	+16	17
Fagus sylvatica	1	N	70	21	330	421	84	+7	+19	13
Betula pendula	1	N	77	40	270	387	82	+5	+12	17
Pinus sylvestris	2	N	116	36	232	384	79	+17	+40	15
Ulmus glabra	1	N	70	63	245	378	77	-4	-11	19
Betula pubescens	1	N	76	40	252	368	74	+5	+11	17
Prunus avium	1	N	141	31	178	350	82	+28	+55	14
Acer campestre	1, 3	N	61	10	226	297	86	+11	+20	9
Salix fragilis	1, 14	AR	59	28	196	283	73	+5	+10	14
Ligustrum vulgare	1, 3	N	68	29	182	279	74	+9	+16	14
Tilia x europaea	1	NH	95	17	145	257	65	+26	+40	11
Malus domestica	3	AR	167	14	75	256		+56	+78	11
Taxus baccata	1	N	78	30	144	252	67	+15	+24	15
Viburnum opulus	1	N	95	45	107	247	68	+18	+30	19
Prunus domestica	3, 17	AR	100	33	102	235	72	+26	+40	16
Cornus sanguinea	1, 3	N	48	14	152	214	80	+10	+15	11
Populus tremula	1, 16	N	78	30	106	214	50	+19	+28	16
Quercus petraea	1	N	49	56	103	208	59	-12	-18	18
Ulmus procera	3	NA	40	48	118	206	74	-12	-18	16
Salix viminalis	11, 13, 14	AR	79	33	93	205	50	+19	+29	17
Salix alba	14	AR	62	28	101	191	59	+13	+19	16
Malus sylvestris	3	N	97	33	60	190		+33	+48	18
Euonymus europaeus	1, 3	N	48	33	95	176	70	+3	+4	19
Castanea sativa	1	AR	56	18	79	153	47	+20	+27	15
Carpinus betulus	1	N	70	20	60	150	54	+31	+40	16
Sorbus aria agg.	17	N	64	20	43	127		+33	+41	19
Prunus padus	1	N	52	16	54	122	50	+26	+32	17
Populus nigra sens. lat.	3, 14	N	68	9	22	99		+58	+66	17
Crataegus laevigata	1	N	23	15	34	72	53	+6	+7	25
Buxus sempervirens	1, 3	N	34	16	20	70	35	+25	+29	26
Ulmus minor	1, 3	N	31	14	25	70	60	+22	+25	25
Tilia cordata	1	N	34	7	15	56	35	+47	+51	23
Frangula alnus	1	N	14	6	20	40	35	+15	+16	27
Salix pentandra	1	N	17	12	9	38	28	+11	+12	39
Pyrus communis sens. lat.	1, 3, 17	AR	20	8	9	37	30	+33	+35	33
Tilia platyphyllos	1	N	27	3	5	35	27	+67	+70	26
Sorbus torminalis	1	N	9	3	16	28	26	+15	+16	28
Prunus cerasus	1, 3	AR	6	9	5	20	31	-30	-31	47

NS: Native Status   G: Gains   L: Losses   R: Re-finds   TF: Tetrad Frequency   RC: Relative Change   CF: Change Factor (weighted)

Trees and shrubs (neophyte)	Broad Habitats	G	L	R	Total	RC	CF	90% Conf. (CF)
Acer pseudoplatanus	1, 3, 17	40	13	462	515	0	+2	17
Aesculus hippocastanum	3, 17	107	27	204	338	+19	+38	13
Symphoricarpos albus	1, 3, 17	85	39	152	276	+12	+22	16
Larix decidua	1, 2, 17	82	41	113	236	+14	+22	18
Acer platanoides	1, 3, 17	127	14	72	213	+50	+66	12
Picea abies	2	112	28	58	198	+42	+59	16
Picea sitchensis	2	107	9	70	186	+48	+61	11
Populus x canadensis		69	23	68	160	+26	+34	17
Ligustrum ovalifolium	3, 17	73	21	58	152	+32	+41	17
Prunus laurocerasus	1, 17	96	8	47	151	+54	+65	12
Syringa vulgaris	3, 17	66	23	35	124	+35	+44	20
Populus alba	3, 17, 19	54	27	36	117	+22	+28	23
Larix x marschlinsii	2, 17	79	11	22	112	+59	+69	17
Quercus cerris	1, 3, 17	44	20	40	104	+20	+25	21
Chamaecyparis lawsoniana	17	76	7	15	98	+68	+76	16
Lonicera nitida		78	4	14	96	+72	+79	15
Laburnum anagyroides	3, 17	45	23	24	92	+24	+29	25
Pinus nigra	1, 2, 17, 19	64	11	17	92	+57	+66	19
Prunus cerasifera	1, 3, 17	65	6	18	89	+63	+70	16
Populus x canescens	1, 3	43	22	15	80	+28	+34	28
Pseudotsuga menziesii	1, 2, 17	56	10	12	78	+59	+67	20
Larix kaempferi	2, 17	35	16	25	76	+23	+27	25
Rosa rugosa	3, 18, 19	50	9	15	74	+55	+61	21
Mahonia aquifolium	1, 3	25	22	26	73	-2	-3	27
Populus nigra 'Italica'		60	4	9	73	+73	+79	18
Sorbus intermedia agg.		49	8	12	69	+59	+65	21
Spiraea agg.		34	12	19	65	+33	+37	25
Alnus incana	1, 3	51	3	6	60	+76	+81	19
Juglans regia	1, 3	44	8	7	59	+62	+69	23
Pinus contorta	2	37	5	14	56	+54	+59	21
Tsuga heterophylla	1, 2, 17	36	9	8	53	+53	+59	26
Lycium barbarum agg.		25	10	17	52	+27	+30	27
Fallopia baldschuanica		43	6	1	50	+76	+94	22
Thuja plicata	2, 17	33	3	13	49	+57	+60	20
Quercus ilex	1, 17, 19	22	4	19	45	+36	+38	22
Robinia pseudoacacia	3, 17	30	8	7	45	+51	+56	28
Quercus rubra		39	1	1	41	+87	+90	24
Rubus armeniacus		24	4	5	33	+60	+64	29
Alnus cordata		31	1	0	32	+88		

G: Gains   L: Losses   R: Re-finds   RC: Relative Change   CF: Change Factor (weighted)

Trees and shrubs (neophyte)	Broad Habitats	G	L	R	Total	RC	CF	90% Conf. (CF)
Hypericum calycinum	3	19	5	6	30	+47	+50	33
Rhus typhina		28	0	0	28	+92		
Sambucus racemosa	1, 3	12	5	10	27	+23	+24	36
Prunus lusitanica	1, 17	21	2	3	26	+71	+73	30
Fuchsia magellanica	3, 17	17	3	4	24	+58	+60	34
Cornus sericea	1, 3, 17	18	2	2	22	+71	+74	33
Forsythia x intermedia		22	0	0	22	+91		
Leycesteria formosa	1, 3, 17	20	0	2	22	+82	+83	14
Abies grandis		13	4	1	18	+56	+60	41
Platanus x hispanica		15	1	2	18	+74	+75	34
Sequoiadendron giganteum		14	1	3	18	+68	+69	33
Populus x jackii		8	4	5	17	+22	+23	49
Philadelphus coronarius		14	2	0	16	30		
Symphoricarpos x chenaultii		16	0	0	16	+91		
Abies procera		8	1	6	15	+41	+42	34
Amelanchier lamarckii		12	0	3	15	+71	+72	15
Rubus laciniatus		7	5	3	15	+11	+12	60
X Cupressocyparis leylandii		14	0	1	15	+85	+85	19

G: Gains   L: Losses   R: Re-finds   RC: Relative Change   CF: Change Factor (weighted)

Other native species

Dactylorhiza maculata was excluded because of technical difficulties with the data from the first survey. *Symphytum officinale* was considered to be greatly over-recorded (for *Symphytum* × *uplandicum*) in the first survey and was excluded for that reason.

Species recorded in fewer than 15 tetrads across the two surveys

Although the sample sizes here are small and little reliance can be placed on the results, there are a number of instances where the apparent trends are of interest.

Native and archaeophyte species which may be declining

The following were recorded in between 8 and 14 tetrads across the two surveys and show a possible decline.

Apera spica-venti, *Euphorbia platyphyllos* and *Lithospermum arvense* are archaeophytic arable weeds that appear to be continuing to decline, possibly with small and scattered seed banks. *Lathyrus sylvestris* has a very low Ellenberg N and may be the victim of competition after eutrophication. The results for *Tofieldia pusilla*, like other montane species, should be interpreted with caution in view of survey limitations.

Natives and archaeophyte species recorded in 8 to 14 tetrads (possibly declining)	Broad Habitats	NS	WD	EN	G	L	R	Total	TF	RC	CF	90% Conf (CF)
Apera spica-venti	3, 4	AR	n	5	1	6	1	8	25	-80	-81	53
Euphorbia platyphyllos	4	AR	s	5	2	7	1	10	38	-71	-72	57
Lathyrus sylvestris	3	N	t	2	0	4	4	8	13	-59	-59	-
Linum bienne	3, 7	N	s	5	2	7	3	12	23	-59	-60	45
Lithospermum arvense	4	AR	s	5	2	8	1	11	23	-75	-77	54
Potamogeton gramineus	13, 14	N	n	3	1	7	1	9	16	-84	-84	49
Spergularia rupicola	18	N	t	5	0	3	6	9	18	-42	-42	-
Tofieldia pusilla	7, 11	N	n	2	1	6	7	14	59	-47	-48	17

NS: Native Status WD: Wider Distribution EN: Ellenberg N G: Gains L: Losses R: Re-finds TF: Tetrad Frequency RC: Relative Change CF: Change Factor (weighted)

Lithospermum arvense
Field Gromwell

Tofieldia pusilla
Scottish Asphodel

Native and archaeophyte species which may be increasing

The following were recorded in between 8 and 14 tetrads across the two surveys and show a possible increase.

The increase in *Agrostemma githago* is entirely due to its inclusion in wild-flower seed mixes. The apparent increases in *Colchicum autumnale*, *Helleborus foetidus* and possibly *Lavatera arborea* are almost

certainly due to increased recording of garden escapes. The southern species with low to mid values for Ellenberg N, *Poa infirma*, *Salvia verbenaca*, *Spiranthes spiralis* and *Trifolium ornithopodioides* may well be benefiting from climate change. Even bearing in mind the small sample sizes, the apparent increases in *Atropa belladonna*, *Bromus secalinus*, *Dipsacus pilosus*, *Goodyera repens*, *Lepidium ruderale* and *Polygonum rurivagum* are intriguing.

Lepidium ruderale
Narrow-leaved Pepperwort

Trifolium ornithopodioides
Bird's-foot Clover

Natives and archaeophyte species recorded in 8 to 14 tetrads (possibly spreading)	Broad Habitats	NS	WD	EN	G	L	R	Total	TF	RC	CF	90% Conf (CF)
Agrostemma githago	4	AR		5	10	1	0	11	20	+81		
Atropa belladonna	1, 3	N	t	6	7	1	5	13	20	+41	+42	38
Bromus secalinus	4	AR		4	10	3	0	13	60	+61		
Carex elata	11	N	t	5	5	3	0	8	23	+31		
Carex viridula subsp. *viridula*	11, 19	N	n	3	7	2	2	11	21	+47	+48	54
Colchicum autumnale	6	N	t	4	10	4	0	14	28	+51		
Dipsacus pilosus	1, 3, 16	N	t	7	5	0	5	10	16	+41	+42	17
Equisetum pratense	11	N	n	4	5	3	0	8	41	+31		
Goodyera repens	2	N	n	2	6	0	7	13	56	+38	+38	15
Helleborus foetidus	1, 3	N	s	3	11	3	0	14	19	+64		
Lavatera arborea	18	N	s	8	8	0	4	12	16	+58	+59	16
Lepidium ruderale	3, 17	AR	t	7	11	1	1	13	23	+75	+76	42
Myosotis stolonifera	11, 14	N	n	4	4	1	3	8	41	+34	+35	56
Orthilia secunda	2, 10, 16	N	n	3	6	2	3	11	46	+36	+36	55
Poa infirma	3	N	s	5	9	0	0	9	61	+91		
Polygonum rurivagum	4	AR	t	5	11	1	0	12	40	+82		
Rumex maritimus	13, 14	N	t	7	6	2	2	10	20	+41	+42	58
Salvia verbenaca	3, 7	N	s	2	5	0	8	13	19	+30	+30	15
Sedum forsterianum	3, 16	N	s	1	6	3	0	9	12	+41		
Spiranthes spiralis	7	N	s	3	7	0	4	11	16	+55	+56	16
Trifolium ornithopodioides	8	N	s	3	6	0	5	11	23	+46	+46	16

NS: Native Status   WD: Wider Distribution   EN: Ellenberg N   G: Gains   L: Losses   R: Re-finds   TF: Tetrad Frequency   RC: Relative Change   CF: Change Factor (weighted)

Neophytes recorded in 8 to 14 tetrads

Of the neophyte species that were recorded in 8 to 14 tetrads across the two surveys, the majority are garden plants that have escaped into the wild or been deliberately introduced there. Results for these may be affected by changes in recording practice; indeed, several of these species were not recorded at all in the first survey but would almost certainly have been present then.

There are suggestions of decline for *Lupinus arboreus* and *Sisymbrium altissimum*. The apparent decline in *Lupinus polyphyllus* is probably due to a better understanding of the genus and it was probably over-recorded in

the first survey for *Lupinus* × *regalis*. Unlike the majority, *Rapistrum rugosum* and the two *Setaria* species are not garden escapes. The apparent increase in these is probably genuine.

Neophytes recently expanding

There are a number of species that are thought to have been increasing quite rapidly in recent years but which are still relatively scarce and localised. For example, *Cardamine corymbosa* was only recorded in 2 tetrads in the 2003/4 survey, *Polypogon viridis* in 5 and *Senecio inaequidens* in 6; there were no records for these in the 1987/88 survey.

Neophyte species recorded in 8 to 10 tetrads	Broad Habitats	EN	G	L	R	Total	TF	RC	CF	90% Conf. (CF)
Arabis caucasica			7	3	1	11	22	+41	+43	58
Aster novi-belgii	3, 17	6	9	0	0	9	10	+91		
Aster x salignus	3, 17	6	6	3	0	9	12	+41		
Azolla filiculoides	13, 14	8	5	6	3	14	11	-20	-20	60
Campanula rapunculoides	3, 17	5	6	5	1	12	24	+6	+6	72
Chionodoxa forbesii			8	0	0	8	34	+91		
Consolida ajacis	3, 4, 17	4	7	3	0	10	23	+48		
Cortaderia selloana			9	0	0	9	22	+91		
Crocosmia paniculata			10	0	0	10	42	+91		
Crocus x stellaris			10	0	0	10	54	+91		
Datura stramonium	17	8	6	3	2	11	13	+29	+30	62
Erigeron karvinskianus	3, 16, 17	2	12	1	1	14	23	+76	+77	40
Erinus alpinus	3, 16	2	4	3	2	9	17	+8	+8	76
Fallopia sachalinensis	3	7	5	4	5	14	19	+1	+1	59
Geranium versicolor			7	2	1	10	25	+54	+55	55
Geranium x magnificum			9	1	1	11	29	+71	+72	46
Hemerocallis fulva			6	2	0	8	22	+58		
Iberis umbellata			7	1	0	8	20	+77		
Iris germanica	3, 17	4	7	2	0	9	25	+63		
Lagarosiphon major	13	6	9	4	0	13	15	+47		
Lilium pyrenaicum			8	2	0	10	27	+66		
Lupinus arboreus	3, 19	3	2	5	5	12	20	-39	-39	42
Lupinus polyphyllus	3, 14, 17	5	2	10	0	12	37	-89		
Lysichiton americanus	13, 14	8	9	0	1	10	28	+81	+82	21
Myriophyllum aquaticum	13	3	10	0	0	10	17	+91		
Papaver atlanticum			6	0	2	8	26	+66	+67	20
Parthenocissus quinquefolia			7	1	1	9	20	+66	+67	52
Pseudosasa japonica			8	3	0	11	33	+54		
Rapistrum rugosum			7	1	1	9	23	+66	+67	52
Setaria pumila			10	0	0	10	20	+91		
Setaria viridis	3, 4, 17	7	10	0	0	10	20	+91		
Sisymbrium altissimum	3, 17	4	3	6	3	12	18	-42	-43	54
Solanum physalifolium			11	2	0	13	39	+73		
Stachys byzantina			8	1	0	9	32	+79		
Symphytum grandiflorum			12	1	0	13	27	+83		
Tolmiea menziesii	1	7	6	1	1	8	17	+63	+64	57

EN: Ellenberg N   G: Gains   L: Losses   R: Re-finds   TF: Tetrad Frequency   RC: Relative Change   CF: Change Factor (weighted)

Rapistrum rugosum
Bastard Cabbage

Setaria viridis
Green Bristle-grass

7. Local Assessment of Change

16th July 1988

23rd August 2003

Photographs taken during the two surveys looking east along the rampart of an Iron Age fort, Castell Moeddyn, in tetrad SN45W. There are signs of bracken increasing, but otherwise little change is apparent. Arthur Chater

Introduction

The Local Change instructions asked recorders to try to assess which recorded gains and losses were thought likely to be real on the basis of physical changes observed in the field together with information about the routes and localities of notable species from the Monitoring Scheme survey. While a number of recorders felt emboldened to make such assessments the results are not homogeneous: recorders had varying levels of detail available to them and some were inclined to construe observed changes as real whereas others were very disinclined to do so.

In consequence the planned analysis of the assessments to gather circumstantial evidence of change on a species by species basis has proved impractical and instead a selection of them have been examined, from six areas, to look for regional trends and for information on species which are suspected of having undergone a mixture of real gains and real losses rather than the more usual trend of either predominant increase or decline. This is of interest, as the statistics alone cannot distinguish a mixture of real gains and losses from a mixture of real changes and 'missed' species.

Scottish Borders VCs 80 and 81

Michael Braithwaite, with some help, surveyed five tetrads in VC 80 Roxburghshire and VC 81 Berwickshire. These tetrads are largely agricultural (both grass and arable) with some forestry and more natural features but very little habitation.

The changes considered to be real have been tabulated and analysed using the Change Factor. Some changes observed related to trees, shrubs and planted crops or to species that are scarce nationally but, as none of these have yielded a valid Change Factor, they are excluded from the analysis. It was notable that a number of tree and shrub species, both native and alien, had been recently introduced in amenity plantings.

The results for neophyte species other than planted species are in line with this report as a whole with a net gain of 6.4 species per tetrad, as are the results for coastal species colonising salted road verges with a gain of 1.4 species per tetrad.

The results for arable weeds are broadly in line with those of that Broad Habitat as a whole. There are thus gains of 2 species per tetrad and losses of 0.6 species per tetrad: a predominance of gains. The number of gains was influenced by the reseeding of a refuse tip in one tetrad, which led to the presence there in 2003-04 of many species having been brought in with the topsoil as casuals.

The aquatic species showed much change because new ponds had been dug in two tetrads and a pond was lost to drainage in a further tetrad. This resulted in the gain of 3 species per tetrad and a loss of 1.2 species per tetrad.

This leaves the remaining native and archaeophyte species. The tetrad records showing change for these species may be summarised as:

Native and archaeophyte species (excluding arable and aquatic species)	Species per tetrad	Average CF
Gains	1.2	0.07
Losses	5.4	-0.01
Net losses	4.2	0.00

6 of 33 tetrad records showing change show gains and 27 show losses. It is very striking that the considerable net loss of species for identifiable reasons of habitat loss show a nil average CF.

The species lost are predominantly moorland species. There is an interesting lesson in this as only one of the tetrads had any obvious moorland in 1987-88 and that but a small patch at a quarry. The moorland species lost relate to moorland that was effectively destroyed fifty years ago and more and the species have hung on in tiny habitat fragments in woodland and on rocky knowes. The final losses have been caused by very minor events.

Excluding two special cases, the species with apparent losses but a substantial positive CF are *Koeleria macrantha*, *Senecio sylvaticus*, *Carex binervis*, *Carex nigra*, *Cerastium semidecandrum* and *Phleum bertolonii*. *Carex binervis* is shown by this report to be possibly increasing, perhaps in forestry rides, but must suffer losses if an area of moorland is lost, as here. If this is discounted the remaining five are species which might reasonably be expected to be declining nationally as they are specialists of unproductive habitats, though of a greater diversity of habitat than the purely moorland species with a negative CF that also show losses. This appears to offer some support for the suspicion that if a measure of absolute change was available it would show more losses than the relative change model used in this report, but it must be admitted that these five are species that are only at risk in a limited area on the fringes of their distribution, at least at tetrad scale. This matter is discussed further at the end of this section.

Cardiganshire VC 46

Arthur Chater was responsible for ten tetrads in Ceredigion, VC 46 Cardiganshire, in both surveys. These tetrads are somewhat similar to those in the Scottish Borders as they are rural, but with some hamlets, less arable and much more forestry. What most distinguishes them is the extreme thoroughness with which they were recorded including the compilation of extensive habitat notes. It is no surprise therefore that more real gains and losses per tetrad are believed to have been observed than in the Scottish Borders.

Although this sample is the nearest we have to a complete survey with the possibility of detecting absolute change it is sobering that about as many species are still believed to have been missed in one or other survey as to have shown real gains or losses: the extra effort has resulted in more small populations being found but these are just the ones that are hard to re-find.

The results for neophyte species other than planted species are again in line with this report as a whole with a net gain of 8.7 species per tetrad. On the other hand little can be said

about the coastal species colonising salted road verges as this is much less a feature in the far west and only one such arrival was reported, namely *Cochlearia danica*.

Arable weeds show an almost equal number of gains and losses, 1.7 and 1.9 species per tetrad respectively. There is no mention of set-aside as a factor, reflecting the broadly pastoral nature of the agriculture. Interestingly a number of the gains and losses of arable weeds have occurred in small areas of disturbed soil on roadsides and the like rather than in fields. These are essentially casual occurrences.

Aquatic species gains were detected in five water bodies: two new ponds, a new quarry pool and two existing features. This resulted in the gain of 1.4 species per tetrad.

The tetrad records showing change for the remaining native and archaeophyte species may be summarised as:

Native and archaeophyte species (excluding arable and aquatic species)	Species per tetrad	Average CF
Gains	5.7	0.12
Losses	5.3	-0.02
Net losses	0.4	0.05

57 of 110 tetrad records showing change show gains and 55 show losses. This contrasts strikingly with the net decline in the Scottish Borders. Analysis shows that it is the gains rather than the losses which differ.

The 57 gains comprise 19 related to forestry tracks, 6 to sowings, 18 that are essentially casuals of roadsides and the like and 14 others. It is particularly interesting to have circumstantial evidence of the colonisation of upland areas by lowland species along forestry tracks, as this is a trend picked up from the species maps but with some hesitation. The species colonising were *Aphanes australis*, *Hypericum humifusum*, *Juncus bufonius* (2), *Lapsana communis*, *Medicago lupulina*, *Ornithopus perpusillus* (2), *Persicaria hydropiper*, *Rumex crispus*, *Scrophularia nodosa*, *Sonchus asper* (2), *Spergularia rubra*

(2), *Torilis japonica, Trifolium dubium, Tussilago farfara* and *Veronica officinalis*. This list includes two species that have become specialists of this habitat, *Ornithopus perpusillus* and *Spergularia rubra*.

The 53 losses comprise 18 for species that might be half-expected to show losses, mainly the scarcer species of moorland and moorland-edge habitats, and 35 that would not be expected to show losses. These last include a considerable number of annuals or short-lived perennials and are comparable to some of the species showing gains. The very detailed survey has thus detected a turnover in the more ruderal elements of the flora, which those recorders who have not worked in such detail would have been inclined to attribute to species 'missed'.

Overall, the continuing loss of the scarcer native species has been balanced by the colonisation of forestry tracks, mostly by much more widespread species.

Nottinghamshire VC 56

The LC recording in five tetrads in Nottinghamshire has been conducted under the leadership of David Wood. The nature of the country is very different to those of the previous examples with urban and suburban habitat and a relatively rich flora.

The results for neophyte species excluding planted species and the rarer casuals show a net gain of 13.6 species per tetrad, a considerably higher average than that for the Scottish Borders and Wales. There is surprisingly only one instance of a coastal species colonising salted road verges.

The results for arable weeds are broadly in line with those for the Broad Habitat as a whole. There are thus gains of 2.6 species per tetrad and losses of 0.4 species per tetrad: a predominance of gains. Here again, few of the gains and losses relate to the arable habitat, instead they relate to largely casual occurrences in other disturbed habitats.

The aquatic species showed change because a new pond had been dug in one tetrad and a pit tip pool had become more suitable for aquatic vegetation. This resulted in a gain of 1.4 species per tetrad.

This leaves the remaining native and archaeophyte species. The tetrad records showing change for these species may be summarised as:

Native and archaeophyte species (excluding arable and aquatic species)	Species per tetrad	Average CF
Gains	5.2	0.14
Losses	3.0	-0.09
Net gains	**2.2**	**0.06**

Unlike the tables for the Scottish Borders and Wales the gains show an average positive CF fairly comparable to the negative CF of the losses.

26 of 41 tetrad records showing change show gains and 15 show losses. 10 of the gains relate to a pit tip area where recolonisation of relatively widespread native species occurred after landscaping and four of the gains relate to *Lactuca virosa*. The remaining gains relate mainly to colonisation of disturbed ground.

The losses include a due proportion relating to species thought to be in general decline such as *Aira caryophyllea, Campanula rotundifolia, Daucus carota, Eriophorum angustifolium, Euphrasia officinalis* agg., *Festuca ovina* agg., *Potentilla erecta* and *Rumex acetosella*.

Worcestershire VC 37

John Day has reported on five tetrads in Worcestershire in country with a wide range of habitats in both rural and suburban situations.

The results for neophyte species excluding planted species and the rarer casuals are startling with a net gain of 21.8 species per tetrad, but there must be doubt as to how recent some of the arrivals have been. Thus *Vinca major* is recorded as newly arrived in all five tetrads when this is just the sort of species that many recorders formerly chose not to record.

An average of 1.4 coastal species per tetrad have colonised salted road verges, a very marked change in line with this report as a whole.

There have been few changes in arable weeds. There are thus gains of 1.0 species per tetrad and losses of 0.4 species per tetrad: a predominance of gains. The gains relate to set-aside and one species only shows a loss, with *Mentha arvensis* not being re-found in two tetrads.

The aquatic species showed some decline with a net loss of 1.2 species per tetrad. Gains related to a new pool, the introduction of *Nuphar lutea* and *Nymphaea alba* and to colonisation by *Typha latifolia*. Losses related to drainage and management by angling interests.

This leaves the remaining native and archaeophyte species. The tetrad records showing change for these species may be summarised as:

Native and archaeophyte species (excluding arable and aquatic species)	Species per tetrad	Average CF
Gains	11.4	0.27
Losses	7.6	-0.11
Net gains	**3.8**	**0.12**

Although the gains show an average positive and the losses an average negative CF, the average for the gains is considerably larger than the losses.

57 of 95 tetrad records showing change show gains and 38 show losses. There is a higher turnover in species than further north, partly but not wholly relating to the richer flora. The gains show a strong bias towards species of disturbed ground and include *Anthriscus caucalis* at a roadside, *Carex pendula* on a verge, *Dipsacus fullonum*, *Epilobium parviflorum*, *Filago vulgaris* in an urban area, *Geranium lucidum* (3), *G. rotundifolium* (2), *Iris foetidissima* (2), *Lactuca virosa* (2) and *Valerianella carinata*.

The losses include a majority thought to be in general decline such as *Centaurea scabiosa* (2), *Equisetum palustre* (3), *Helictotrichon pratense*, *H. pubescens*, *Myosotis ramosissima*, *Plantago media*, *Potentilla anglica*, *Polygala vulgaris* (2) and *Succisa pratensis*.

West Kent and Middlesex VCs 16 and 21

Rodney Burton has reported on five tetrads in West Kent and Middlesex in predominantly suburban situations, but nevertheless with a wide range of habitat and a rich flora.

The results for neophyte species excluding planted species and the rarer casuals show a large net gain of 15.4 species per tetrad. There are strong trends for species now demonstrated to be increasing such as *Conyza sumatrensis*, *Hirschfeldia incana*, *Lactuca serriola*, *Mercurialis annua*, *Papaver somniferum*, *Soleirolia soleirolii* and *Vulpia myuros*.

An average of 1.6 coastal species per tetrad have colonised salted road verges, a marked change in line with the report as a whole but embracing as many as seven different species. These are *Atriplex littoralis*, *Catapodium marinum*, *Cerastium diffusum*, *Cochlearia danica*, *Plantago coronopus*, *Puccinellia distans* and *Spergularia marina*.

There have been changes in the arable weed flora with gains of 3.0 species a tetrad and losses of 1.8 species a tetrad: a predominance of gains.

The aquatic species showed some decline with a net loss of 1.2 species per tetrad. 3 gains related to *Lythrum salicaria* while *Typha latifolia* had colonised a road drainage lagoon. The losses could not be clearly related to specific changes.

This leaves the remaining native and archaeophyte species. The tetrad records showing change for these species may be summarised as:

Native and archaeophyte species (excluding arable and aquatic species)	Species per tetrad	Average CF
Gains	11.6	0.24
Losses	11.0	-0.07
Net gains	0.6	0.09

On average the gains show a larger positive CF than the negative CF of the losses.

58 of 113 tetrad records showing change show gains and 55 show losses. This is a high turnover in species. The gains again show a strong bias towards ruderal species. Species with two or three gains are *Allium vineale*, *Carex pendula*, *Dipsacus fullonum*, *Geranium pusillum*, *G. rotundifolium*, *Lactuca virosa*, *Myosotis sylvatica*, *Picris echioides* and *Viola odorata*.

The losses relate mainly to species of long-established habitats and include *Adoxa moschatellina*, *Cardamine pratensis*, *Cerastium arvense*, *Clinopodium acinos* (2), *Knautia arvensis*, *Plantago media*, *Potentilla erecta* (2), *Succisa pratensis* and *Trifolium arvense* (2).

Hampshire VCs 11 and 12

The LC recording in Hampshire has been conducted by a very enthusiastic group of recorders under the leadership of the late Pete Selby, Martin Rand and Tony Mundell. The country surveyed includes much suburban habitat along with a good variety of more natural habitats and has a rich flora. A sample of eight of these tetrads has been analysed.

The results for neophyte species excluding planted species and the rarer casuals are once again in line with this report as a whole with a net gain of 11.6 species per tetrad, as are the results for coastal species colonising salted road verges with a gain of 1.1 species per tetrad.

The results for arable weeds are broadly in line with the Broad Habitat account. There are

thus gains of 3.5 species a tetrad and losses of 1.4 species a tetrad: a predominance of gains. The gains and losses relate hardly at all to the arable habitat, instead they relate to largely casual occurrences in a great variety disturbed habitats including roadsides, car parks, quarries and military ranges.

The aquatic species showed change because new ponds had been dug in three tetrads and gravel pits had flooded in two further tetrads. A gain of *Zannichellia palustris* was attributed to the observation that it 'moves in river with current'. This resulted in the gain of 1.5 species per tetrad and a loss of 1.1 species per tetrad.

This leaves the remaining native and archaeophyte species. The tetrad records showing change for these species may be summarised as:

Native and archaeophyte species (excluding arable and aquatic species)	Species per tetrad	Average CF
Gains	14.5	0.23
Losses	8.9	-0.07
Net gains	5.6	0.12

This is no exception to the pattern by which the average positive CF of the gains exceeds the average negative CF of the losses.

116 of 187 tetrad records showing change show gains and 71 show losses. This is a very high turnover of species even allowing for the rich flora.

Species showing gains include *Allium vineale*, *Anacamptis pyramidalis*, *Blackstonia perfoliata*, *Carex spicata*, *Catapodium rigidum*, *Crepis vesicaria*, *Dipsacus fullonum*, *Epilobium parviflorum*, *Erodium cicutarium*, *Filago vulgaris*, *Geranium rotundifolium*, *Lactuca serriola*, *Papaver somniferum*, *Picris echioides* and *Picris hieracioides*. The great majority of these species favour linear and urban habitats with a particular emphasis on ruderal habitats.

The losses include species of long-established habitat thought to be in general decline such as *Apium inundatum*, *Blechnum spicant*, *Carex pallescens*, *Carex panicea*, *Erica cinerea*, *Galium saxatile* and *Genista tinctoria*.

Scottish Highlands

None of the six areas considered above is from the Scottish highlands. This reflects the different character of the reports that we have received from that region.

Ian Strachan in Westerness VC 97 has submitted assessments for the large group of tetrads that he coordinated in an area centred on Fort William. We have sought trends in montane species from those with land above 500 m. While there were a mixture of observed gains and losses in all tetrads all were assessed as 'missed' except for the arrival of one neophyte, *Cotoneaster simonsii*. We have spoken to a number of members who recorded in the hills and they have all reported in similar terms: the limitations of coverage in montane areas coupled with a lack of precise locality data for previous records have precluded a reasoned approach to the assessment of real gains and losses. We have pressed them further regarding the general condition of montane habitats. While there has been reference to new access roads, forestry and other disturbance with some associated species, no major fundamental changes in such habitats have been observed. Where there have been changes in vegetation associated with changes in grazing regimes it is the flowering of plants, rather than their survival, that is perceived to have been affected.

The main changes in the flora of the hills are thus perceived to have been the arrival of some widespread species associated with access roads and other disturbance. Nevertheless there is acceptance that there is a limit to what is observable on the ground and that statistics covering an adequate sample of montane areas might show more significant changes.

Discussion of the average CF of gains and losses of native and archaeophyte species

Given that the Change Factor is an index of relative change, being change relative to the average for a broad suite of native species, it is surprising that the tables above show such a marked difference between the positive CF of gains and the negative CF of losses. There is a temptation to see this as an indication of an overall absolute decline of native species with all the CF values being high compared with what a measure of absolute change would give. This may not be the most likely explanation.

It is necessary to consider by what criteria a recorder will assess whether an observed gain or loss is real. For gains he is likely to be strongly influenced by his perception of what is increasing nationally and in his county. As roadside halophytes are known to have been increasing nationally there is every reason to accept such gains as real, while the recorder's assessment of a small colony of *Vulpia bromoides* where it was not previously recorded will be influenced by whether or not that species is perceived to have been increasing locally. This means that the gains assessed as real will tend to either be those of species that are increasing strongly or those of obviously new habitats such as re-seeded grassland or freshly disturbed sites. This biases the results for gains in favour of those species with strong national trends and a positive CF.

The same does not apply to losses. Losses assessed as real will tend to be those where the plant was known from a particular small feature, such as a relict fragment of species-rich grassland, wetland or heath, and where the fragment has been destroyed. The species lost will tend to be habitat specialists but may not be those at risk in Britain as a whole, as there is a large element of chance in just what species were present in the fragment. Perhaps, therefore, it is not so surprising that species with a wide range of CF appear to have been suffering losses and that there is much less repetition between the individual species assessed to be lost than those assessed to have increased.

It thus does not seem possible to infer any indication of trends as to absolute change from the local assessments.

Conclusions

The evidence fed back from recorders in this way provides a valuable insight into the detail of change in the flora and into the recording process.

There is much support for the conclusions of the analysis by Broad Habitat: for the general decline of some native species particularly those of nutrient poor habitats; for the spread of neophytes; for the spread of coastal species along roadsides. This is a considerable comfort to us.

There is valuable insight into the incidence of species with both real gains and real losses: valuable because the main analysis makes the simplifying assumption that a particular species is either increasing across its range or decreasing and any evidence to the contrary is due to the species being 'missed' in one or other survey. A mixture of gains and losses is seen to be significant in two main species groups: those of arable ground and those of aquatic habitats.

More often than might be thought, the gains and losses of arable weeds are seen to relate to occurrences at roadsides and in other non-agricultural habitats, so some of the increase shown by such species may relate not to agri-environment options but to the increased disturbance of ruderal ground. It is something of an open issue as to how much such occurrences are essentially casual, being dependent on introduction from arable habitats, and how much they relate to species that are now part of a wider and well-established ruderal flora.

Many gains and losses of aquatic species are seen to relate to the surprisingly large turnover in ponds: many new ones have been dug and some have been filled in. This goes a considerable way to explain the relatively low proportion of 're-finds' for many aquatic species and the low significance of the trends shown by the Broad Habitat studies.

The losses of native species are not strongly linked to large-scale losses of habitat. Instead there is evidence of a link to tiny fragments of habitat left over after major habitat losses at some time in the past, often many years ago. The tiny fragments finally succumb to eutrophication or physical disturbance. The corollary of this is that any major habitat losses between the two surveys may have given rise to rather few losses at tetrad scale as fragments may remain. It seems therefore that only small plot studies or actual habitat mapping can be expected to measure current habitat loss effectively and small plots are not suitable for studies of the less widespread species as they occur too infrequently in the plots.

Gains recorded, on the contrary, tend to relate to physical or environmental change in the period between the two surveys. Tetrad studies are much more effective than studies of small plots in detecting species colonising an area.

Colonisation of the uplands by some widespread lowland species which may exploit forestry tracks is suggested in some of the single species studies in this report. It is interesting to find that we do indeed have direct evidence of this.

The sowing of redeveloped land with grass seed with or without wildflower mixes leads to gains of native species more often than might have been guessed but the species involved are often quite widespread ones, so it is only in a few instances that the overall results for a species appear to have been significantly affected by such sowings.

Particularly interesting are the gains in species of ruderal habitats as these include so many of those species thought to be increasing because of climate change. This seems a fruitful ground for further studies.

8. 'Probability' Compared between Species

The model that we have used for analysis recognises that observers do not record all the species that are present in a tetrad in a finite amount of recording time and that some species are recorded much more readily than others. This concept of the probability of a species being recorded where present differing from species to species is perceived to be one of the fundamentals of plant recording. The Probability calculated for each species represents the average chance of a recorder finding the species in a tetrad in which it is present in this particular survey. The outcome is instructive as it provides feedback on the inherent limitations of the recording process.

One of the factors that most influences the Probability of a species is how common it is, so the more widespread species generally have a high Probability:

Here Probability LC is plotted against the estimate of the real range in LC. All the very widespread species are well-recorded but there is much greater variation for the scarcer species. While 0.75 is about average for the scarcer species, many are recorded much better than that and it is only a few that are as low as 0.5.

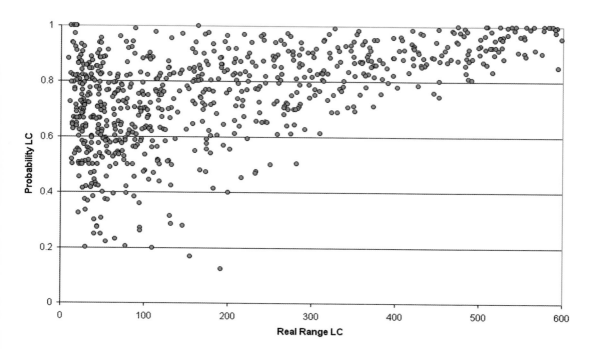

The model used estimates the range of a species from its observed range and its Probability. Ten species are selected below to show the effect of Probability on observed range for well-recorded and less well-recorded species.

Species	Local Change		
	Probability	Observed Range	Real Range
Cytisus scoparius	0.88	244	278
Ballota nigra	0.86	165	192
Alchemilla xanthochlora	0.78	64	82
Arabidopsis thaliana	0.75	228	303
Festuca pratensis	0.50	125	250
Myosotis ramosissima	0.50	33	66
Sagina nodosa	0.42	19	45
Rorippa microphylla	0.42	34	81
Ornithogalum angustifolium	0.31	52	166
Ophioglossum vulgatum	0.26	25	95

It must be emphasised that most species have been well-recorded and that this selection is deliberately biased to include a disproportionate number of less well-recorded species.

Cytisus scoparius and *Ballota nigra* are typical well-recorded species. But even for a species with a Probability of 0.87 the estimate of the real range entails adding 15% to the observed range.

A Probability of 0.75 is typical of the scarcer species. Here the estimate of the real range entails adding 33% to the observed range. Where the Probability is as low as 0.50 the estimate of the real range entails doubling the observed range.

Cytisus scoparius and *Ballota nigra* typify many plants that, while easy to identify, are not confined to a very particular habitat and may be easily overlooked in a tetrad where they are scarce and the habitat is fragmented.

Arabidopsis thaliana is uncommon in some areas and, where this is so, may be present only as a small colony in a ruderal habitat or a garden and may thus be overlooked. *Alchemilla xanthochlora* is a more critical species of a group that not all recorders have experience in.

Festuca pratensis is an interesting species that well demonstrates the difficulties of recording. It is shown by Local Change to be by no means as ubiquitous at tetrad as opposed to 10-km square scale. Where it is scarce it may occur in modest quantity in damp pasture and is only likely to be recorded when the flowers have not been grazed off and are fresh: this may leave only a narrow season for recording as the species does not prosper in grassland that is not grazed.

Myosotis ramosissima is only likely to be recorded when in flower during a short season in the spring. In contrast *Sagina nodosa* is only likely to be recorded when in flower during its short season in the late summer when it is still elusive. *Rorippa microphylla* requires well-formed fruits for safe identification and these are only available rather late in the season. *Ornithogalum angustifolium* is most likely to be recorded during its short season in the late spring though it can also be recorded earlier vegetatively, but this requires specialist experience. *Ophioglossum vulgatum* is the classic under-recorded plant: it is highly inconspicuous at the best of times and, in most habitats, is very soon obscured by the taller grasses with which it grows.

These examples show that the calculated Probability really does mirror what is known from field experience about the ease or otherwise with which species are recorded. The Probability of a recorder finding a species where it is present is thus of value in helping to assess any survey results which are suspected to suffer from incomplete coverage of target species.

9. Tetrad Frequency

The Atlases of the British flora have studied plant distribution at hectad scale only. County studies at tetrad scale have indicated a fairly strong relationship between hectad frequency and tetrad frequency. The Local Change surveys have given us an opportunity to study this relationship across Britain. By comparing data from Local Change with data from the *New Atlas* the frequency of species within 10km Atlas 'dots' can be studied at tetrad scale.

The predominance of widespread species

The total number of tetrads in which a species is present in Britain may be estimated from the Local Change sample. The extent to which the rather few widespread species dominate is apparent even at hectad scale. At tetrad scale the dominance becomes much more pronounced, and it is not difficult to imagine an extrapolation to even finer scales to obtain an insight into just how much Britain's vegetation is dominated by a small group of species.

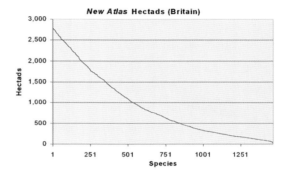

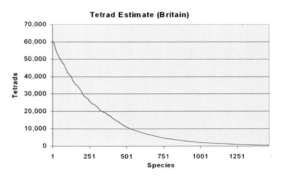

The 1,467 species presented in these charts are those with 5 or more Local Change tetrad records, a sample which excludes nationally rare or scarce species present in less than about 100 hectads in Britain.

Hectad and tetrad frequencies compared

The comparison between hectad and tetrad frequency for individual species may be presented as:

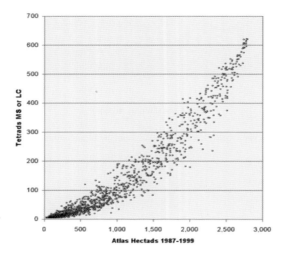

The plethora of scarce species that make little contribution to the vegetation shows up as the dense colour in the bottom left of the chart.

A few of the most widespread species are seen to be really ubiquitous, being present in almost every tetrad as well as almost every hectad.

There are no dots above a diagonal from bottom left to top right, as that would imply a species being present in more than 25 tetrads per hectad.

Tetrad Frequency

It is more helpful to consider the tetrad frequency within the range of a species than across Britain as a whole. The tetrad frequency per hectad is the average number of tetrads in which a species is present in a hectad in which it is present. This may be converted to a proportion so that the maximum is one.

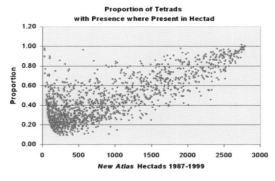

It is quite surprising that the blue dots, those species with at least 30 MS or LC tetrad records, have an average tetrad frequency of over 0.5. This means that within their recorded range they are on average present in over 12 tetrads per hectad. Given that many such species are scarce at the fringes of their range, the tetrad frequency in their heartlands is high indeed. Nevertheless there are wide variations. For example predominantly coastal species are seldom present in more than about 5 or 6 tetrads per hectad as the coastal strip is just that, a line across the tetrad, albeit a remarkably convoluted one at times. Similar considerations limit some habitat specialists like the aquatic species of still water. Other habitat specialists, like calcareous grassland and montane species, may be quite frequent in those limited areas where the habitat occurs.

Tetrad frequencies below 0.2, or four tetrads per hectad, are infrequent. If these species were evenly distributed over their range they would have been expected to show next to no losses in the *New Atlas* at hectad scale as four tetrad extinctions in a hectad implies a high level of change. This is not the case, as most species have a heartland where they are frequent surrounded by a fringe where they are scarce and it is in this fringe that they are subject to change at hectad scale.

With this in mind it is interesting to examine the species present in less than 30 tetrads in the sample, the red dots. Many have a surprisingly high tetrad frequency of around 0.2 rather than the minimum possible of 0.04 or one tetrad per hectad: so even our scarcest plants tend to have a rather clustered distribution. The increased variation in tetrad frequency for very low tetrad scores is due to the effects of chance on how many tetrads with the species present were selected in the Local Change sample. Species with less than 5 tetrad records are excluded.

A very few species have a frequency factor just over 1, an anomaly related to the exclusion of poorly recorded tetrads but not poorly recorded hectads and to problems with coastal hectads which may have very little land area and a paucity of even very widespread species.

Example species

The difference between recording at tetrad scale and recording at hectad scale may be illustrated by selecting some individual species. In the following chart the hectad and tetrad frequencies are sorted into descending order independently so sample dots for individual species are needed to bring out the variation between species. *Alopecurus pratensis* is little more frequent than *Anemone nemorosa* at hectad scale but considerably more so at tetrad scale. Similarly *Crepis paludosa* is little more frequent than *Ophrys apifera* at hectad scale but considerably more so at tetrad scale.

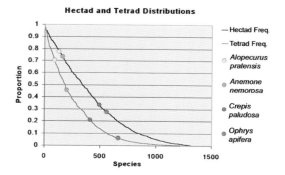

Statistics for selected species

The following table shows statistics of tetrad frequency for a selection of species. Some of the results may be found startling. *Sedum rosea* is present in about 3,200 tetrads in Britain, *Pinguicula lusitanica* 3,600, *Arctostaphylos uva-ursi* 4,200, *Veronica polita* 9,000, *Selaginella selaginoides* 12,500 and *Lotus corniculatus* in even more tetrads than *Urtica dioica*.

Chrysanthemum segetum is present in about one third of the tetrads within its range, *Helianthemum nummularium* one third, *Juniperus communis* and *Pinguicula lusitanica* one half, *Vaccinium vitis-idea* and *Calystegia silvatica* two thirds and *Selaginella selaginoides* three quarters.

See table on following page.

The recent *Flora of Assynt* (Evans *et al.* 2002), with its tetrad atlas, offers comfort regarding the frequency estimates of some of the highland species with *Arctostaphylos uva-ursi*, *Juniperus communis* and *Vaccinium vitis-idea* being recorded in around half the tetrads in that area.

Calculation of tetrad frequency

There are 2,852 Atlas hectads in Britain in the sense used by the *New Atlas* and 244,266 1 km squares. About 818 hectads are coastal.

Dividing the 1 km square total by four gives a crude tetrad estimate of 61,067. This differs from 2,852 x 25 = 71,300 because parts of the coastal hectads are sea.

The tetrad estimate of 61,067 is too low as tetrads also have some sea. A refinement to reflect this leads to an estimate of 62,090 tetrads of which 4,093 are coastal.

There are thus on average 62,090/2,852 = 21.77 tetrads with some land per hectad in Britain. 6.6% of British tetrads are coastal.

Species	Atlas Hectads 1987+	Britain Tetrad Estimate	Tetrad Frequency
Zannichellia palustris	735	2,836	0.18
Doronicum pardalianches	610	2,738	0.21
Carlina vulgaris	778	3,716	0.22
Ophrys apifera	785	4,107	0.24
Spergularia media	503	2,738	0.25
Carex arenaria	599	3,422	0.26
Glaux maritima	791	4,595	0.27
Armeria maritima	1,048	7,431	0.33
Myriophyllum alterniflorum	990	7,138	0.33
Chrysanthemum segetum	887	6,747	0.35
Helianthemum nummularium	757	5,769	0.35
Rhynchospora alba	370	2,836	0.35
Sedum rosea	407	3,227	0.36
Claytonia sibirica	947	8,311	0.40
Menyanthes trifoliata	1,526	13,493	0.41
Cotoneaster simonsii	832	7,627	0.42
Juniperus communis	748	7,333	0.45
Viola lutea	334	3,324	0.46
Pinguicula lusitanica	332	3,618	0.50
Allium ursinum	1,811	20,337	0.52
Veronica polita	793	8,995	0.52
Thalictrum alpinum	300	3,813	0.58
Erica cinerea	1,732	22,489	0.60
Primula veris	1,447	19,360	0.61
Vaccinium vitis-idaea	723	9,875	0.63
Arctostaphylos uva-ursi	305	4,204	0.63
Anemone nemorosa	2,100	29,431	0.64
Eriophorum angustifolium	1,749	24,737	0.65
Calystegia silvatica	1,550	22,782	0.68
Calluna vulgaris	2,250	34,222	0.70
Rorippa nasturtium-aquaticum agg.	2,074	31,582	0.70
Phalaris arundinacea	2,287	36,471	0.73
Mercurialis perennis	2,063	33,342	0.74
Ulex europaeus	2,488	40,871	0.75
Selaginella selaginoides	754	12,515	0.76
Galeopsis tetrahit agg.	2,168	37,351	0.79
Aegopodium podagraria	2,378	41,653	0.80
Silene dioica	2,348	41,653	0.81
Lonicera periclymenum	2,501	44,684	0.82
Hyacinthoides non-scripta	2,291	41,359	0.83
Veronica beccabunga	2,185	39,893	0.84
Filipendula ulmaria	2,609	49,475	0.87
Veronica persica	1,976	37,644	0.88
Tussilago farfara	2,488	48,888	0.90
Centaurea nigra	2,580	50,942	0.91
Capsella bursa-pastoris	2,452	48,693	0.91
Heracleum sphondylium	2,626	52,408	0.92
Lotus corniculatus	2,771	58,275	0.97
Veronica chamaedrys	2,556	53,973	0.97
Urtica dioica	2,723	57,590	0.97

10. Conclusions and Recommendations

This section first summarises the achievements of the Local Change project against its objectives and redefines the niche which the survey is perceived to fill. It also presents recommendations for the future.

Measuring achievements against the key objective

Change at species level

The key objective of Local Change has been to measure distributional changes in the individual species of the British Flora at tetrad scale by a repeat survey during 2003-04 of sample tetrads previously surveyed in 1987-88. This is a finer scale than the hectads used by the *New Atlas* and is coarser than the small plots used by the Countryside Survey. The *New Atlas* project was not primarily designed to measure change, but measuring change in the period 1930-1999 was a secondary objective. On the whole it was achieved more successfully for scarce species than for widespread ones, as scarce species tend to show more genuine change at hectad scale and differences in recording coverage at different dates therefore have less effect on the results. The Countryside Survey is designed primarily to measure change in habitats rather than individual species and is only successful in measuring change for the most widespread species as too little data are available for less widespread ones.

Local Change has met this objective by generating useful statistics on change for 726 native and archaeophyte species and 134 neophyte species that have been found in 15 or more of the sample tetrads. The scarcer species that the *New Atlas* covered so well are thus excluded. In so doing it has filled an important niche in an overall endeavour to monitor change in the British flora that cannot be met by any single survey.

Some species were not consistently recorded in the two surveys, especially those that are planted. These are mainly neophytes but also include most trees and shrubs, whether native in Britain or not, as these are often planted. For these species more limited statistics have been generated showing something of their relative frequency. No estimate of change could be calculated for the 39 most widespread species as any possible small changes at tetrad scale were masked by observer bias, but good estimates of the tetrad frequency of these species have been obtained.

Statistical robustness of the results

There was always an uncertainty as to how much differences in recording between the two surveys would mask any significant change. We believe that it is a considerable achievement by our volunteer recorders to have attained as high a degree of consistency between the two surveys as they have. Nevertheless the confidence limits in the measures of change at species level are relatively wide and we have placed great importance on analysis by groups of species with similar characteristics in our search for statistically robust trends.

We have developed a model to facilitate analysis which recognises that observers do not record all the species that are present in a tetrad in a finite amount of recording time and that some species are recorded much more readily than others. The concept that the probability of a species being recorded where it is present differs from species to species is perceived to be one of the fundamentals of plant recording. Ironically we have not been able to carry through this concept quite as we would have liked in the adjustment that is made for over-recording in the second survey relative to the first, as a circular argument arises where the calculation of the probability of finding a species is dependent on knowing the relative recording effectiveness of the two surveys and vice versa.

We present two separate but related measures of change whose definitions may be found in the Glossary. Relative Change gives a measure of the change in the tetrad distribution of a species. Relative Change is the observed change in proportion to recorded range, adjusted for relative over-recording. The Change Factor is used for the analysis of groups of species. The Change Factor is found by applying a weighting to the Relative Change seeking to make the small gains and losses of widespread species in response to environmental change comparable to the proportionately larger gains and losses of scarce species in response to the same change.

Change in the 726 native and archaeophyte species selected for analysis is shown in the chart below. At a 90% confidence level 480 species or 66% show no material change, 132 or 18% show a relative increase and 114 or 16% show a relative decrease.

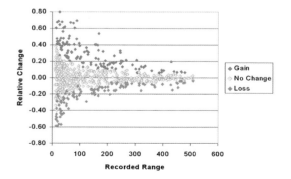

About one third of the species show substantial change and perhaps as many again are likely to have changed to a lesser extent, though our statistics are not robust enough to demonstrate it with confidence.

It has been a disappointment to find that there was such a degree of difference in recording effort between the two surveys that it has masked real change and led to change being assessed on a relative change model only. In this model change is related to an average for typical native species. The suspicion that native species as a whole have declined in absolute terms, and in particularly that this is true of the scarcer ones, has been left as an untested hypothesis.

Analysis of change

Native and archaeophyte species are analysed in groups related to Broad Habitat. A summary of this analysis is to be found in Chapter 3. This analysis is the key section of our report and is of interest both at individual species level and in relation to the statistical trends for groups of species. The most important findings are the following.

- There has been a loss of species of infertile habitats, particularly calcareous grassland and dwarf shrub heath. Habitat fragmentation may have been the main underlying cause but much of the fragmentation occurred some time ago and isolated fragments suffer species loss for many reasons, including eutrophication and both over and under grazing.

- Eutrophication may be the main driving force affecting change in wetland species. Many species of wetland habitats show an increase or decline though no overall change has been detected in the group as a whole. The more specialised wetland communities may have suffered a loss in diversity while in other habitats, such as riversides, there may have been a change in species composition with little loss in diversity.

- It seems inescapable that climate change has been one of the factors that has led to an increase in some species, particularly ruderal species found in urban habitats and the transport network. Such ruderal species tend to be those which are readily dispersed and which can thus respond rapidly to conditions that favour them. Southerly species have also fared better than northerly species in Neutral and Calcareous grassland. It is much more difficult to point to cases where climate change has led to losses but this may reflect the extraordinary persistence of many upland plants rather than any suggestion that they will remain unaffected indefinitely.

- One of the most striking trends shown by the *New Atlas* and other studies has been the great decline of the weed species of arable fields. The Local Change survey indicates that such species are no longer declining as a class and indeed there is some evidence of modest recovery, though some of the more specialised species do continue to decline. Agri-environment policies including set-aside are thought have contributed to this reversal of fortune, but the exclusion of the scarcer arable species from the Local Change results may also be a factor.

It must be emphasised that not all species in the species groupings have changed in the same way: there are many examples of species that have increased while apparently similar species have declined and vice versa. We present a selection of species accounts to illustrate this. This varied response is indicative of the wide range of ecological strategies adopted by our flora.

A summary of the analysis of neophyte species is to be found in pages 293 to 294. Neophytes included in the analysis are almost by definition those that are continuing to increase, as less successful species do not qualify as they are too infrequent in the sample tetrads. The spread of species that have been widespread since the first Atlas survey in 1960 continues and they are being joined by further introductions, but neophytes still represent only about 16% of the species analysed. Although a very large number of plant species have been introduced to Britain, the majority have very local distributions. On average the more recent introductions included in our analysis are increasing faster than long-established species but this may be biased because the recent introductions that are increasing more slowly have not qualified for analysis. Southern England is being colonised by aliens to a

greater extent than other areas and climate change may be a factor here, perhaps allied to higher levels of habitat disturbance.

While there are striking examples of recent spread, most of these were heralded in the *New Atlas*. However, *Conyza sumatrensis* and *Lemna minuta* are seen to have become notably frequent very recently within their increasing ranges.

Tetrad frequency

The Atlases of the British Flora have studied plant distribution at hectad scale only. County studies at tetrad scale have indicated a fairly strong relationship between hectad frequency and tetrad frequency. The Local Change surveys have given us an opportunity to study this relationship across Britain. By comparing data from Local Change with data from the *New Atlas* the frequency of species within 10km Atlas 'dots' can be studied at tetrad scale. Even those botanists who live in northern and western areas may be surprised by our estimate that *Selaginella selaginoides*, a relatively inconspicuous species, is present in about 12,500 tetrads in Britain.

These tetrad frequencies and tetrad estimates are a major step towards establishing the relative abundance of species, though they would need to be combined with studies at yet finer scale before the ideal of measuring the abundance of a species across Britain could be fully realised.

Measuring achievements against secondary objectives

Local Change has also achieved educational objectives and has enabled improvements in the technical ability of BSBI to carry out survey work

Training a new generation of botanists

One of the objectives of Local Change has been to pass on skills in field botany to those new to plant recording by one-to-one training in the field. It is difficult to measure this quantitatively but the very success of the survey in achieving almost nationwide coverage speaks for itself: such coverage could not have been achieved without the comradeship that is an essential element in an enjoyable project and this is fully borne out both by reports from recorders and by the number of those who took part who had not participated in previous surveys.

Accurate Grid References for locally scarce species

One of the clear successes of the Local Change survey, and the companion project to record scarce plants for County Rare Plant Registers, has been the use of GPS equipment to record plant localities routinely to a precision of 10m. This has much enhanced the quality of the data as a baseline for future survey.

MapMate hub

Another clear success of the Local Change survey has been the use of the MapMate recording program to enable the data recorded to be computerised locally and to be transmitted electronically to a central hub. This has transformed the capability of BSBI to carry out survey projects such as this as it has eliminated most of the central data processing costs which have previously been associated with such projects. This success has enabled resources to be reallocated productively to data interpretation.

Comparison with other studies

Studies of woodland plots

We have sought to compare the results of the Local Change surveys with Kirby's (2005) studies of woodland plots. There is in some ways a surprisingly low degree of correlation, with Kirby's studies showing more decline than Local Change. However the surveys cover different time periods and relate to different plot sizes. There is reason to suspect that the decline in woodland species has been lower in recent years than in the period since 1971 and that it is less evident at the scale of a tetrad than at plot scale.

The New Atlas and Local Change results compared

The chart below compares the Change Factor applied to Local Change data and the Change Index applied to the *New Atlas* data. The comparison is limited to the native and archaeophyte species that were selected to derive the Change Factor by excluding the scarcest and most widespread species and species thought to have been affected by differences in recording methodology between the two Local Change surveys. Although the two indexes are calculated differently they are in fact closely comparable and, to a first approximation, the Change Factor is similar to the Change Index divided by three. The high random element in the chart thus relates substantially to the underlying data, not to differences in the two models used for analysis.

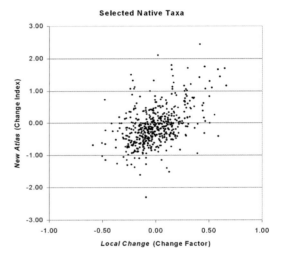

In the individual species accounts we have often compared the results of Local Change with those of the *New Atlas*. Again there is a surprisingly low degree of correlation. While the reasons sometimes include deficiencies in the surveys, mainly relating to poorer coverage or taxonomic understanding in the earlier surveys, the different time periods and the different size of the recording unit are usually thought to be more important. Thus we do have reason to believe that the fortunes of arable plants have improved in recent years and equally it is not unreasonable to find that the distribution of a species like *Cytisus scoparius* has declined at tetrad scale but has remained largely unaltered at hectad scale.

Nevertheless the degree of divergence between the change at species level shown by recent studies of the British flora at different spatial scales is interesting, as much of our subjective perception points to relatively constant trends of decline in many native species over the last half century and less constant and often surprising increases in some other native and alien species.

Table 10.1 selects some individual species for discussion. Five trends are picked out that are suggested to be particularly significant in explaining the divergence. There is evidence that change at tetrad scale is fundamentally different to change at hectad scale. The main results of this report are seen to be reflected in the comparison with arable species showing improved fortune in recent years and some species appearing to respond to climate change. Some species are recognised to have been under-recorded for the first Atlas. Finally there are species that show variation for which we cannot suggest one simple explanation.

This comparison is salutary as it reinforces our belief that there is no one simple index that adequately describes how a plant species is faring in Britain. Plants have individual distribution patterns at so many different spatial scales that the situation is inherently complex. Despite these reservations, our belief is that both the *New Atlas* and Local Change datasets are valid bases for analysis as long as their limitations are taken into account.

The unique niche of Local Change in monitoring change in the British flora

Recent country-wide botanical surveys include the *New Atlas*, BSBI's Vice-county Rare Plant Register programme (CRPRs), BSBI Local Change, the Countryside Survey (CS), Plantlife's Common Plant Survey (CPS) and the National Vegetation Classification (NVC).

The *New Atlas* is the definitive current record of the national distribution of the whole of our flora except for certain critical groups. The comparison of the results of the 1987-99 survey with those obtained for the 1962 *Atlas* was used to assess changes at hectad scale. The main changes revealed were the expansion of range of some species (many of which are neophytes), the apparent increase through improved recording of species which are now better known to recorders or which it has only recently become acceptable to record, and the decrease of species that are relatively scarce at this scale. Expanding species are always likely to be detected more readily than declining species as colonisation of hectads may be rapid whereas decline to extinction can be a protracted process. Because of this, declining species will be lost from a hectad more rapidly if they are represented there by few populations than if they are frequent. For more widespread species change in the hectad distribution may be

Table 10.1 Species	Change Factor	CI/3	Change Index
Species showing notably more change at tetrad scale			
Caltha palustris	-0.36	-0.09	-0.26
Campanula latifolia	-0.47	-0.08	-0.23
Saxifraga granulata	-0.40	-0.09	-0.26
Arable species showing improved fortune			
Anagallis arvensis	0.15	-0.24	-0.73
Chenopodium album agg.	0.02	-0.24	-0.73
Persicaria maculosa	-0.12	-0.32	-0.95
Species possibly increasing in response to climate change			
Geranium pusillum	0.45	0.05	0.16
Lactuca virosa	0.66	0.39	1.16
Sherardia arvensis	0.39	-0.31	-0.94
Species under-recorded for the first Atlas			
Dryopteris carthusiana	0.16	0.35	1.06
Holcus mollis	0.06	0.27	0.80
Species showing unexplained variation from the *New Atlas*			
Rorippa sylvestris	-0.48	0.24	0.73
Viola riviniana	-0.24	0.36	1.07

unrepresentative of change at finer scales. In particular a species may decline substantially at population or tetrad scale before it begins to show significant losses at hectad scale even at the fringes of its distribution. The *New Atlas*, like Local Change, is based on a presence or absence survey, so it is unable to give any indication of the abundance of species.

BSBI is addressing the need for distribution and abundance data for rare or scarce plants through its Vice-county Rare Plant Register programme (CRPRs) and occasional single species studies. More detailed studies of a limited set of species and sites is being carried out as part of the Common Standards Monitoring (CSM) programme of EN/SNH/CCW, a programme to which BSBI is contributing. Local Change is designed to measure change for a different suite of species and indeed to start roughly where the CRPRs break off and to be ineffective for only a small number of very widespread species which are too frequent at tetrad scale for change to be measurable. The very comprehensive coverage has meant that it has not been practical to measure abundance during the Local Change survey: abundance is a difficult concept to quantify in a recording unit of 400 hectares.

Meanwhile the Countryside Survey (CS) has worked with small plots from 200 m² downwards in 1 km squares. Changes in presence at this scale are tantamount to a measure of abundance but in such small plots it is only widespread species that occur frequently enough to be available for the measurement of change so CS has therefore been much more successful in measuring change in vegetation type than in measuring change at individual species level. Plantlife's Common Plant Survey (CPS) also works with small plots but with only a very limited set of species.

Another approach to monitoring vegetation is to use the National Vegetation Classification (NVC). Considerable progress has now been made towards preparing national inventories of NVC vegetation types. However the species frequency tables that underlie the NVC are not stable enough to support a project to estimate the abundance of individual species in the countryside from such inventories, except possibly at a crude level for widespread and very widespread species. Thus, while changes in these inventories of habitats may be chronicled, loss or gain of habitats cannot be related to changes in the individual species present in them.

Local Change species data has been attributed to Broad Habitats in an attempt to relate changes in groups of species with similar attributes to changes affecting the Broad Habitat as a whole. It is doubtful if the data is suitable for a similar exercise in relation to the NVC.

To summarise how BSBI Local Change, LC, fits into a coherent scheme to monitor the British flora see table 10.3 (opposite).

This table divides the flora into four categories, species that are rare or scarce, local, widespread or very widespread. To give these terms some meaning table 10.2 (below) is presented based on the 4,111 species covered by the *New Atlas* survey.

The correspondence between spatial scales is approximate only, as not all the species vary across spatial scales in the same way.

No one survey can expect to measure all the elements of change in Britain's plant diversity, both at habitat and species level. Overall Local Change is clearly complementary to other

Table 10.2		Estimated Species Coverage of Botanical Survey Methods					
The correspondence between spatial scales is approximate only, as not all the species vary across spatial scales in the same way							
	Species	*New Atlas* Hectads	% Hectads	LC Tetrads	% Tetrads	CS Plots
Rare or Scarce	2,726	1-100	0.04-3	0-4	0.01-0.7	0
Local	1,014	101-1,445	4-53	5-200	0.8-31	0-4
Widespread	332	1,446-2,615	54-96	201-500	32-78	5-50
Very Widespread	39	2,616-2,852	97-100	501-635	79-100	50+

12. Acknowledgements

The authors acknowledge with much gratitude the teamwork within BSBI and its partners that has made this survey and its report not only possible but also enjoyable.

Thanks are due to our sponsor, the Heritage Lottery Fund, without whose contribution BSBI's Research Fund would not have been able to fund the Volunteers Officer post to coordinate the survey. Thanks are also due to Plantlife International for making the bid for the 'Making it Count for People and Plants' project as a whole and for help with grant administration.

The BSBI Vice-county recorders and others who organised the fieldwork and submission of data for the survey are listed below:

K.J. Adams, R. Aisbitt, A.G. Amphlett, G.H. Ballantyne, B.R.& C.B. Ballinger, M. Barron, B.D. Batty, G.& K.A. Beckett, I. Bennalick, P.M. Benoit, I.R. Bonner, C.R. Boon, M.E. Braithwaite, M. Briggs, N.H. Brown, E.R. Bullard, S.J. Bungard, R.M. Burton, J.K. Butler, A.O. Chater, P.J. Cook, R.W.M. Corner, M.J. Crawley, J.J. Day, D.P. Earl, R.W. Ellis, P.A. Evans, S.B. Evans, T.G. Evans, L. Farrell, J.H.C. Fenton, C.N. French, P. Follett, P.G. Garner, G.M. Gent, A.C. Godfrey, I.P. Green, J.A. Green, P.R. Green, E.F. Greenwood, Q.J. Groom, G. Halliday, A.C. Hannah, P.A. Harmes, D.M. Hawker, J.E. Hawksford, P. Harvey, D.M. Henderson, A. Hoare, R.M.H. Hodgson, B.G. Hogarth, D.R. Humphreys, E.H. Jackson, T. J. James, M.B. Jeeves, G.M. Kay, Q.O.N. Kay, H.J. Killick, P.R. Kirby, M.A.R.& C. Kitchen, A.G. Knapp, A.C. Leslie, A. Lockton, P. Macpherson, R. Maycock, W.N. McCarthy, D.J. McCosh, J.W. McIntosh, D. McKean, T.F. Medd, R. Middleton, C. Miles, N.P. Millar, D.J. Millward, R.J. Mitchell, A.J. Morton, A.R.G. Mundell, R.J. Murphy, C.W. Murray, M.E. Murray, J. Muscott, M.A. Ogilvie, J. O'Reilly, R.J. Pankhurst, S.J. Parker, R.E. Parslow, J.W. Partridge, D.A. Pearman, B.W. Phillips, E.G. Philp, S. Pilkington, M.D. Pool, C.R. Pope, M. Porter, R.D. Pryce, M.W. Rand, A.W. Reid, M.C. Robinson, G. Rothero, A. Rutherford, M.N. Sanford, P.A. Sankey, W. Scott, P.J. Selby, A.J. Silverside, P.A. Smith, R.E.N. Smith, E.W. Stewart, S.E. Stille, I.M. Strachan, G.A. Swan, N.W. Taylor, S.E. Thomson, G.N. Toone, M. Woods, M. Wainwright, K.J. Watson, D. Welch, T.C.E. Wells, I. Weston, S.J. Whild, A. Willmot, G.T.D. Wilmore, R.J. Wilson, D.C. Wood, J. Woodman, G. Wynne, P.A. Zagni.

Their achievement is reflected in the outstanding coverage achieved and the computerisation of the data. The individual contributors, who include many people new to such recording, are listed in Appendix 5.

We are most grateful for the cooperation of landowners and land managers in allowing access to land which has continued a tradition that is crucial to the success of such surveys.

Within BSBI the Volunteers Officers, the late Pete Selby and Bob Ellis, were supported by a steering committee comprising, in addition to the other authors, D. A. Pearman, G.E Hemery and I. R. Bonner. David Pearman, as BSBI Projects Manager and BSBI Records Committee chairman, has been a constant support in many ways and Ian Bonner assisted in the partnership with Plantlife for the 'Making it Count for People and Plants' project as a whole. We thank K. J. Walker for detailed comments on Chapter 4, and A. Amphlett, G. P. Rothero and C. E. Pinches for additional help with this section. C. R. Boon has reviewed the proofs and R. G. Ellis has assisted with the distribution of this report.

The majority of the data were collected and collated using the recording package MapMate. We are grateful to Mark Yeates and Teknica Ltd. for their support throughout the project. The maps were produced using DMAPW by Alan Morton.

BSBI has worked in a productive partnership with the Centre for Ecology and Hydrology, Monks Wood, in preparing this report. CEH provided the services of one of the authors, Dr C. D. Preston, and also supported the project through the work of Dr P. Rothery and Dr D. B. Roy. We are particularly grateful to Peter Rothery for the statistical analyses reported in Chapter 4 and for his review of the work reported in Appendix 2.

We are grateful to Adrian Darby and Malcolm Vincent of the Joint Nature Conservation Committee for contributing the Foreword. JNCC has also, through Dr C. M. Cheffings, provided facilities for meetings and has given general support.

Thanks are extended on behalf of BSBI to all these individuals and organisations for their contributions.

13. References

Andreasen C, Stryhn H, Streibig JC. 1996. Decline of the flora in Danish arable fields. *Journal of Applied Ecology* 33: 619-26.

Barr CJ, Gillespie MK. 2000. Estimating hedgerow length and pattern characteristics in Great Britain using Countryside Survey data. *Journal of Environmental Management* 60: 23-32.

Braithwaite ME. 2004. *Berwickshire vice-county rare plant register (together with a check list of vascular plants).* Hawick: privately published.

Brown A, Hall R, Townshend A, eds. 2001. *State of Nature: the upland challenge.* Peterborough: English Nature.

Bunce RGH, Smart SM, van de Poll HM, Watkins JW, Scott WA. 1999. *Measuring change in British vegetation.* ECOFACT volume 2. Grange-over-Sands: Institute of Terrestrial Ecology.

Byfield A, Pearman D. 1996. *Dorset's disappearing heathland flora.* London: Plantlife.

Chater AO, Oswald PH, Preston CD. 2000. Street floras in Cambridge and Aberystwyth. *Nature in Cambridgeshire* 42: 3-26.

Clutton-Brock TH, Coulson T, Milner JM. 2004. Red deer stocks in the Highlands of Scotland. *Nature* 429: 261-2.

Cooke AS, Farrell L. 2001. Impact of muntjac deer (*Muntiacus reevesi*) at Monks Wood National Nature Reserve, Cambridgeshire, eastern England. *Forestry* 74: 241-50.

Corner RWM. 2004. *Carex vaginata* Tausch (Cyperaceae): a sedge new to England. *Watsonia* 25: 127-30.

Cox DR, Snell EJ. 1981. *Applied statistics.* London: Chapman & Hall.

Department for Transport. 2003. *Transport Statistics Great Britain.* www.dft.gov.uk.

Dickson JH, Macpherson P, Watson K. 2000. *The changing flora of Glasgow.* Edinburgh: Edinburgh University Press.

Dodd M, Silvertown J, McConway K, Potts J, Crawley M. 1995. Community stability - a 60-year record of trends and outbreaks in the occurrence of species in the Park Grass Experiment. *Journal of Ecology* 83: 277-85.

Dony JG. 1974. Changes in the flora of Hertfordshire. *Transactions of the Hertfordshire Natural History Society* 27: 255-64.

Dony JG. 1977. Change in the flora of Bedfordshire, England, from 1798 to 1976. *Biological Conservation* 11: 307-20.

Dunn ST. 1905. *Alien Flora of Britain.* London: West, Newman & Co.

Dunnett NP, Willis AJ, Hunt R, Grime JP. 1998. A 38-year study of relations between weather and vegetation dynamics in road verges near Bibury, Gloucestershire. *Journal of Ecology* 86: 610-23.

Evans PA, Evans IM, Rothero GP. 2002. *Flora of Assynt.* Privately published.

Firbank LG, Arnold HR, Eversham BC, Mountford JO, Radford GL, Telfer MG, Treweek JR, Webb NRC, Wells TCE. 1993. *Managing set-aside land for wildlife.* London: HMSO.

Firbank LG, Ellis NE, Hill MO, Lockwood AJ, Swetnam RD. 1998. Mapping the distribution of weeds in Great Britain in relation to national survey data and to soil type. *Weed Research* 38: 1-10.

Firbank LG, Smart SM, van de Poll HM, Bunce RGH, Hill MO, Howard DC, Watkins JW, Stark GJ. 2000. *Causes of change in British vegetation*. ECOFACT volume 3. Grange-over-Sands: Institute of Terrestrial Ecology.

Foley MJY. 1992. The current distribution and abundance of *Orchis ustulata* L. (Orchidaceae) in the British Isles - an updated summary. *Watsonia* 19: 121-6.

French DD, Miller GR, Cummins RP. 1997. Recent development of high-altitude *Pinus sylvestris* scrub in the northern Cairngorm mountains, Scotland. *Biological Conservation* 79: 133-44.

George M. 1992. *The land use, ecology and conservation of Broadland*. Chichester: Packard Publishing.

Greenwood EF. 1999. Vascular plants: a game of chance? In *Ecology and landscape development: a history of the Mersey basin*, ed. EF Greenwood, pp. 195-211. Liverpool: Liverpool University Press & National Museums and Galleries on Merseyside.

Greenwood EF. 2003. Understanding change: a Lancashire perspective. *Watsonia* 24: 337-50.

Greenwood EF. 2005. The changing flora of the Lancaster canal in West Lancaster (v.c. 60). *Watsonia* 25: 231-53.

Grime JP. 1979. *Plant strategies and vegetation processes*. Chichester: John Wiley & Sons.

Grime JP, Hodgson JG, Hunt R. 1988. *Comparative plant ecology: a functional approach to common British species*. London: Unwin Hyman.

Haines-Young R, Barr CJ, Black HIJ, Briggs DJ, Bunce RGH, et al. 2000. *Accounting for nature: assessing habitats in the UK countryside*. London: Department of the Environment, Transport and the Regions.

Harris S, Morris P, Wray S, Yalden D. 1995. *A review of British mammals: population estimates and conservation status of British mammals other than cetaceans*. Peterborough: Joint Nature Conservation Committee.

Hill MO, Mountford JO, Roy DB, Bunce RGH. 1999. *Ellenberg's indicator values for British plants*. Huntingdon: Institute of Terrestrial Ecology.

Hill MO, Preston CD, Roy DB. 2004. *PLANTATT Attributes of British and Irish plants: status, size, life history, geography and habitats*. Huntingdon: Centre for Ecology and Hydrology.

Hodgson JG. 1986. Commonness and rarity in plants with special reference to the Sheffield flora. Part II: the relative importance of climate, soils and land use. *Biological Conservation* 36: 253-74.

Jackson DL. 2000. *Guidance on the interpretation of the Biodiversity Broad Habitat Classification (terrestrial and freshwater types): Definitions and the relationship with other habitat classifications*. JNCC Report no. 307. Peterborough: Joint Nature Conservation Committee.

James TJ. 1997. The changing flora of Hertfordshire. *Transactions of the Hertfordshire Natural History Society* 33: 62-83.

Jefferson R. 2005. The conservation management of upland hay meadows in Britain: a review. *Grass and Forage Science* 60: 322-31.

Kirby KJ, Smart SM, Black HIJ, Bunce RGH, Corney PM, Smithers RJ. 2005. *Long term ecological change in British woodland (1971-2001)*. English Nature Research reports no. 653. Peterborough: English Nature.

Le Duc MG, Hill MO, Sparks TH. 1992. A method for predicting the probability of species occurrence using data from systematic surveys. *Watsonia* 19: 97-105.

Lee JA, Tallis JH, Woodin SJ. 1988. Acid deposition and British upland vegetation. In *Ecological change in the uplands*, ed. MB Usher, DBA Thompson, pp. 151-62. Oxford: Blackwell Scientific Publications.

Leslie AC, Walters SM. 1983.
The occurrence of *Lemna minuscula* Herter in the British Isles. *Watsonia* 14: 243-8.

McCollin D, Moore, L. & Sparks, T.H. 2000. The flora of a cultural landscape: environmental determinants of change revealed using landscape sources. *Biological Conservation* 92: 249-63.

Margules CR, Nicholls AO, Usher MB. 1994. Apparent species turnover, probability of extinction and the selection of nature reserves: a case study of the Ingleborough limestone pavements. *Conservation Biology* 8: 398-409.

Matheson J, Summerfield C, eds. 2000. *Social trends 30*. London: The Stationery Office.

Moore NW. 1962. The heaths of Dorset and their conservation. *Journal of Ecology* 60: 369-91.

Mountford JO. 1994.
Floristic change in English grazing marshes: the impact of 150 years of drainage and land-use change. *Watsonia* 20: 3-24.

Palmer MA, Bratton JH. 1995. *A sample survey of the flora of Britain and Ireland.* U.K. Conservation no. 8. Peterborough: Joint Nature Conservation Committee.

Parr TW, Way JM. 1988. Management of roadside vegetation: the long-term effects of cutting. *Journal of Applied Ecology* 25: 1073-87.

Pearman DA, Preston CD. 2000.
A flora of Tiree, Gunna and Coll. Dorchester: privately published.

Perring FH, Walters SM, eds. 1962. *Atlas of the British Flora*. London: Thomas Nelson & Sons.

Preston CD. 2000. Engulfed by suburbia or destroyed by the plough: the ecology of extinction in Middlesex and Cambridgeshire. *Watsonia* 23: 59-81.

Preston CD, Hill MO. 1997.
The geographical relationships of British and Irish vascular plants. *Botanical Journal of the Linnean Society* 124: 1-120.

Preston CD, Pearman DA, Dines TD. 2002a. *New Atlas of the British and Irish flora.* Oxford: Oxford University Press.

Preston CD, Sheail J, Armitage PD, Davy-Bowker J. 2003a. The long-term impact of urbanisation on aquatic plants: Cambridge and the River Cam. *Science of the Total Environment* 314-316: 67-87.

Preston CD, Telfer MG, Arnold HR, Carey PD, Cooper JM, Dines TD, Pearman DA, Roy DB, Smart, SM. 2002b. *The changing flora of the UK.* London: Department for Environment, Food and Rural Affairs.

Preston CD, Telfer MG, Roy DB, Carey PD, Hill MO, Meek WR, Rothery P, Smart SM, Smith GM, Walker KJ, Pearman DA. 2003b. *The changing distribution of the flora of the United Kingdom: technical report.* Huntingdon: Centre for Ecology and Hydrology.

Prince SD, Carter RN, Dancy KJ. 1985. The geographical distribution of prickly lettuce (*Lactuca serriola*). II. Characteristics of populations near its distribution limit in Britain. *Journal of Ecology* 73: 39-48.

Rackham O. 2003. *Ancient woodland, edn 2.* Dalbeattie: Castlepoint Press.

Rich TCG, Woodruff ER. 1990. The BSBI Monitoring Scheme, *1987-1988*. 2 vols. Nature Conservancy Council Report no. 1265. London: Botanical Society of the British Isles.

Rich TCG, Woodruff ER. 1992. Recording bias in botanical surveys. *Watsonia* 19: 73-95.

Rich TCG, Woodruff ER. 1996.
Changes in the vascular plant floras of England and Scotland between 1930-1960 and 1987-1988: the BSBI monitoring scheme. *Biological Conservation* 75: 217-29.

Roberts FJ. 2003. After foot and mouth, Cross Fell in bloom. *The Carlisle Naturalist* 10: 33-42.

Robinson RA, Sutherland WJ. 2002.
Post-war changes in arable farming and biodiversity in Great Britain. *Journal of Applied Ecology* 39: 157-76.

Rodwell JS, ed. 1991a. *British plant communities, 1. Woodlands and scrub.* Cambridge: Cambridge University Press.

Rodwell JS, ed. 1991b. *British plant communities, 2. Mires and heaths.* Cambridge: Cambridge University Press.

Rodwell JS, ed. 1992. *British plant communities, 3. Grasslands and montane communities.* Cambridge: Cambridge University Press.

Rodwell JS, ed. 1995. *British plant communities, 4. Aquatic communities, swamps and tall-herb fens.* Cambridge: Cambridge University Press.

Rodwell JS, ed. 2000. *British plant communities, 5. Maritime communities and vegetation of open habitats.* Cambridge: Cambridge University Press.

Roy DB, Hill MO, Rothery P. 1999. Effects of urban land cover on the local species pool in Britain. *Ecography* 22: 507-15.

Sell P. 1989. The changing face of nature in Bassingbourn (1930s-1980s). *Nature in Cambridgeshire* 31: 12-18.

Smart SM, Bunce RGH, Marrs R, LeDuc M, Firbank LG, Maskell LC, Scott WA, Thompson K, Walker KJ. 2005. Large-scale changes in the abundance of common higher plant species across Britain between 1978, 1990 and 1998 as a consequence of human activity: tests of hypothesised changes in trait representation. *Biological Conservation* 124: 355-71.

Smart SM, Clarke RT, van de Poll HM, Robertson EJ, Shield ER, Bunce RGH, Maskell LC. 2003. National-scale vegetation change across Britain: an analysis of sample-based surveillance data from the Countryside Surveys of 1990 and 1998. *Journal of Environmental Management* 67: 239-54.

Sokal RR, Rohlf FJ. 1981. *Biometry.* New York: W.H. Freeman & Company.

Spence DHN. 1964. The macrophytic vegetation of freshwater lochs, swamps and associated fens. In *The vegetation of Scotland*, ed. JH Burnett, pp. 306-425. Edinburgh & London: Oliver & Boyd.

Stace CA. 1997. *New Flora of the British Isles, edn 2.* Cambridge: Cambridge University Press.

Stevens CJ, Dise NB, Mountford JO, Gowing DJ. 2004. Impact of nitrogen deposition on the species richness of grasslands. *Science* 303: 1876-9.

Stoate C. 1996. The changing face of lowland farming and wildlife, part 2: 1945-1995. *British wildlife* 7: 162-72.

Sutcliffe OL, Kay QON. 2000. Changes in the arable flora of central southern England since the 1960s. *Biological Conservation* 93: 1-8.

Tamis WLM, van't Zelfde M, van der Meijden R, Groen CLG, Uno de Haes HA. 2005. Ecological interpretation of changes in the Dutch flora in the 20th century. *Biological Conservation* 125: 211-24.

Townshend D, Stace H, Radley D. 2004. *State of nature: Lowlands - future landscapes for wildlife.* Peterborough: English Nature.

Valle Pacha MJ del. 2004. *Fragmentation of northern hay meadows and populations of Geranium sylvaticum in the Yorkshire Dales National Park.* PhD thesis, Lancaster University.

van der Waal R, Pearce I, Brooker R, Scott D, Welch D, Woodin S. 2003. Interplay between nitrogen deposition and grazing causes habitat degradation. *Ecology Letters* 6: 141-6.

Wade PM. 1999. The impact of human activity on the aquatic macroflora of Llangorse Lake, South Wales. *Aquatic Conservation - Marine and Freshwater Ecosystems* 9: 441-59.

Walker KJ, Preston CD. in press. Ecological predictors of extinction risk in the flora of lowland England, UK. *Biodiversity and Conservation.*

Welch D, Scott D. 1995. Studies in the grazing of heather moorland in north-east Scotland. VI. 20-year trends in botanical composition. *Journal of Applied Ecology* 32: 596-611.

Wells TCE. 1968. Land-use changes affecting *Pulsatilla vulgaris* in England. *Biological Conservation* 1: 37-43.

Wells TCE. 1989. The effects of changes in land use on the flora of Huntingdonshire and the Soke of Peterborough in the period 1949-89. In *40 years of change in the county 1949-89*, ed. TCE Wells, JH Cole, PEG Walker, pp. 10-20. Huntingdon: Huntingdonshire Flora and Fauna Society.

Appendix 1
Species index and tabulated results

This appendix lists alphabetically all the species that were recorded by the two surveys in 15 tetrads or more and presents statistics for each.

The list acts as an index for chapters 4, 5 and 6. The page numbers indicate the Broad Habitat, Neophyte or sundry groups of which the species is a representative. A species may be a representative of several Broad Habitat groups. Page numbers in bold relate to case studies of individual species that comprise a map, data and a caption discussing trends observed.

The column headings, which are further defined in the Glossary on page 329, are G: Gains, L: Losses, R: Re-finds, T: Total, TF: Tetrad Frequency, RC: Relative Change, CF: Change Factor (weighted), 90% confidence limits for CF, P_2: Probability, N_2: Real Range.

An example of the derivation of the statistics is presented on pages 11 and 12.

Species	G	L	R	Total	TF	RC	CF	90% conf. (CF)	P_2	N_2	Page(s)
Abies grandis	13	4	1	18	27	+56	+60	41	0.20	70	300
Abies procera	8	1	6	15	37	+41	+42	34	0.86	16	300
Acer campestre	61	10	226	297	86	+11	+20	9	0.96	300	299
Acer platanoides	127	14	72	213	73	+50	+66	12	0.84	238	300
Acer pseudoplatanus	40	13	462	515	93	0	+2	17	0.97	516	300
Achillea millefolium	20	19	565	604	99	-4	-59	23	1.00	585	297
Achillea ptarmica	60	57	165	282	63	-6	-11	17	0.79	285	168
Aconitum napellus sens. lat.	12	4	7	23	17	+34	+35	38	0.64	30	42, 176, 238
Acorus calamus	8	7	7	22	27	-2	-2	46	0.51	29	265
Adoxa moschatellina	39	36	76	151	48	-5	-7	19	0.72	160	31
Aegopodium podagraria	52	38	336	426	80	-2	-7	15	0.92	422	230
Aesculus hippocastanum	107	27	204	338	75	+19	+38	13	0.88	352	300
Aethusa cynapium	53	40	124	217	69	0	0	17	0.76	234	80, 238
Agrimonia eupatoria	29	37	163	229	65	-11	-17	11	0.92	209	95
Agrimonia procera	9	8	3	20	20	0	0	53	0.27	44	28, 90
Agrostis canina sens. lat.	72	80	186	338	86	-10	-22	19	0.77	333	131, 168
Agrostis capillaris	93	46	426	565	95	+4	+37	41	0.90	575	297
Agrostis curtisii	3	3	9	15	40	-9	-9	40	0.82	15	135, 145
Agrostis gigantea	62	65	47	174	63	-11	-17	27	0.47	232	67
Agrostis stolonifera	101	41	450	592	97	+6	+71	49	0.92	601	297
Aira caryophyllea	29	32	38	99	31	-12	-15	24	0.62	108	146, 217
Aira praecox	69	70	133	272	58	-8	-14	20	0.71	285	131, 217
Ajuga reptans	63	50	260	373	75	-2	-6	17	0.86	376	35
Alcea rosea	30	1	1	32	48	+85	+88	27	0.50	62	289
Alchemilla alpina	6	10	40	56	82	-16	-18	14	0.96	48	124, 201, **205**, 220
Alchemilla filicaulis	30	37	34	101	48	-18	-22	24	0.58	110	122, 201, 217
Alchemilla glabra	16	40	125	181	75	-22	-30	8	0.97	145	104, 201, **205**, 220
Alchemilla mollis	94	2	7	103	59	+83	+89	14	0.78	130	285
Alchemilla xanthochlora	19	30	45	94	57	-23	-27	19	0.78	82	104, 122
Alisma lanceolatum	8	6	2	16	25	+11	+12	60	0.25	40	158, 182
Alisma plantago-aquatica	51	46	98	195	56	-4	-6	19	0.71	209	161, 186
Alliaria petiolata	37	20	344	401	94	-1	-4	11	0.96	397	56
Allium paradoxum	10	3	2	15	26	+50	+51	46	0.40	30	265, **277**
Allium triquetrum	24	2	4	30	45	+70	+72	27	0.67	42	265, **277**

Species	G	L	R	Total	TF	RC	CF	90% conf. (CF)	P_2	N_2	Page(s)
Allium ursinum	62	24	122	208	52	+13	+20	14	0.84	220	35, **37**
Allium vineale	42	14	45	101	46	+24	+29	19	0.76	114	90, **94**, 116
Alnus cordata	31	1	0	32	49	+88					300
Alnus glutinosa	80	37	308	425	79	+5	+16	17	0.89	435	299
Alnus incana	51	3	6	60	43	+76	+81	19	0.67	86	300
Alopecurus geniculatus	79	76	233	388	74	-5	-15	21	0.80	391	101
Alopecurus myosuroides	44	22	91	157	81	+9	+11	16	0.81	168	71
Alopecurus pratensis	62	41	347	450	91	0	-2	19	0.90	455	101
Amaranthus retroflexus	18	2	0	20	30	+80					289, **290**
Amelanchier lamarckii	12	0	3	15	57	+71	+72	15	1.00	15	300
Ammophila arenaria	4	2	22	28	27	-1	-1	21	0.92	28	249
Amsinckia micrantha	13	2	6	21	33	+49	+51	33	0.75	25	265, 273
Anacamptis pyramidalis	23	3	17	43	28	+42	+44	21	0.85	47	111, 115
Anagallis arvensis	74	36	190	300	82	+8	+15	15	0.84	314	67
Anagallis tenella	15	16	33	64	33	-10	-12	24	0.75	64	156
Anchusa arvensis	26	21	51	98	43	-2	-2	21	0.72	107	67
Anemone nemorosa	50	58	193	301	64	-10	-19	15	0.85	284	35, 217
Angelica sylvestris	49	55	397	501	85	-7	-29	18	0.94	474	164, 217
Anisantha diandra	23	0	4	27	50	+77	+78	12	1.00	27	265, **273**
Anisantha sterilis	50	16	281	347	91	+4	+9	11	0.95	350	67, 232
Antennaria dioica	18	12	39	69	52	+2	+3	23	0.76	75	124, 148
Anthemis arvensis	5	11	1	17	36	-59	-63	52	0.20	30	71, **73**
Anthemis cotula	20	27	11	58	48	-27	-31	33	0.40	78	71
Anthoxanthum odoratum	32	39	503	574	94	-6	-48	20	0.99	542	297
Anthriscus caucalis	23	9	10	42	45	+34	+37	31	0.53	63	71, 135
Anthriscus sylvestris	33	16	443	492	94	-2	-7	13	0.98	485	56
Anthyllis vulneraria	17	24	51	92	30	-17	-20	18	0.82	83	120
Antirrhinum majus	40	6	6	52	27	+66	+71	23	0.50	92	285
Aphanes arvensis agg.	99	58	129	286	65	+11	+22	21	0.69	331	76, **131**, 217
Apium inundatum	3	7	7	17	18	-37	-38	37	0.80	13	156, **157**, 188
Apium nodiflorum	63	28	161	252	74	+9	+14	14	0.85	263	161, 186
Aquilegia vulgaris	53	14	23	90	34	+43	+50	21	0.62	122	296
Arabidopsis thaliana	101	42	127	270	63	+19	+33	17	0.75	303	214, 232, **233**
Arabis hirsuta	7	18	10	35	27	-48	-50	29	0.68	25	111, 212
Arctium lappa	37	25	50	112	64	+6	+7	22	0.67	131	52
Arctium minus	70	48	308	426	82	0	0	19	0.87	437	56
Arctium nemorosum	29	71	18	118		-55	-72	22	0.45	104	
Arctostaphylos uva-ursi	12	9	22	43	63	0	0	30	0.71	48	148, 201
Arenaria serpyllifolia sens. lat.	53	59	101	213	55	-11	-18	19	0.71	217	214
Armeria maritima	8	8	60	76	33	-8	-9	12	0.96	71	247
Armoracia rusticana	31	30	120	181	60	-7	-10	14	0.86	176	54
Arrhenatherum elatius	40	17	478	535	93	0	-2	20	0.97	534	297
Artemisia absinthium	15	11	16	42	34	+4	+5	34	0.59	52	214, 234
Artemisia vulgaris	59	20	247	326	78	+6	+13	12	0.93	331	232
Arum italicum	13	1	2	16	23	+71	+73	37	0.67	23	296
Arum maculatum	33	16	266	315	82	-1	-2	10	0.95	314	31
Asparagus officinalis	19	5	12	36	28	+37	+39	29	0.71	44	52
Asperula cynanchica	1	3	14	18	32	-20	-21	12	1.00	15	111
Asplenium adiantum-nigrum sens. lat.	55	29	73	157	41	+13	+17	19	0.72	179	217
Asplenium marinum	10	3	10	23	24	+26	+27	34	0.77	26	247, **248**
Asplenium ruta-muraria	51	32	128	211	49	+3	+5	17	0.80	224	214, 230
Asplenium trichomanes	51	39	143	233	54	-1	-2	16	0.79	244	214, 230
Asplenium viride	4	7	14	25	37	-23	-24	27	0.86	21	201, **206**, 220
Aster agg.	25	26	24	75	33	-10	-12	29	0.54	92	279
Aster tripolium	10	5	21	36	29	+8	+8	27	0.81	38	249
Athyrium filix-femina	52	38	317	407	78	-2	-6	15	0.91	404	38, 217
Atriplex glabriuscula	8	8	11	27	27	-9	-9	40	0.63	30	249
Atriplex littoralis	28	2	6	36	31	+68	+71	24	0.75	45	249, **251**
Atriplex patula	92	51	220	363	82	+7	+16	19	0.81	384	76
Atriplex portulacoides	2	1	12	15	24	-1	-1	26	0.94	15	249
Atriplex prostrata	130	38	115	283	80	+31	+53	16	0.75	326	67, 245
Aubrieta deltoidea	16	2	1	19	22	+74	+77	34	0.33	51	285
Avena fatua	64	34	122	220	74	+9	+14	17	0.78	238	67
Avena sativa	58	3	5	66	46	+79	+84	19	0.63	101	298
Avena sterilis	6	7	2	15	43	-20	-21	62	0.28	29	265
Ballota nigra	47	19	118	184	67	+10	+15	14	0.86	192	52
Barbarea intermedia	19	15	9	43	41	+6	+7	39	0.38	75	265
Barbarea verna	9	7	3	19	27	+8	+9	56	0.30	40	265

Species	G	L	R	Total	TF	RC	CF	90% conf. (CF)	P_2	N_2	Page(s)
Barbarea vulgaris	67	49	128	244	68	+2	+3	20	0.72	270	161
Bellis perennis	28	15	562	605	98	-2	-36	34	1.00	593	297
Berberis vulgaris	9	7	1	17	16	+11	+13	62	0.13	80	42
Berula erecta	19	11	15	45	25	+15	+16	32	0.58	59	158, 182
Beta vulgaris subsp. *maritima*	8	4	17	29	28	+7	+8	30	0.81	31	249
Beta vulgaris subsp. *vulgaris*	10	3	3	16	31	+45	+47	45	0.50	26	298
Betula pendula	77	40	270	387	82	+5	+12	17	0.87	398	299
Betula pubescens	76	40	252	368	74	+5	+11	17	0.86	380	299
Bidens cernua	15	12	10	37	32	+3	+4	40	0.45	55	158
Bidens tripartita	10	11	11	32	21	-13	-14	38	0.58	37	158
Blackstonia perfoliata	13	9	18	40	30	+4	+5	33	0.67	47	111
Blechnum spicant	45	32	258	335	78	-2	-5	13	0.91	333	38, 45, 146, 217
Bolboschoenus maritimus	8	11	22	41	29	-18	-19	25	0.81	37	182, 249, **252**
Borago officinalis	23	6	4	33	24	+54	+58	31	0.40	68	289
Botrychium lunaria	6	8	5	19	16	-24	-25	49	0.51	22	124, 220
Brachypodium pinnatum	14	10	22	46	42	+3	+3	30	0.69	52	111
Brachypodium sylvaticum	56	25	260	341	72	+3	+7	13	0.91	346	35
Brassica napus	117	18	61	196	59	+48	+64	13	0.77	231	298
Brassica nigra	24	21	19	64	38	-1	-2	30	0.48	89	80
Brassica oleracea	11	4	0	15	29	+55					298
Brassica rapa	44	36	21	101	46	+4	+6	32	0.37	176	298
Briza media	30	46	105	181	53	-18	-25	14	0.85	159	120, **121**
Bromopsis erecta	9	26	32	67	47	-38	-41	16	0.88	46	111, **113**
Bromopsis ramosa	48	46	152	246	67	-6	-10	16	0.82	244	31
Bromus commutatus	36	11	14	61	54	+42	+47	25	0.56	89	52
Bromus hordeaceus	98	38	297	433	91	+9	+28	17	0.89	446	76, **77**, 101
Bromus racemosus	12	3	4	19	28	+48	+49	40	0.57	28	90
Bryonia dioica	23	8	129	160	79	+2	+3	11	0.94	161	52
Buddleja davidii	119	7	58	184	60	+56	+70	10	0.89	198	279
Butomus umbellatus	11	3	5	19	16	+41	+43	40	0.63	26	182
Buxus sempervirens	34	16	20	70	35	+25	+29	26	0.56	97	299
Cakile maritima	10	5	9	24	25	+18	+19	40	0.64	30	249
Calamagrostis epigejos	13	13	16	42	28	-8	-9	34	0.60	48	158
Calendula officinalis	23	8	2	33	25	+51	+59	33	0.20	125	289
Callitriche hamulata sens. lat.	28	32	19	79	32	-16	-20	30	0.44	106	168, 188
Callitriche obtusangula	7	12	4	23	23	-40	-42	45	0.42	27	182
Callitriche stagnalis sens. lat.	83	91	160	334	64	-10	-23	22	0.71	343	164, 186
Calluna vulgaris	23	26	301	350	70	-7	-15	7	0.99	327	146, **147**, 196
Caltha palustris	55	84	236	375	67	-15	-36	15	0.87	334	164, **166**
Calystegia pulchra	16	13	3	32	32	+7	+9	49	0.19	101	265
Calystegia sepium	101	32	234	367	82	+14	+32	14	0.88	381	164
Calystegia silvatica	74	29	130	233	68	+15	+23	15	0.82	250	265
Campanula glomerata	5	7	7	19	30	-23	-24	44	0.65	19	111
Campanula latifolia	6	18	15	39	25	-45	-47	23	0.82	26	31, **33**
Campanula persicifolia	16	1	2	19	30	+75	+76	33	0.67	27	285
Campanula portenschlagiana	14	1	0	15	20	+84					279
Campanula poscharskyana	31	0	3	34	34	+83	+84	12	1.00	34	279, **283**
Campanula rotundifolia	39	51	213	303	67	-11	-21	12	0.91	277	120, **121**
Campanula trachelium	12	10	10	32	30	+1	+1	42	0.50	44	28
Capsella bursa-pastoris	39	33	426	498	91	-4	-17	15	0.97	481	78, 230
Cardamine amara	27	22	38	87	46	-1	-1	24	0.64	102	31, 161
Cardamine flexuosa	95	40	355	490	90	+7	+29	22	0.90	501	35
Cardamine hirsuta	116	65	279	460	89	+7	+27	26	0.81	487	217
Cardamine pratensis	70	62	394	526	90	-3	-21	30	0.90	518	101, 164
Carduus crispus	34	28	84	146	54	-3	-4	17	0.77	153	54
Carduus nutans	26	24	46	96	41	-5	-6	22	0.70	104	90, 116
Carduus tenuiflorus	5	5	5	15	18	-9	-9	56	0.55	18	90
Carex acuta	10	6	2	18	22	+25	+26	52	0.25	48	158
Carex acutiformis	24	20	39	83	30	-2	-2	23	0.67	93	161
Carex arenaria	9	4	22	35	26	+8	+8	26	0.85	37	249
Carex bigelowii	6	4	18	28	43	0	0	28	0.82	29	201
Carex binervis	53	21	173	247	68	+7	+12	13	0.89	253	131, 146, 217
Carex caryophyllea	47	42	63	152	48	-3	-5	22	0.62	177	122
Carex curta	25	34	44	103	54	-20	-24	21	0.70	98	171, **173**
Carex dioica	37	16	58	111	67	+14	+17	18	0.78	121	171
Carex distans	10	3	8	21	19	+30	+31	37	0.73	25	249
Carex disticha	17	21	24	62	32	-17	-19	27	0.64	64	161, **163**
Carex divulsa	48	10	30	88	65	+41	+46	18	0.75	104	90, 116
Carex echinata	41	30	207	278	72	-2	-4	12	0.90	277	171, 196

Species	G	L	R	Total	TF	RC	CF	90% conf. (CF)	P_2	N_2	Page(s)
Carex extensa	8	2	5	15	23	+38	+38	42	0.71	18	249
Carex flacca	103	80	234	417	75	+1	+2	29	0.75	452	120, 164
Carex hirta	93	34	152	279	71	+17	+30	15	0.82	300	95, **98**
Carex hostiana	35	23	83	141	54	+2	+3	18	0.78	151	171
Carex laevigata	20	13	15	48	31	+12	+13	33	0.54	65	31, 217
Carex limosa	7	4	12	23	40	+7	+8	37	0.75	25	174, 190, 198
Carex muricata	30	10	10	50	35	+42	+46	28	0.50	80	116, 135
Carex nigra	52	47	259	358	69	-5	-11	15	0.89	350	168
Carex otrubae	35	23	91	149	47	+2	+2	17	0.80	158	158
Carex ovalis	80	51	184	315	68	+4	+9	19	0.78	337	146
Carex pallescens	31	31	50	112	46	-8	-10	22	0.67	121	38
Carex panicea	45	40	245	330	67	-5	-10	13	0.90	321	168
Carex paniculata	20	18	36	74	30	-5	-5	24	0.70	80	31, 161
Carex pauciflora	15	9	21	45	86	+8	+9	29	0.70	51	198
Carex pendula	82	8	72	162	56	+41	+51	11	0.90	171	31, 161
Carex pilulifera	93	38	122	253	66	+18	+31	17	0.76	282	131, **133**
Carex pseudocyperus	16	4	8	28	27	+41	+43	33	0.67	36	158
Carex pulicaris	40	31	132	203	63	-2	-3	15	0.83	208	171, 217
Carex remota	65	20	134	219	59	+15	+23	13	0.87	229	35, 164, **166**
Carex riparia	26	18	40	84	38	+4	+5	24	0.69	96	158
Carex rostrata	43	27	126	196	58	+2	+3	16	0.82	205	171, 188
Carex spicata	41	14	28	83	45	+31	+36	22	0.67	104	90, 116
Carex strigosa	9	3	6	18	25	+31	+32	42	0.67	23	28, 158
Carex sylvatica	70	25	115	210	57	+17	+25	15	0.82	225	31, **33**
Carex vesicaria	7	4	4	15	14	+19	+19	54	0.50	22	156, 182
Carex viridula subsp. brachyrrhyncha	22	29	27	78	44	-21	-24	25	0.61	81	171
Carex viridula subsp. *oedocarpa*	48	47	199	294	69	-6	-12	14	0.87	286	168
Carlina vulgaris	8	11	19	38	22	-18	-20	27	0.78	35	111
Carpinus betulus	70	20	60	150	54	+31	+40	16	0.75	173	299
Carum verticillatum	4	3	11	18	33	-2	-2	36	0.80	19	171
Castanea sativa	56	18	79	153	47	+20	+27	15	0.81	166	299
Catabrosa aquatica	13	6	6	25	25	+28	+30	41	0.50	38	158, **160**
Catapodium marinum	10	4	7	21	24	+27	+28	41	0.64	27	249
Catapodium rigidum	32	14	24	70	32	+24	+27	25	0.63	89	116, 234
Centaurea cyanus	11	2	2	15	17	+61	+62	42	0.50	26	71, 234
Centaurea montana	37	8	4	49	32	+62	+70	25	0.33	123	285
Centaurea nigra	34	16	471	521	91	-1	-7	15	0.98	515	101, 120
Centaurea scabiosa	11	27	62	100	45	-26	-30	12	0.94	78	90, 116, **118**
Centaurium erythraea	63	41	84	188	52	+7	+11	20	0.67	219	116, 245
Centaurium pulchellum	10	8	5	23	34	+5	+5	51	0.38	39	245
Centranthus ruber	83	9	40	132	49	+52	+62	14	0.82	151	279
Cerastium arvense	8	14	16	38	38	-28	-30	28	0.75	32	135, **137**
Cerastium diffusum	19	16	27	62	32	-2	-2	27	0.64	72	247
Cerastium fontanum	15	7	599	621	100	-3	-73	66	1.00	614	297
Cerastium glomeratum	145	37	284	466	86	+20	+60	17	0.88	485	81, **83**
Cerastium semidecandrum	24	16	10	50	29	+15	+17	35	0.38	88	135, 245
Cerastium tomentosum	48	26	22	96	39	+23	+29	26	0.46	153	279
Ceratocapnos claviculata	27	8	30	65	33	+25	+28	21	0.79	72	31, 139, **140**
Ceratophyllum demersum	17	9	13	39	24	+18	+20	33	0.59	51	182
Ceterach officinarum	20	9	26	55	30	+16	+17	25	0.74	62	214
Chaenorhinum minus	27	37	20	84	39	-26	-31	28	0.47	99	67, **69**, 234
Chaerophyllum temulum	39	51	193	283	81	-12	-21	12	0.90	259	54
Chamaecyparis lawsoniana	76	7	15	98	56	+68	+76	16	0.68	134	300
Chamerion angustifolium	45	34	458	537	97	-3	-17	22	0.96	525	297
Chelidonium majus	58	32	69	159	51	+13	+17	20	0.68	186	54
Chenopodium album	69	50	294	413	90	-1	-2	19	0.86	421	76
Chenopodium bonus-henricus	13	20	12	45	31	-30	-33	32	0.54	46	54, **55**
Chenopodium ficifolium	47	11	14	72	53	+51	+57	22	0.56	109	71, **74**
Chenopodium polyspermum	63	15	33	111	61	+42	+50	18	0.69	140	71, **75**
Chenopodium rubrum	72	43	39	154	62	+18	+27	25	0.48	233	67, 158
Chrysanthemum segetum	18	30	21	69	35	-32	-36	26	0.60	65	64, **65**
Chrysosplenium alternifolium	10	12	12	34	28	-17	-18	36	0.60	37	156
Chrysosplenium oppositifolium	42	26	213	281	68	-1	-1	12	0.90	285	38, 168
Cicerbita macrophylla	13	6	10	29	25	+22	+23	36	0.63	37	265
Cichorium intybus	6	10	4	20	13	-37	-39	47	0.45	22	52
Circaea lutetiana	54	37	196	287	68	0	0	15	0.84	297	31
Circaea x intermedia	11	9	17	37	44	-1	-1	32	0.66	42	40
Cirsium acaule	9	22	28	59	47	-34	-37	19	0.85	43	111, **113**

Species	G	L	R	Total	TF	RC	CF	90% conf. (CF)	P_2	N_2	Page(s)
Cirsium arvense	11	10	545	566	95	-4	-34	18	1.00	556	297
Cirsium eriophorum	5	9	13	27	39	-27	-28	30	0.81	22	111
Cirsium heterophyllum	18	17	27	62	53	-6	-7	27	0.65	69	104, 220
Cirsium palustre	34	39	433	506	87	-6	-28	14	0.98	477	164
Cirsium vulgare	17	14	561	592	97	-4	-44	21	1.00	578	297
Claytonia perfoliata	14	10	12	36	32	+7	+7	38	0.55	48	265
Claytonia sibirica	31	17	37	85	40	+12	+14	23	0.69	99	265
Clematis vitalba	22	14	90	126	50	-1	-1	14	0.87	128	52
Clinopodium acinos	2	8	6	16	30	-51	-52	31	0.88	9	214, **216**
Clinopodium ascendens	9	10	3	22	22	-16	-18	53	0.28	44	214
Clinopodium vulgare	28	23	57	108	50	-2	-3	20	0.73	117	116
Cochlearia danica	73	5	15	93	35	+69	+76	16	0.75	117	245, **246**
Cochlearia officinalis sens. lat.	17	5	57	79	34	+8	+9	14	0.92	81	247
Coeloglossum viride	5	8	8	21	25	-27	-28	40	0.69	19	124
Conium maculatum	67	35	144	246	69	+8	+13	16	0.80	262	54
Conopodium majus	59	66	293	418	79	-8	-23	17	0.89	397	35, 101
Convallaria majalis	12	5	6	23	25	+30	+32	41	0.55	33	28, 111
Convolvulus arvensis	38	28	226	292	82	-3	-5	12	0.92	288	67
Conyza canadensis	78	6	38	122	57	+54	+63	13	0.86	134	265, **271**
Conyza sumatrensis	20	0	1	21	58	+87	+88	18	1.00	21	265, **271**
Cornus sanguinea	48	14	152	214	80	+10	+15	11	0.92	218	299
Cornus sericea	18	2	2	22	30	+71	+74	33	0.50	40	300
Coronopus didymus	80	18	63	161	63	+36	+46	15	0.78	184	265, **274**
Coronopus squamatus	66	16	100	182	73	+23	+31	13	0.86	193	71
Corylus avellana	64	18	372	454	86	+5	+17	14	0.95	457	299
Cotoneaster horizontalis	57	13	11	81	46	+57	+66	21	0.46	148	279
Cotoneaster integrifolius	6	8	4	18	19	-25	-26	52	0.45	22	279
Cotoneaster rehderi	15	0	1	16	57	+85	+86	19	1.00	16	279
Cotoneaster simonsii	50	17	11	78	42	+46	+56	24	0.39	155	265
Crassula helmsii	33	2	3	38	30	+78	+81	24	0.60	60	279, **282**
Crataegus laevigata	23	15	34	72	53	+6	+7	25	0.69	82	299
Crataegus monogyna	21	9	492	522	98	-3	-13	11	1.00	513	299
Crepis biennis	8	5	3	16	26	+19	+19	56	0.38	29	90
Crepis capillaris	76	48	294	418	81	+2	+5	20	0.86	430	120
Crepis paludosa	28	25	90	143	67	-5	-7	16	0.83	143	171, 220
Crepis vesicaria	54	35	94	183	72	+5	+8	19	0.73	203	265
Crocosmia x crocosmiiflora	86	7	42	135	48	+54	+64	12	0.86	149	279
Crocus tommasinianus	14	1	0	15	42	+84					285
Crocus vernus	20	1	0	21	35	+86					285
Cruciata laevipes	22	18	122	162	59	-5	-6	12	0.92	157	99
Cryptogramma crispa	8	5	10	23	36	+8	+8	41	0.67	27	148, 201, 220
Cyclamen hederifolium	13	2	0	15	27	+76					285
Cymbalaria muralis	66	40	126	232	56	+6	+10	18	0.76	253	265
Cynoglossum officinale	3	5	14	22	24	-19	-20	25	0.91	19	111, 245
Cynosurus cristatus	64	57	413	534	90	-4	-23	29	0.91	523	81, 101
Cystopteris fragilis	16	23	37	76	46	-20	-23	21	0.77	69	220, **222**
Cytisus scoparius	45	57	199	301	64	-11	-21	14	0.88	278	56
Dactylis glomerata	21	11	518	550	93	-3	-19	13	1.00	539	297
Dactylorhiza fuchsii	65	51	96	212	50	+1	+2	22	0.65	247	164
Dactylorhiza incarnata	14	19	7	40	27	-28	-31	38	0.37	56	156, **157**
Dactylorhiza maculata	150	1	9	160	45	+86	+94	10	0.90	177	301
Dactylorhiza praetermissa	22	6	23	51	28	+27	+29	23	0.79	57	158
Dactylorhiza purpurella	26	21	35	82	39	0	0	24	0.63	98	171
Danthonia decumbens	90	39	117	246	58	+17	+29	17	0.75	276	122, 131
Daphne laureola	15	8	18	41	24	+13	+14	30	0.69	48	28
Daucus carota	30	40	112	182	52	-14	-20	14	0.86	166	95, 116
Deschampsia cespitosa	44	41	460	545	95	-4	-28	22	0.96	525	297
Deschampsia flexuosa	41	32	282	355	78	-3	-8	12	0.93	347	131, 146
Descurainia sophia	4	2	15	21	31	+2	+2	30	0.88	22	64, **66**
Digitalis purpurea	66	32	396	494	89	+2	+10	21	0.93	499	131, 139
Diphasiastrum alpinum	14	6	21	41	52	+14	+15	27	0.78	45	201
Diplotaxis muralis	19	9	18	46	34	+19	+20	29	0.67	56	265
Diplotaxis tenuifolia	14	5	4	23	30	+41	+43	40	0.44	41	214, 234
Dipsacus fullonum sens. lat.	87	26	123	236		+22	+34	14	0.83	254	106, 238
Doronicum pardalianches	6	9	13	28	21	-22	-23	32	0.76	25	279
Drosera anglica	8	6	34	48	61	-4	-4	19	0.88	48	174, 198
Drosera intermedia	4	15	8	27	48	-56	-58	28	0.80	15	174, **175**, 198
Drosera rotundifolia	23	21	147	191	63	-6	-9	11	0.93	182	196
Dryopteris affinis	114	29	190	333	71	+22	+42	13	0.87	350	38, 217

Species	G	L	R	Total	TF	RC	CF	90% conf. (CF)	P_2	N_2	Page(s)
Dryopteris carthusiana	47	28	47	122	47	+12	+16	22	0.63	150	31
Dryopteris dilatata	59	36	429	524	91	0	-2	26	0.93	527	35, 45
Dryopteris expansa	5	14	4	23	62	-59	-61	39	0.54	17	40, 201, 220
Dryopteris filix-mas	59	46	415	520	94	-2	-13	25	0.92	514	35, 45
Dryopteris oreades	4	7	5	16	39	-34	-35	47	0.63	14	201, 220
Echinochloa crus-galli	17	1	0	18	36	+86					289, 290
Echium vulgare	16	9	15	40	24	+14	+15	33	0.63	50	116
Eleocharis multicaulis	26	8	26	60	41	+26	+29	22	0.76	68	174, 198, **199**
Eleocharis palustris	77	46	113	236	46	+9	+15	19	0.71	267	164, 186
Eleocharis quinqueflora	26	21	46	93	50	-1	-1	22	0.70	104	171
Eleocharis uniglumis	3	11	7	21	26	-53	-54	30	0.83	12	156
Eleogiton fluitans	15	2	12	29	24	+40	+41	25	0.86	32	190, **191**
Elodea canadensis	26	42	27	95	31	-31	-38	24	0.57	93	265, **269**
Elodea nuttallii	32	8	15	55	32	+43	+47	24	0.65	72	265, **269**
Elymus caninus	50	37	50	137	49	+5	+7	24	0.57	174	31
Elytrigia atherica	6	6	16	28	38	-9	-9	31	0.80	28	249
Elytrigia juncea	4	6	9	19	20	-22	-23	38	0.77	17	249
Elytrigia repens	62	34	357	453	87	+1	+4	19	0.91	459	76, 245
Empetrum nigrum	24	18	121	163	63	-3	-5	12	0.90	161	148, 196, 201
Epilobium anagallidifolium	6	3	7	16	49	+14	+15	46	0.70	19	174, 201
Epilobium brunnescens	66	11	69	146	65	+33	+41	13	0.86	157	265, **275**
Epilobium ciliatum	128	54	183	365	86	+17	+41	19	0.77	403	265, **275**
Epilobium hirsutum	49	14	341	404	92	+3	+9	11	0.96	406	161
Epilobium montanum	74	60	352	486	88	-2	-10	25	0.87	487	214, 230
Epilobium obscurum	130	55	136	321	78	+21	+44	19	0.71	374	168
Epilobium palustre	56	46	227	329	72	-3	-6	15	0.86	330	168
Epilobium parviflorum	142	45	102	289	75	+33	+59	17	0.69	352	161, **163**
Epilobium roseum	20	16	6	42	38	+7	+8	42	0.27	95	158
Epilobium tetragonum	108	32	50	190	85	+41	+58	18	0.61	259	234
Epipactis helleborine	21	17	18	56	30	+2	+2	33	0.51	76	31, 116
Equisetum arvense	60	38	419	517	91	-1	-3	25	0.92	520	78
Equisetum fluviatile	61	53	127	241	50	-3	-5	19	0.73	258	168, 186
Equisetum palustre	52	79	128	259	54	-20	-34	16	0.77	232	164
Equisetum sylvaticum	45	32	74	151	59	+3	+4	20	0.70	171	40, 220
Equisetum telmateia	14	10	55	79	35	-2	-3	16	0.87	80	161
Eranthis hyemalis	21	7	5	33	34	+45	+49	34	0.42	62	285
Erica cinerea	21	18	191	230	60	-6	-9	8	0.97	219	146
Erica tetralix	27	28	203	258	68	-7	-12	10	0.95	242	146, 196
Erigeron acer	20	12	21	53	31	+11	+12	29	0.64	64	214
Eriophorum angustifolium	24	23	206	253	65	-7	-11	9	0.96	239	196, **197**
Eriophorum latifolium	17	3	9	29	41	+45	+47	29	0.75	35	174
Eriophorum vaginatum	37	13	147	197	70	+6	+8	11	0.92	200	196, **197**
Erodium cicutarium agg.	49	18	50	117	40	+23	+29	19	0.74	135	245
Erophila verna sens. lat.	106	53	84	243	60	+21	+36	21	0.61	310	214, 232
Erysimum cheiranthoides	16	23	15	54	48	-27	-30	30	0.54	58	71
Erysimum cheiri	23	8	5	36	24	+45	+49	33	0.38	73	296
Eschscholzia californica	18	1	0	19	29	+86					289
Euonymus europaeus	48	33	95	176	70	+3	+4	19	0.74	193	299
Eupatorium cannabinum	33	29	101	163	49	-5	-6	16	0.82	164	161
Euphorbia amygdaloides	7	16	38	61	43	-25	-27	14	0.94	48	28
Euphorbia exigua	23	17	28	68	50	+3	+4	28	0.62	82	71
Euphorbia helioscopia	90	39	162	291	74	+13	+25	16	0.81	313	67, 232
Euphorbia lathyris	56	7	9	72	42	+67	+74	20	0.56	116	214, 234, **237**
Euphorbia peplus	100	32	153	285	76	+20	+35	15	0.83	306	67, 232
Euphrasia officinalis agg.	49	50	236	335	68	-7	-14	14	0.89	322	104, 122, 131, 146
Fagopyrum esculentum	10	5	0	15	35	+41					298
Fagus sylvatica	70	21	330	421	84	+7	+19	13	0.94	426	299
Fallopia baldschuanica	43	6	1	50	38	+76	+94	22	0.14	308	300
Fallopia convolvulus	68	57	169	294	78	-2	-4	18	0.77	309	67
Fallopia japonica	58	41	123	222	53	+2	+3	18	0.75	241	265
Festuca arundinacea	97	43	123	263	63	+17	+30	18	0.74	297	95, **97**, 120
Festuca filiformis	15	10	11	36	34	+11	+12	38	0.52	50	135
Festuca gigantea	52	60	130	242	65	-11	-19	17	0.77	235	31
Festuca ovina agg.	72	71	301	444	79	-6	-15	21	0.86	435	122, 131
Festuca pratensis	68	84	57	209	60	-19	-34	26	0.50	251	95, **97**
Festuca rubra agg.	62	31	512	605	99	+1	+22	81	0.94	609	297
Festuca vivipara	11	5	100	116	73	-2	-3	8	0.98	114	201, 220
Filago minima	10	8	7	25	27	+3	+3	47	0.47	36	214
Filago vulgaris	22	5	8	35	32	+48	+51	29	0.62	49	52, **53**

Species	G	L	R	Total	TF	RC	CF	90% conf. (CF)	P_2	N_2	Page(s)
Filipendula ulmaria	41	17	448	506	87	0	-1	17	0.96	507	164
Filipendula vulgaris	5	5	13	23	22	-9	-9	35	0.79	23	111
Foeniculum vulgare	41	14	11	66	37	+44	+50	26	0.44	118	214, 234
Forsythia x intermedia	22	0	0	22	62	+91					300
Fragaria ananassa	15	9	1	25	26	+29	+37	50	0.10	160	285
Fragaria vesca	59	61	200	320	69	-8	-15	17	0.83	313	35, 120
Frangula alnus	14	6	20	40	35	+15	+16	27	0.77	44	299
Fraxinus excelsior	23	10	484	517	95	-2	-12	9	1.00	507	299
Fuchsia magellanica	17	3	4	24	35	+58	+60	34	0.57	37	300
Fumaria bastardii	7	5	5	17	30	+8	+8	54	0.50	24	64
Fumaria densiflora	6	4	5	15	47	+10	+10	55	0.56	20	71
Fumaria muralis	73	19	49	141	64	+36	+46	17	0.72	169	64, **66**
Fumaria officinalis	80	55	100	235	65	+7	+11	22	0.65	279	67
Galanthus nivalis	123	36	71	230	65	+38	+58	17	0.66	292	279
Galega officinalis	16	4	6	26	49	+46	+48	34	0.60	37	279
Galeopsis speciosa	5	15	16	36	40	-41	-43	22	0.87	24	64, **65**
Galeopsis tetrahit agg.	69	78	235	382	79	-9	-23	19	0.83	368	56, 78
Galinsoga parviflora	12	3	1	16	26	+61	+64	41	0.25	52	265, **272**
Galinsoga quadriradiata	18	6	2	26	33	+51	+56	36	0.25	80	265, **272**
Galium aparine	15	6	495	516	90	-3	-16	16	1.00	510	78, 230, **231**
Galium boreale	13	16	24	53	62	-16	-17	26	0.71	52	124, **125**, 220
Galium mollugo	48	20	132	200	65	+8	+12	14	0.87	207	116
Galium odoratum	33	36	60	129	41	-11	-14	20	0.70	132	38, **39**
Galium palustre	70	41	324	435	78	+2	+5	19	0.89	444	164
Galium saxatile	27	47	323	397	77	-11	-28	8	0.98	356	131, **133**, 139
Galium uliginosum	28	24	38	90	41	-2	-3	24	0.63	105	161
Galium verum	71	37	241	349	69	+5	+10	16	0.87	360	120
Genista anglica	5	3	18	26	30	0	0	29	0.86	27	148
Genista tinctoria	6	9	9	24	19	-25	-26	38	0.67	22	90, **92**
Gentianella amarella	7	12	11	30	24	-30	-32	33	0.69	26	111, **114**
Gentianella campestris	10	10	12	32	36	-9	-9	38	0.60	37	124
Geranium columbinum	14	11	12	37	29	+3	+3	39	0.52	50	111
Geranium dissectum	68	15	291	374	83	+9	+20	11	0.95	378	76, **77**
Geranium endressii	14	2	2	18	22	+66	+68	37	0.50	32	285
Geranium lucidum	69	19	55	143	52	+33	+41	17	0.74	167	214
Geranium molle	67	57	222	346	73	-3	-7	18	0.82	352	76
Geranium pratense	58	25	81	164	50	+16	+22	17	0.76	182	101
Geranium pusillum	55	9	43	107	53	+39	+45	15	0.83	119	52
Geranium pyrenaicum	62	11	45	118	49	+40	+47	15	0.80	133	265, **274**
Geranium robertianum	55	18	453	526	96	+2	+13	20	0.96	528	35, 217
Geranium rotundifolium	32	5	7	44	44	+61	+65	25	0.58	67	214, 234
Geranium sanguineum	13	4	3	20	23	+48	+50	41	0.43	37	111, 214
Geranium sylvaticum	14	18	42	74	63	-15	-17	19	0.82	68	104, **105**, 220
Geranium x oxonianum	34	3	2	39	64	+78	+83	24	0.40	90	285
Geum rivale	31	28	110	169	55	-6	-8	15	0.84	167	38, 217
Geum urbanum	49	11	371	431	87	+3	+11	11	0.97	433	35
Geum x intermedium	11	14	6	31	32	-24	-26	42	0.39	43	
Glaux maritima	6	4	37	47	27	-4	-4	16	0.94	46	249
Glechoma hederacea	40	23	348	411	87	-1	-4	12	0.95	408	35
Glyceria declinata	82	59	60	201	62	+9	+15	26	0.50	282	168
Glyceria fluitans	88	90	248	426	77	-7	-22	25	0.79	427	164, 186
Glyceria maxima	26	18	76	120	45	0	0	16	0.81	126	158, 182
Glyceria notata	47	42	29	118	50	-2	-2	28	0.42	183	161, 182
Glyceria x pedicellata	8	16	1	25	38	-56	-66	48	0.13	68	
Gnaphalium sylvaticum	6	7	6	19	27	-16	-17	49	0.55	22	148
Gnaphalium uliginosum	119	55	170	344	73	+16	+35	19	0.76	383	164
Gymnadenia conopsea	19	15	18	52	29	+2	+3	33	0.55	68	122, 168
Gymnocarpium dryopteris	19	21	39	79	55	-12	-13	22	0.74	79	40, **41**, 220
Hedera helix	24	28	450	502	92	-6	-26	7	1.00	474	35
Helianthemum nummularium	15	9	35	59	35	+4	+4	23	0.80	63	111
Helianthus annuus	35	2	2	39	63	+81	+84	24	0.50	74	298
Helictotrichon pratense	15	22	20	57	35	-25	-28	27	0.64	55	111
Helictotrichon pubescens	32	39	28	99	37	-19	-23	26	0.51	117	99, 111
Heracleum mantegazzianum	17	14	17	48	27	0	0	34	0.55	62	265
Heracleum sphondylium	13	11	512	536	92	-4	-25	13	1.00	525	297
Hesperis matronalis	38	37	28	103	35	-7	-9	28	0.46	143	265
Hieracium agg.	66	80	219	365	79	-11	-26	18	0.82	346	
Hippocrepis comosa	1	4	11	16	26	-29	-29	13	1.00	12	111
Hippophae rhamnoides	9	3	8	20	22	+27	+28	38	0.73	23	249

Species	G	L	R	Total	TF	RC	CF	90% conf. (CF)	P_2	N_2	Page(s)
Hippuris vulgaris	7	13	11	31	18	-34	-35	32	0.69	26	158, 182, **184**
Hirschfeldia incana	19	1	5	25	33	+66	+68	26	0.83	29	265, **270**
Holcus lanatus	27	10	579	616	100	-1	-37	48	1.00	608	297
Holcus mollis	84	55	330	469	89	+1	+6	25	0.86	483	35, 139
Honckenya peploides	5	3	16	24	20	+1	+1	31	0.84	25	249
Hordeum distichon sens. lat.	89	3	0	92	64	+89					298
Hordeum murinum	57	19	130	206	68	+13	+19	13	0.87	214	234, **236**
Hordeum secalinum	38	24	40	102	60	+10	+12	24	0.63	125	81
Humulus lupulus	53	31	97	181	60	+7	+10	18	0.76	198	54
Huperzia selago	12	14	66	92	64	-11	-12	13	0.92	85	201, 220
Hyacinthoides hispanica	65	27	18	110	65	+38	+50	24	0.40	208	285, **287**
Hyacinthoides non-scripta	52	47	324	423	83	-5	-13	16	0.92	411	**34**, 35, 139
Hyacinthoides x massartiana	165	5	8	178	80	+85	+97	12	0.62	281	279, **283**
Hydrocotyle vulgaris	16	33	110	159	42	-20	-25	9	0.96	132	168
Hymenophyllum wilsonii	12	14	15	41	52	-15	-17	33	0.61	44	40, 220
Hypericum androsaemum	62	16	66	144	54	+28	+36	15	0.80	159	31
Hypericum calycinum	19	5	6	30	30	+47	+50	33	0.55	46	300
Hypericum elodes	10	3	19	32	39	+16	+16	25	0.86	34	156, 188
Hypericum hirsutum	28	24	66	118	50	-4	-5	18	0.76	123	95, 116
Hypericum humifusum	51	39	46	136	48	+4	+6	25	0.54	179	56
Hypericum maculatum	26	19	45	90	48	+2	+2	23	0.70	101	31, 214
Hypericum perforatum	76	43	176	295	74	+6	+12	17	0.80	314	120
Hypericum pulchrum	63	47	224	334	70	-1	-2	16	0.84	344	146, 217
Hypericum tetrapterum	83	46	107	236	57	+12	+20	19	0.70	272	164
Hypericum x desetangsii	16	3	0	19	29	+73					
Hypochaeris radicata	74	41	445	560	93	+2	+14	40	0.92	567	297
Ilex aquifolium	64	23	356	443	90	+4	+14	15	0.94	447	299
Impatiens capensis	8	1	8	17	29	+35	+36	30	0.89	18	265, **276**
Impatiens glandulifera	57	24	74	155	49	+17	+23	17	0.76	174	265, **276**
Impatiens parviflora	8	6	6	20	29	+6	+6	51	0.50	28	265
Inula conyzae	8	13	17	38	25	-25	-27	28	0.76	33	111, 214
Iris foetidissima	57	9	30	96	51	+47	+54	17	0.77	113	28, **30**
Iris pseudacorus	100	36	221	357	66	+14	+30	15	0.86	373	164
Isoetes lacustris	5	5	5	15	17	-9	-9	56	0.55	18	190
Isolepis setacea	59	47	39	145	43	+4	+6	28	0.45	216	168
Jasione montana	12	17	36	65	42	-18	-20	20	0.83	58	131, 145
Juglans regia	44	8	7	59	39	+62	+69	23	0.47	109	300
Juncus acutiflorus	111	57	203	371	74	+11	+27	20	0.78	402	164
Juncus articulatus	92	52	347	491	83	+4	+17	26	0.87	505	164
Juncus bufonius sens. lat.	102	65	329	496	85	+3	+16	32	0.84	516	164
Juncus bulbosus	58	52	201	311	71	-4	-9	16	0.83	311	168, 188
Juncus conglomeratus	89	68	274	431	80	0	-1	24	0.80	452	164
Juncus effusus	32	20	538	590	97	-2	-29	29	0.99	577	297
Juncus gerardii	7	5	35	47	27	-4	-4	18	0.91	46	249
Juncus inflexus	52	23	220	295	79	+4	+7	13	0.91	300	95, 161
Juncus maritimus	2	0	13	15	23	+5	+5	13	1.00	15	249
Juncus squarrosus	29	17	220	266	74	-2	-3	10	0.95	263	131, 196
Juncus subnodulosus	6	5	6	17	17	0	0	50	0.55	22	158
Juncus tenuis	33	15	43	91	51	+16	+18	21	0.74	103	265
Juniperus communis	19	19	37	75	45	-8	-9	23	0.72	78	124, 148, 201, 220
Kickxia elatine	42	15	26	83	56	+32	+37	22	0.63	107	71
Kickxia spuria	23	13	24	60	61	+13	+14	27	0.65	73	71
Knautia arvensis	31	40	102	173	55	-14	-19	15	0.84	159	95, 116
Koeleria macrantha sens. lat.	26	17	27	70	34	+9	+10	27	0.61	86	111
Laburnum anagyroides	45	23	24	92	43	+24	+29	25	0.51	135	300
Lactuca serriola	104	2	63	169	80	+54	+65	8	0.97	172	234, **237**
Lactuca virosa	36	5	8	49	42	+62	+66	23	0.62	72	214, **216**
Lamiastrum galeobdolon subsp. *montanum*	18	27	76	121	27	-17	-20	14	0.89	106	28
Lamiastrum galeobdolon subsp. *argentatum*	117	3	14	134	58	+79	+88	12	0.82	159	279
Lamium album	34	27	263	324	86	-4	-8	10	0.95	314	232
Lamium amplexicaule	37	36	44	117	51	-7	-9	24	0.59	137	67
Lamium confertum	8	8	7	23	51	-9	-9	47	0.51	29	62
Lamium hybridum	48	18	42	108	55	+25	+31	20	0.70	129	67, **69**
Lamium maculatum	43	21	4	68	45	+38	+59	34	0.16	294	285
Lamium purpureum	62	42	311	415	87	-1	-2	17	0.89	421	76, 232
Lapsana communis	42	15	428	485	94	+1	+2	15	0.97	487	238
Larix decidua	82	41	113	236	61	+14	+22	18	0.73	266	300

Species	G	L	R	Total	TF	RC	CF	90% conf. (CF)	P_2	N_2	Page(s)
Larix kaempferi	35	16	25	76	46	+23	+27	25	0.61	98	300
Larix x marschlinsii	79	11	22	112	67	+59	+69	17	0.67	152	300
Lathraea squamaria	9	3	5	17	19	+34	+35	44	0.63	22	28
Lathyrus latifolius	23	8	9	40	29	+38	+41	31	0.53	60	285
Lathyrus linifolius	37	38	126	201	57	-8	-12	15	0.84	195	131, 217
Lathyrus nissolia	15	12	10	37	35	+3	+4	40	0.45	55	90, 116
Lathyrus pratensis	48	26	445	519	92	-1	-3	21	0.95	519	101
Legousia hybrida	4	7	9	20	30	-27	-28	36	0.77	17	71
Lemna gibba	9	7	3	19	20	+8	+9	56	0.30	40	182
Lemna minor	83	53	174	310	69	+5	+10	19	0.77	335	186
Lemna minuta	49	2	1	52	43	+86	+92	20	0.33	150	265, **270**
Lemna trisulca	19	21	18	58	30	-14	-15	31	0.53	69	182
Leontodon autumnalis	107	70	399	576	96	+2	+32	75	0.85	595	297
Leontodon hispidus	45	55	110	210	63	-14	-20	17	0.77	201	116, **118**
Leontodon saxatilis	47	39	35	121	44	+2	+2	28	0.47	173	116
Lepidium campestre	11	9	8	28	29	+2	+2	45	0.47	40	71
Lepidium draba	31	16	30	77	39	+16	+19	24	0.65	94	265
Lepidium heterophyllum	19	18	22	59	38	-6	-7	29	0.59	70	56
Leucanthemum vulgare	81	53	266	400	79	+2	+6	21	0.83	416	101, 120
Leucanthemum x superbum	29	7	9	45	28	+49	+53	27	0.56	68	279
Leycesteria formosa	20	0	2	22	26	+82	+83	14	1.00	22	300
Leymus arenarius	5	2	9	16	21	+13	+13	38	0.82	17	249
Ligusticum scoticum	4	3	11	18	30	-2	-2	36	0.80	19	247
Ligustrum ovalifolium	73	21	58	152	57	+32	+41	17	0.73	178	300
Ligustrum vulgare	68	29	182	279	74	+9	+16	14	0.86	290	299
Linaria purpurea	85	17	42	144	50	+46	+57	16	0.71	178	279
Linaria repens	7	9	3	19	19	-25	-27	53	0.33	30	116
Linaria vulgaris	31	38	137	206	55	-11	-17	13	0.88	190	95
Linum catharticum	56	55	172	283	56	-7	-12	17	0.81	281	122
Linum usitatissimum	30	3	2	35	22	+76	+80	26	0.40	80	298
Listera cordata	38	11	17	66	65	+41	+46	24	0.61	91	45, 148, 198
Listera ovata	24	31	25	80	27	-21	-25	26	0.56	87	31, 161
Lithospermum officinale	7	5	5	17	19	+8	+8	54	0.50	24	28, 111
Littorella uniflora	14	14	41	69	32	-8	-9	21	0.81	68	171, 190
Lobelia dortmanna	4	5	19	28	27	-13	-13	23	0.91	25	190
Lobelia erinus	16	1	1	18	25	+80	+81	35	0.50	34	289
Lobularia maritima	19	9	5	33	26	+33	+36	37	0.36	67	289, **291**
Lolium multiflorum	75	61	69	205	65	+2	+4	26	0.53	271	298
Lolium perenne	27	11	505	543	92	-2	-11	13	1.00	534	297
Lonicera nitida	78	4	14	96	66	+72	+79	15	0.78	118	300
Lonicera periclymenum	63	28	366	457	82	+3	+9	17	0.93	462	35
Lotus corniculatus	53	24	519	596	97	+1	+11	57	0.96	599	297
Lotus pedunculatus	58	57	267	382	78	-6	-15	16	0.88	371	164
Lunaria annua	115	25	41	181	58	+50	+68	16	0.62	251	279, **282**
Lupinus x regalis	19	1	0	20	31	+86					285
Luzula campestris	95	80	301	476	85	-2	-9	31	0.81	491	101
Luzula forsteri	7	6	13	26	48	-4	-4	36	0.71	28	28
Luzula multiflora	57	48	266	371	76	-3	-8	16	0.88	368	131
Luzula pilosa	49	49	122	220	57	-7	-12	17	0.77	222	38, 45
Luzula sylvatica	52	23	159	234	58	+4	+10	13	0.87	242	38, 217
Lychnis coronaria	16	5	1	22	30	+56	+62	37	0.17	102	285
Lychnis flos-cuculi	66	55	168	289	56	-2	-4	18	0.77	303	164
Lycium barbarum agg.	25	10	17	52	28	+27	+30	27	0.63	67	300
Lycopersicon esculentum	28	2	0	30	32	+84					298
Lycopodium clavatum	23	14	19	56	51	+13	+15	30	0.58	73	148
Lycopus europaeus	54	18	85	157	48	+18	+24	15	0.83	168	161
Lysimachia nemorum	49	45	199	293	67	-5	-10	14	0.86	288	38
Lysimachia nummularia	66	37	46	149	58	+18	+25	23	0.55	202	95, 158
Lysimachia punctata	48	9	27	84	38	+44	+50	18	0.75	100	285
Lysimachia vulgaris	21	12	20	53	26	+14	+15	29	0.63	66	161
Lythrum portula	28	15	27	70	38	+15	+17	26	0.64	86	156
Lythrum salicaria	50	26	74	150	46	+12	+15	18	0.74	168	161
Mahonia aquifolium	25	22	26	73	40	-2	-3	27	0.56	92	300
Malus domestica	167	14	75	256		+56	+78	11	0.84	287	299
Malus sylvestris	97	33	60	190		+33	+48	18	0.65	243	299
Malva moschata	69	19	60	148	51	+31	+40	16	0.76	170	95
Malva neglecta	49	14	33	96	50	+35	+41	20	0.70	117	52
Malva sylvestris	77	12	172	261	73	+19	+31	10	0.93	266	234
Matricaria discoidea	38	29	470	537	94	-3	-19	19	0.97	522	265

Species	G	L	R	Total	TF	RC	CF	90% conf. (CF)	P_2	N_2	Page(s)
Matricaria recutita	93	44	113	250	83	+17	+28	18	0.72	286	67, **70**
Meconopsis cambrica	88	18	38	144	53	+48	+60	16	0.68	186	296
Medicago arabica	34	7	52	93	57	+23	+27	15	0.88	98	234
Medicago lupulina	53	20	284	357	85	+4	+8	12	0.93	361	116, 232
Medicago sativa subsp. *sativa*	11	25	18	54	37	-41	-45	24	0.71	41	279, **281**
Melampyrum pratense	23	36	51	110	43	-23	-28	19	0.76	97	38, **39**, 45
Melica nutans	4	9	5	18	35	-44	-46	42	0.64	14	40, 124, 220
Melica uniflora	24	22	85	131	46	-6	-8	15	0.85	129	31
Melilotus albus	11	12	4	27	22	-15	-16	48	0.29	51	265
Melilotus altissimus	26	24	30	80	42	-5	-6	26	0.58	96	234
Melilotus officinalis	24	30	23	77	42	-20	-23	27	0.54	87	265
Melissa officinalis	40	4	6	50	44	+70	+74	22	0.60	77	279
Mentha aquatica	76	45	255	376	73	+3	+8	18	0.85	389	164
Mentha arvensis	44	55	44	143	48	-19	-26	23	0.55	160	67, 161
Mentha spicata	42	19	14	75	30	+33	+39	27	0.42	132	234
Mentha x *piperita*	20	14	5	39	35	+15	+18	41	0.26	95	
Mentha x *verticillata*	28	29	9	66	38	-11	-14	37	0.27	139	
Mentha x *villosa*	18	18	5	41	25	-9	-10	44	0.24	97	265
Menyanthes trifoliata	32	17	89	138	41	+5	+6	16	0.84	144	168, 188
Mercurialis annua	30	9	24	63	45	+31	+34	23	0.73	74	71, 234, **236**
Mercurialis perennis	28	30	283	341	74	-7	-15	9	0.97	320	35
Milium effusum	23	18	45	86	35	-1	-1	21	0.72	94	31
Mimulus agg.	23	28	60	111	39	-14	-17	18	0.79	105	265
Moehringia trinervia	52	70	159	281	72	-15	-26	16	0.82	259	31
Molinia caerulea	40	26	240	306	70	-2	-3	12	0.92	305	196
Montia fontana	66	45	168	279	68	+2	+4	18	0.79	297	168
Muscari armeniacum	60	1	1	62	53	+88	+93	21	0.50	122	285
Mycelis muralis	28	23	62	113	46	-2	-3	19	0.75	120	31, 214
Myosotis arvensis	69	48	342	459	87	-1	-2	21	0.88	466	78
Myosotis discolor	89	47	84	220	56	+17	+27	20	0.64	270	101
Myosotis laxa	77	63	106	246	55	0	+1	24	0.63	292	164
Myosotis ramosissima	18	20	15	53	28	-14	-16	33	0.50	66	135, 214
Myosotis scorpioides	57	73	115	245	55	-16	-27	18	0.73	237	164
Myosotis secunda	64	31	101	196	65	+13	+18	17	0.77	216	168
Myosotis sylvatica	107	35	75	217	68	+32	+49	17	0.68	267	31
Myosoton aquaticum	27	19	25	71	42	+7	+8	28	0.57	92	158
Myrica gale	8	10	80	98	59	-10	-12	8	0.99	89	198, **199**
Myriophyllum alterniflorum	19	17	37	73	33	-5	-5	23	0.72	78	190
Myriophyllum spicatum	25	18	15	58	26	+9	+10	33	0.45	88	182
Myrrhis odorata	10	21	57	88	44	-22	-25	12	0.94	71	265, **268**
Narcissus agg.	188	17	65	270	82	+61	+85	11	0.79	319	285, **287**
Nardus stricta	24	24	240	288	74	-7	-12	8	0.97	271	131
Narthecium ossifragum	20	15	172	207	67	-5	-7	8	0.97	199	196
Nigella damascena	17	0	0	17	30	+91					289
Nuphar lutea	13	12	31	56	27	-6	-7	24	0.77	57	182
Nymphaea alba	31	13	31	75	27	+21	+24	23	0.70	88	182
Nymphoides peltata	14	4	5	23	23	+44	+46	38	0.56	34	182
Odontites vernus	80	56	154	290	66	+3	+7	20	0.73	319	101
Oenanthe aquatica	4	9	3	16	25	-50	-52	48	0.50	14	158, 182, **184**
Oenanthe crocata	34	20	150	204	63	0	0	13	0.88	209	161
Oenanthe fistulosa	6	9	7	22	23	-27	-28	42	0.60	22	158
Oenanthe lachenalii	4	6	6	16	21	-25	-26	46	0.67	15	156
Oenanthe pimpinelloides	7	0	12	19	44	+28	+29	12	1.00	19	90, **93**
Oenothera agg.	38	16	19	73	33	+30	+35	25	0.54	105	279
Onobrychis viciifolia	7	6	5	18	24	0	0	51	0.46	26	126
Ononis repens	27	27	65	119	40	-8	-10	19	0.77	120	116
Onopordum acanthium	21	4	1	26	23	+69	+75	30	0.20	110	234
Ophioglossum vulgatum sens. lat.	19	17	6	42	15	-1	-1	40	0.26	95	99
Ophrys apifera	25	3	14	42	24	+48	+51	22	0.82	47	116, **119**
Orchis mascula	27	37	36	100	32	-22	-27	23	0.63	100	31, 116, 217
Oreopteris limbosperma	37	31	130	198	72	-4	-6	14	0.84	199	40, 220
Origanum vulgare	24	20	28	72	36	-1	-1	26	0.59	89	111, 214
Ornithogalum angustifolium	42	22	10	74	42	+30	+38	30	0.31	166	285
Ornithopus perpusillus	15	14	16	45	28	-5	-6	33	0.56	55	135
Orobanche minor	12	10	3	25	19	+5	+5	52	0.23	65	71, 81
Osmunda regalis	7	9	12	28	23	-18	-19	35	0.70	27	31, 156
Oxalis acetosella	38	33	306	377	77	-5	-11	11	0.95	363	38, 45, 217
Oxalis articulata	33	2	3	38	35	+78	+81	24	0.60	60	285
Oxalis corniculata	48	5	10	63	38	+66	+71	20	0.67	87	279

Species	G	L	R	Total	TF	RC	CF	90% conf. (CF)	P_2	N_2	Page(s)
Oxalis exilis	20	1	0	21	31	+86					279
Oxalis stricta	11	6	0	17	41	+37					285
Oxyria digyna	4	6	17	27	57	-17	-18	25	0.89	24	201, 220
Panicum miliaceum	21	0	0	21	35	+91					298
Papaver argemone	8	9	4	21	28	-16	-17	52	0.37	33	71
Papaver dubium	78	42	79	199	57	+15	+24	20	0.65	241	67
Papaver rhoeas	52	22	176	250	74	+6	+10	13	0.89	257	67
Papaver somniferum	133	13	50	196	62	+58	+75	12	0.79	231	296
Parietaria judaica	32	15	35	82	31	+17	+20	22	0.70	96	214, 234
Parnassia palustris	15	16	33	64	42	-10	-12	24	0.75	64	171
Pastinaca sativa	19	31	47	97	48	-24	-28	18	0.79	84	90, 116
Pedicularis palustris	21	26	64	111	44	-14	-16	17	0.82	103	171
Pedicularis sylvatica	24	40	161	225	60	-15	-23	10	0.94	196	146, 168, **170**, 196
Pentaglottis sempervirens	99	17	77	193	56	+39	+53	13	0.82	215	265, **278**
Persicaria amphibia	37	26	107	170	44	0	0	17	0.80	179	161, 186
Persicaria bistorta	17	21	33	71	36	-16	-18	23	0.73	69	99, **100**
Persicaria hydropiper	69	58	127	254	67	-2	-3	20	0.70	281	164
Persicaria lapathifolia	83	44	105	232	67	+13	+22	19	0.70	267	67, 161
Persicaria maculosa	72	61	343	476	91	-3	-12	23	0.88	474	78
Persicaria vivipara	6	9	21	36	55	-18	-20	24	0.86	31	124, 201
Persicaria wallichii	4	8	4	16	30	-42	-43	48	0.57	14	285
Petasites albus	5	2	8	15	32	+14	+15	41	0.80	16	279
Petasites fragrans	28	10	39	77	31	+19	+21	20	0.80	84	285
Petasites hybridus	24	26	72	122	35	-10	-12	17	0.82	118	161
Petroselinum segetum	10	3	7	20	30	+33	+34	38	0.70	24	71
Phacelia tanacetifolia	17	0	0	17	46	+91					298
Phalaris arundinacea	77	39	257	373	73	+5	+13	16	0.87	385	164
Phalaris canariensis	19	17	1	37	27	+1	+3	90	0.06	360	289
Phegopteris connectilis	19	10	78	107	63	+1	+2	15	0.89	109	40, 220
Philadelphus coronarius	14	2	0	16	30	+77					300
Phleum pratense sens. lat.	72	51	362	485	94	-1	-3	24	0.88	492	81, 101
Phragmites australis	50	20	113	183	42	+11	+15	14	0.85	192	164, **167**, 186
Phyllitis scolopendrium	84	16	163	263	62	+21	+33	11	0.91	271	35, 217, **219**
Picea abies	112	28	58	198	66	+42	+59	16	0.67	252	300
Picea sitchensis	107	9	70	186	77	+48	+61	11	0.89	200	300
Picris echioides	77	9	89	175	73	+34	+44	11	0.91	183	71
Picris hieracioides	20	11	23	54	38	+13	+14	28	0.68	64	116
Pilosella aurantiaca	73	11	11	95	38	+66	+77	18	0.50	168	279
Pilosella officinarum	101	75	238	414	76	+2	+5	27	0.76	446	120
Pimpinella major	8	12	15	35	37	-23	-25	30	0.72	32	90, **92**
Pimpinella saxifraga	39	52	113	204	55	-15	-23	15	0.81	188	120
Pinguicula lusitanica	16	7	14	37	50	+22	+23	31	0.67	45	148, 174
Pinguicula vulgaris	9	15	155	179	67	-11	-15	5	1.00	164	171, 196
Pinus contorta	37	5	14	56	59	+54	+59	21	0.74	69	300
Pinus nigra	64	11	17	92	44	+57	+66	19	0.61	133	300
Pinus sylvestris	116	36	232	384	79	+17	+40	15	0.87	402	299
Plantago coronopus	42	14	65	121	42	+18	+22	16	0.82	130	101, 247
Plantago lanceolata	14	7	600	621	100	-3	-75	65	1.00	614	297
Plantago major	21	12	544	577	96	-3	-27	17	1.00	565	297
Plantago maritima	18	13	76	107	42	-3	-3	14	0.88	107	201, 247
Plantago media	24	30	68	122	54	-14	-17	17	0.81	114	116
Platanthera bifolia	4	10	5	19	25	-49	-50	40	0.65	14	40, 148
Platanthera chlorantha	5	4	7	16	11	0	0	47	0.64	19	31, 90
Platanus x hispanica	15	1	2	18	32	+74	+75	34	0.67	26	300
Poa annua	18	20	570	608	100	-5	-68	24	1.00	588	297
Poa compressa	32	23	9	64	42	+14	+17	35	0.28	146	52
Poa nemoralis	56	61	80	197	57	-11	-17	21	0.64	213	31
Poa pratensis sens. lat.	71	62	429	562	95	-3	-28	41	0.90	554	297
Poa trivialis	75	53	421	549	96	-1	-4	39	0.89	555	297
Polygala serpyllifolia	41	35	182	258	66	-4	-7	13	0.88	254	131, 146, 196
Polygala vulgaris	31	44	53	128	38	-21	-27	20	0.70	121	122, **123**
Polygonatum multiflorum	9	13	9	31	38	-27	-28	38	0.56	32	28
Polygonatum x hybridum	20	3	2	25	29	+69	+72	32	0.40	55	285
Polygonum aviculare agg.	52	23	450	525	94	+1	+5	22	0.95	528	78, 230
Polypodium vulgare sens. lat.	76	35	238	349	69	+7	+15	15	0.87	360	38
Polystichum aculeatum	27	33	43	103	38	-16	-19	22	0.67	104	31, 217
Polystichum setiferum	36	13	74	123	51	+13	+16	15	0.85	129	31
Populus alba	54	27	36	117	43	+22	+28	23	0.57	158	300
Populus nigra 'Italica'	60	4	9	73		+73	+79	18	0.69	100	300

Species	G	L	R	Total	TF	RC	CF	90% conf. (CF)	P_2	N_2	Page(s)
Populus nigra sens. lat.	68	9	22	99		+58	+66	17	0.71	127	299
Populus tremula	78	30	106	214	50	+19	+28	16	0.78	236	299
Populus x canadensis	69	23	68	160	58	+26	+34	17	0.75	183	300
Populus x canescens	43	22	15	80	41	+28	+34	28	0.41	143	300
Populus x jackii	8	4	5	17	23	+22	+23	49	0.56	23	300
Potamogeton berchtoldii	22	14	2	38	18	+25	+34	45	0.13	192	182
Potamogeton crispus	28	28	10	66	25	-8	-11	37	0.29	132	182
Potamogeton natans	51	55	74	180	40	-11	-16	21	0.64	194	186
Potamogeton pectinatus	21	17	19	57	28	+2	+2	33	0.53	76	182
Potamogeton perfoliatus	10	12	10	32	21	-18	-19	38	0.55	36	182
Potamogeton polygonifolius	31	40	139	210	61	-12	-18	13	0.89	192	171, 188, **189**, 196
Potamogeton pusillus	13	4	4	21	19	+44	+46	40	0.50	34	182
Potentilla anglica	35	32	31	98	52	-4	-5	27	0.51	129	95
Potentilla anserina	33	27	427	487	85	-4	-16	12	0.98	470	101
Potentilla erecta	29	42	385	456	80	-9	-28	10	0.99	420	131, **134**
Potentilla palustris	32	26	76	134	46	-2	-3	18	0.76	141	168
Potentilla reptans	30	20	314	364	91	-3	-7	9	0.97	354	95
Potentilla sterilis	42	46	225	313	72	-8	-16	13	0.90	295	35
Potentilla x mixta sens. lat.	25	7	5	37	44	+52	+56	31	0.42	72	
Primula veris	53	30	115	198	61	+6	+9	17	0.79	212	95, 116
Primula vulgaris	77	40	306	423	76	+4	+12	18	0.88	433	35, 217
Primula x polyantha	9	14	10	33	24	-29	-31	35	0.59	32	
Prunella vulgaris	45	12	534	591	97	+1	+18	37	0.98	592	297
Prunus avium	141	31	178	350	82	+28	+55	14	0.85	375	299
Prunus cerasifera	65	6	18	89	52	+63	+70	16	0.75	111	300
Prunus cerasus	6	9	5	20	31	-30	-31	47	0.51	22	299
Prunus domestica	100	33	102	235	72	+26	+40	16	0.76	267	299
Prunus laurocerasus	96	8	47	151	58	+54	+65	12	0.85	167	300
Prunus lusitanica	21	2	3	26	27	+71	+73	30	0.60	40	300
Prunus padus	52	16	54	122	50	+26	+32	17	0.77	137	299
Prunus spinosa	33	18	386	437	88	-2	-6	11	0.98	430	56
Pseudofumaria lutea	43	8	36	87	34	+36	+41	17	0.82	97	279
Pseudotsuga menziesii	56	10	12	78	43	+59	+67	20	0.55	125	300
Pteridium aquilinum	28	30	419	477	83	-6	-21	10	0.99	451	35, 139, **140**
Puccinellia distans	63	7	12	82	44	+67	+74	18	0.63	119	245, **246**
Puccinellia maritima	10	8	16	34	26	-1	-1	33	0.67	39	249
Pulicaria dysenterica	43	31	126	200	65	0	0	15	0.81	210	95, 158
Pulmonaria officinalis	18	8	7	33	34	+31	+34	36	0.47	54	285
Pyrus communis sens. lat.	20	8	9	37	30	+33	+35	33	0.53	55	299
Quercus cerris	44	20	40	104	43	+20	+25	21	0.67	126	300
Quercus ilex	22	4	19	45	29	+36	+38	22	0.83	50	300
Quercus petraea	49	56	103	208	59	-12	-18	18	0.74	207	299
Quercus robur	37	27	368	432	91	-3	-10	12	0.96	421	299
Quercus rubra	39	1	1	41	49	+87	+90	24	0.50	80	300
Ranunculus acris	30	22	556	608	100	-3	-52	38	0.99	591	297
Ranunculus aquatilis sens. lat.	36	41	30	107	63	-15	-20	26	0.50	132	182
Ranunculus auricomus	24	33	42	99	42	-20	-24	21	0.70	94	28, **30**
Ranunculus bulbosus	98	56	172	326	74	+9	+19	20	0.75	358	101, 120
Ranunculus ficaria	81	62	358	501	91	-1	-6	29	0.86	509	35
Ranunculus flammula	38	49	318	405	74	-9	-23	12	0.95	374	168
Ranunculus hederaceus	34	38	39	111	43	-13	-17	24	0.58	125	168, 188
Ranunculus lingua	10	7	2	19	14	+16	+18	54	0.22	54	158, 182
Ranunculus omiophyllus	28	20	29	77	58	+6	+7	27	0.59	96	156, 188
Ranunculus parviflorus	13	0	4	17	30	+68	+69	14	1.00	17	90, **93**
Ranunculus repens	10	3	595	608	100	-3	-51	88	1.00	605	297
Ranunculus sardous	8	7	9	24	35	-3	-3	42	0.58	29	106, 176
Ranunculus sceleratus	42	41	81	164	57	-7	-10	19	0.71	172	158
Ranunculus trichophyllus	16	17	9	42	30	-12	-14	39	0.40	63	182
Raphanus raphanistrum subsp. *raphanistrum*	61	42	66	169	80	+7	+11	22	0.61	208	67
Reseda lutea	21	20	49	90	39	-7	-8	20	0.76	92	58
Reseda luteola	77	28	79	184	55	+24	+34	17	0.74	211	234
Rhamnus cathartica	27	24	44	95	60	-4	-5	22	0.67	105	28
Rheum x hybridum	20	9	2	31	42	+41	+48	38	0.18	121	285
Rhinanthus minor	55	75	152	282	55	-16	-28	16	0.80	260	101, **103**
Rhododendron ponticum	55	28	111	194	49	+9	+13	16	0.80	208	265
Rhus typhina	28	0	0	28	45	+92					300
Rhynchospora alba	11	5	13	29	35	+16	+17	34	0.72	33	198
Ribes nigrum	51	44	38	133	44	0	0	26	0.46	192	265

Species	G	L	R	Total	TF	RC	CF	90% conf. (CF)	P_2	N_2	Page(s)
Ribes rubrum	86	47	95	228	63	+14	+23	20	0.67	271	42
Ribes sanguineum	52	21	15	88	46	+38	+47	25	0.42	161	279
Ribes uva-crispa	77	58	142	277	66	+2	+3	21	0.71	309	279
Robinia pseudoacacia	30	8	7	45	43	+51	+56	28	0.47	79	300
Rorippa amphibia	8	7	9	24	26	-3	-3	42	0.58	29	158, 182
Rorippa nasturtium-aquaticum agg.	84	74	165	323	70	-3	-6	22	0.71	350	164, 186
Rorippa palustris	34	24	25	83	37	+9	+11	28	0.51	116	158
Rorippa sylvestris	13	27	13	53	30	-43	-48	28	0.57	45	158, **160**
Rosa arvensis	46	29	172	247	80	+1	+1	15	0.86	255	54
Rosa canina agg.	51	39	394	484		-3	-11	18	0.94	476	296
Rosa mollis agg.	51	51	88	190		-8	-11	20	0.69	203	296
Rosa pimpinellifolia	12	10	17	39	26	-2	-2	32	0.64	45	145, 232, 247
Rosa rubiginosa agg.	28	15	13	56		+23	+26	31	0.46	88	296
Rosa rugosa	50	9	15	74	45	+55	+61	21	0.63	104	300
Rosa stylosa	11	9	4	24	51	+5	+5	52	0.31	49	28
Rubus armeniacus	24	4	5	33		+60	+64	29	0.56	52	300
Rubus caesius	50	46	63	159	67	-4	-6	22	0.61	187	52
Rubus chamaemorus	6	5	26	37	57	-5	-6	22	0.89	36	148, 198
Rubus fruticosus agg.	18	12	490	520	94	-4	-19	11	1.00	508	35
Rubus idaeus	54	61	272	387	79	-8	-21	15	0.89	366	35
Rubus laciniatus	7	5	3	15		+11	+12	60	0.38	27	300
Rubus saxatilis	12	13	16	41	36	-12	-13	33	0.63	45	40, 124, 220
Rumex acetosa	40	16	555	611	99	0	-5	74	0.97	611	297
Rumex acetosella	47	87	346	480	83	-15	-51	15	0.94	420	131, **134**, 139, 217
Rumex conglomeratus	72	48	123	243	69	+5	+9	19	0.72	271	161
Rumex crispus	56	40	409	505	88	-2	-9	22	0.93	501	101, 245
Rumex hydrolapathum	19	9	17	45	27	+19	+21	30	0.65	55	158, 182
Rumex longifolius	21	10	23	54	58	+17	+18	26	0.70	63	171
Rumex obtusifolius	31	11	524	566	96	-1	-8	21	0.99	561	297
Rumex pulcher	8	5	7	20	24	+11	+12	47	0.58	26	81, 90
Rumex sanguineus	90	27	240	357	84	+13	+28	13	0.90	367	31
Ruscus aculeatus	15	11	16	42	30	+4	+5	34	0.59	52	28
Sagina apetala	104	27	59	190	53	+40	+55	16	0.69	238	232, **233**
Sagina maritima	10	7	5	22	24	+11	+12	49	0.42	36	249
Sagina nodosa	12	22	7	41	31	-43	-47	34	0.42	45	171, **173**, 247
Sagina procumbens	81	43	414	538	89	+3	+18	32	0.91	546	297
Sagina subulata	10	6	7	23	26	+15	+16	44	0.54	32	135, 148
Sagittaria sagittifolia	16	3	14	33	30	+35	+36	25	0.82	36	182, **185**
Salicornia agg.	4	1	12	17	22	+10	+10	28	0.92	17	249
Salix alba	62	28	101	191	59	+13	+19	16	0.78	208	299
Salix aurita	41	42	158	241	64	-8	-12	14	0.86	233	38, 217
Salix caprea	72	59	330	461	92	-2	-9	22	0.87	462	35
Salix cinerea	94	34	371	499	91	+8	+33	21	0.92	508	35, 164
Salix fragilis	59	28	196	283	73	+5	+10	14	0.88	291	299
Salix herbacea	9	1	14	24	38	+26	+27	22	0.93	25	201, **206**
Salix pentandra	17	12	9	38	28	+11	+12	39	0.43	61	299
Salix phylicifolia	8	5	5	18	31	+14	+15	51	0.50	26	174, 220
Salix purpurea	16	16	13	45	27	-8	-9	36	0.49	59	161
Salix repens	24	23	69	116	45	-7	-9	17	0.81	115	146, 247
Salix triandra	14	9	6	29	26	+16	+18	43	0.40	50	158
Salix viminalis	79	33	93	205	50	+19	+29	17	0.74	233	299
Salix x multinervis	38	10	6	54	57	+55	+63	26	0.38	117	
Salix x reichardtii	59	4	6	69	64	+76	+82	19	0.60	108	
Salix x rubens	9	5	2	16	35	+28	+29	54	0.29	39	
Salix x sepulcralis	28	0	0	28	65	+92					
Salix x sericans	26	4	3	33	30	+67	+71	28	0.43	68	
Salix x smithiana	13	7	2	22	29	+31	+34	46	0.22	68	
Sambucus nigra	28	8	451	487	91	-1	-4	10	0.99	483	230
Sambucus racemosa	12	5	10	27	47	+23	+24	36	0.67	33	300
Samolus valerandi	13	6	9	28	22	+23	+24	37	0.60	37	156
Sanguisorba minor	14	17	65	96		-12	-14	14	0.90	88	116
Sanguisorba officinalis	16	17	41	74	44	-10	-11	21	0.79	73	99
Sanicula europaea	35	51	97	183	50	-18	-26	16	0.80	164	35, **37**
Saponaria officinalis	25	16	9	50	26	+18	+21	35	0.36	94	234
Saxifraga aizoides	9	6	34	49	67	-1	-2	20	0.86	50	124, 174, 201, 220
Saxifraga granulata	7	15	12	34	22	-38	-40	30	0.72	26	99, **100**, 111
Saxifraga hypnoides	8	7	5	20	29	-1	-1	50	0.42	31	124, 201, 220
Saxifraga oppositifolia	1	4	17	22	49	-23	-24	10	1.00	18	124, 201, 220
Saxifraga stellaris	7	8	32	47	63	-11	-12	19	0.90	43	174, 201, 220

Species	G	L	R	Total	TF	RC	CF	90% conf. (CF)	P_2	N_2	Page(s)
Saxifraga tridactylites	17	10	14	41	27	+14	+15	34	0.58	53	214
Saxifraga x urbium	14	6	7	27	27	+30	+31	38	0.54	39	285
Scabiosa columbaria	7	13	26	46	36	-24	-25	20	0.87	38	111, **114**
Schoenoplectus lacustris	15	11	34	60	29	0	0	23	0.76	65	182
Schoenoplectus tabernaemontani	9	9	8	26	23	-9	-9	44	0.51	33	158, 182
Schoenus nigricans	15	4	32	51	44	+15	+16	19	0.89	53	174
Scilla verna	2	4	11	17	29	-22	-22	25	0.94	14	104, 145
Scirpus sylvaticus	10	4	10	24	21	+21	+22	36	0.71	28	31, 158
Scleranthus annuus	7	8	6	21	29	-16	-16	48	0.51	26	64, 135, 148, 214
Scrophularia auriculata	54	18	144	216	71	+11	+16	13	0.89	223	158
Scrophularia nodosa	73	52	233	358	75	0	+1	19	0.82	374	35
Scutellaria galericulata	30	13	40	83	28	+16	+19	21	0.75	93	161
Scutellaria minor	19	7	23	49	39	+20	+22	25	0.77	55	156
Sedum acre	65	50	95	210	51	+2	+3	22	0.66	244	217
Sedum album	63	26	44	133	44	+27	+35	20	0.63	170	296
Sedum anglicum	20	12	59	91	46	+2	+2	18	0.83	95	214, 247
Sedum rosea	7	4	22	33	36	+2	+2	27	0.85	34	201, 220
Sedum rupestre	46	19	14	79	36	+37	+44	26	0.42	141	279
Sedum spectabile	15	0	0	15	44	+91					285
Sedum spurium	16	6	1	23	23	+50	+58	39	0.14	119	285
Sedum telephium	31	20	23	74	42	+12	+14	28	0.53	101	31, 232
Selaginella selaginoides	34	16	78	128	76	+8	+10	16	0.83	135	124, 174
Sempervivum tectorum	10	4	2	16	34	+41	+43	48	0.33	36	285
Senecio aquaticus	40	52	96	188	46	-16	-22	17	0.77	177	168, **170**
Senecio erucifolius	36	23	94	153	63	+2	+3	17	0.80	162	90
Senecio jacobaea	49	21	482	552	93	+1	+4	27	0.96	554	297
Senecio squalidus	26	48	51	125	45	-30	-37	18	0.74	104	265, **268**
Senecio sylvaticus	58	40	53	151	47	+8	+12	24	0.57	195	45, 131, 139
Senecio viscosus	43	38	46	127	41	-2	-3	24	0.56	158	265
Senecio vulgaris	47	33	400	480	89	-2	-9	17	0.95	473	78, 230
Senecio x ostenfeldii	6	9	3	18	55	-34	-35	52	0.38	24	
Sequoiadendron giganteum	14	1	3	18	27	+68	+69	33	0.75	23	300
Serratula tinctoria	17	11	13	41	28	+12	+13	35	0.54	55	116
Sherardia arvensis	64	19	51	134	51	+31	+39	17	0.73	158	116, **119**, 214
Silaum silaus	16	12	17	45	29	+4	+4	34	0.59	56	90
Silene dioica	56	38	332	426	81	-1	-4	16	0.91	427	35
Silene latifolia	34	53	169	256	71	-16	-25	12	0.90	225	56, **57**
Silene noctiflora	4	11	3	18	34	-59	-60	44	0.52	14	71, **73**
Silene uniflora	8	10	28	46	27	-14	-15	22	0.85	42	247, **248**
Silene vulgaris	18	44	78	140	50	-29	-36	12	0.90	107	95, **98**
Silene x hampeana	64	19	23	106	49	+44	+53	21	0.55	159	
Sinapis alba	22	20	4	46	36	-1	-1	44	0.17	155	71
Sinapis arvensis	68	55	204	327	77	-2	-4	18	0.80	339	76, 232
Sison amomum	32	14	42	88	60	+16	+19	21	0.75	99	52
Sisymbrium officinale	57	27	281	365	84	+3	+6	14	0.91	371	76, 232
Sisymbrium orientale	12	8	7	27	23	+12	+13	44	0.47	41	265
Smyrnium olusatrum	20	3	31	54	35	+25	+27	17	0.91	56	52, **53**
Solanum dulcamara	41	36	275	352	86	-5	-11	12	0.93	340	161
Solanum nigrum	90	24	90	204	79	+29	+42	15	0.79	228	80
Solanum tuberosum	70	5	2	77	63	+82	+94	17	0.29	252	298
Soleirolia soleirolii	28	6	16	50	33	+42	+45	24	0.73	61	279
Solidago canadensis	28	22	17	67	37	+5	+6	33	0.44	103	279
Solidago gigantea	27	9	5	41	34	+48	+53	31	0.36	90	285
Solidago virgaurea	30	41	121	192	53	-14	-20	13	0.87	173	146, 217
Sonchus arvensis	65	43	252	360	77	+1	+1	17	0.85	371	76
Sonchus asper	75	19	404	498	91	+7	+28	16	0.96	502	78
Sonchus oleraceus	80	33	306	419	87	+6	+18	16	0.90	428	76
Sorbus aria agg.	64	20	43	127		+33	+41	19	0.68	157	299
Sorbus aucuparia	83	22	353	458	84	+9	+28	15	0.94	463	299
Sorbus intermedia agg.	49	8	12	69		+59	+65	21	0.60	102	300
Sorbus torminalis	9	3	16	28	26	+15	+16	28	0.84	30	299
Sparganium angustifolium	14	7	17	38	31	+14	+15	31	0.71	44	190
Sparganium emersum	28	12	17	57	27	+27	+30	27	0.59	77	182, **185**
Sparganium erectum	83	41	132	256	59	+18	+21	17	0.76	282	161, 186, **187**
Sparganium natans	5	8	2	15	29	-39	-40	57	0.33	22	190
Spergula arvensis	73	69	95	237	59	-5	-9	23	0.61	275	78, **79**
Spergularia marina	68	13	12	93	46	+61	+72	20	0.48	167	249, **251**
Spergularia media	12	3	13	28	25	+27	+29	29	0.81	31	249
Spergularia rubra	44	15	16	75	37	+40	+47	24	0.52	116	135, **138**, 234

Species	G	L	R	Total	TF	RC	CF	90% conf. (CF)	P_2	N_2	Page(s)
Spiraea agg.	34	12	19	65	36	+33	+37	25	0.61	87	300
Stachys arvensis	37	17	15	69	39	+30	+35	27	0.47	111	67, **70**
Stachys officinalis	29	38	101	168	56	-14	-19	14	0.85	154	95, 116
Stachys palustris	81	50	118	249	56	+8	+15	20	0.70	283	164
Stachys sylvatica	31	24	430	485	92	-4	-15	12	0.98	468	56
Stachys x ambigua	25	11	8	44	31	+34	+38	32	0.42	78	156
Stellaria graminea	74	46	322	442	86	+1	+5	21	0.88	453	101
Stellaria holostea	45	37	296	378	78	-4	-9	13	0.92	369	35
Stellaria media	22	21	522	565	95	-4	-34	12	1.00	544	297
Stellaria neglecta	20	18	20	58	49	-3	-4	30	0.55	73	28
Stellaria nemorum	7	6	9	22	31	-2	-2	42	0.62	26	40, 156
Stellaria pallida	24	1	2	27	28	+80	+82	28	0.67	39	245
Stellaria uliginosa	62	59	298	419	81	-5	-15	18	0.88	409	164
Suaeda maritima	4	3	12	19	22	-2	-2	34	0.82	20	249
Succisa pratensis	57	50	255	362	68	-4	-10	16	0.87	358	101
Symphoricarpos albus	85	39	152	276	66	+12	+22	16	0.80	298	300
Symphoricarpos x chenaultii	16	0	0	16	51	+91					300
Symphytum officinale	62	0	0	62	26	+92					301
Symphytum orientale	23	0	7	30	38	+68	+70	10	1.00	30	265, **278**
Symphytum tuberosum	15	6	20	41	41	+17	+18	27	0.77	46	40, **41**
Symphytum x uplandicum	89	38	116	243	63	+18	+29	17	0.75	272	265
Syringa vulgaris	66	23	35	124	48	+35	+44	20	0.60	167	300
Tamus communis	23	20	211	254	85	-6	-9	8	0.97	242	28
Tanacetum parthenium	121	46	102	269	66	+27	+47	18	0.69	324	232
Tanacetum vulgare	48	38	55	141	39	+2	+2	24	0.59	174	56
Taraxacum agg.	24	15	581	620	102	-3	-70	37	1.00	605	297
Taxus baccata	78	30	144	252	67	+15	+24	15	0.83	268	299
Tellima grandiflora	22	4	1	27	48	+70	+77	29	0.20	115	279
Teucrium scorodonia	33	32	237	302	64	-6	-12	11	0.94	287	38, 139, 217
Thalictrum alpinum	12	6	21	39	58	+10	+10	28	0.78	42	124, 174, 201, 220
Thalictrum flavum	6	3	6	15	16	+16	+17	49	0.67	18	158
Thalictrum minus	7	7	8	22	18	-9	-9	45	0.58	26	214, 245
Thlaspi arvense	48	41	60	149	54	-1	-2	22	0.60	179	67
Thuja plicata	33	3	13	49	42	+57	+60	20	0.81	57	300
Thymus polytrichus	27	27	187	241	56	-7	-11	10	0.94	228	122, **123**, 217
Tilia cordata	34	7	15	56	35	+47	+51	23	0.68	72	299
Tilia platyphyllos	27	3	5	35	27	+67	+70	26	0.63	51	299
Tilia x europaea	95	17	145	257	65	+26	+40	11	0.90	268	299
Torilis japonica	69	60	230	359	81	-3	-8	18	0.82	364	56
Torilis nodosa	20	1	6	27	31	+65	+66	24	0.86	30	90, **94**
Tragopogon pratensis	57	50	181	288	82	-4	-7	16	0.82	291	95
Trichophorum cespitosum	17	25	155	197	68	-12	-17	8	0.98	176	148, 196
Trientalis europaea	14	10	38	62	77	-1	-1	21	0.80	65	40, 45, 148
Trifolium arvense	15	24	17	56	29	-30	-34	28	0.60	54	135, **137**
Trifolium campestre	45	65	87	197	52	-21	-31	18	0.72	183	214, 245
Trifolium dubium	96	37	343	476	90	+8	+30	20	0.90	486	101, **103**
Trifolium fragiferum	12	9	10	31	30	+5	+5	41	0.53	42	90
Trifolium hybridum	45	78	49	172	56	-34	-49	21	0.58	161	279, **281**
Trifolium medium	65	46	67	178	51	+7	+10	23	0.59	223	99
Trifolium micranthum	32	11	11	54	34	+40	+45	27	0.50	86	135, 234
Trifolium pratense	43	21	487	551	93	-1	-4	24	0.96	550	297
Trifolium repens	13	10	599	622	101	-4	-84	50	1.00	612	297
Trifolium striatum	14	10	6	30	24	+11	+12	44	0.38	53	135
Triglochin maritimum	10	8	27	45	30	-3	-3	24	0.80	46	249
Triglochin palustre	39	49	94	182	51	-15	-21	17	0.77	173	168
Tripleurospermum inodorum	82	49	286	417	94	+3	+9	20	0.85	431	76, 232
Tripleurospermum maritimum	15	15	34	64	41	-8	-9	24	0.76	65	247
Trisetum flavescens	63	47	120	230	68	+1	+2	20	0.72	255	95, 116
Triticum aestivum	133	0	1	134	85	+92	+96	14	1.00	134	298
Trollius europaeus	9	16	23	48	40	-26	-28	23	0.80	40	174, **175**, 220
Tropaeolum majus	14	1	1	16	31	+78	+80	37	0.50	30	289
Tsuga heterophylla	36	9	8	53	43	+53	+59	26	0.47	94	300
Tulipa gesneriana	16	0	0	16	49	+91					285
Tussilago farfara	47	77	376	500	90	-12	-47	17	0.94	449	217, **219**
Typha angustifolia	11	14	7	32	25	-23	-25	41	0.43	42	158, 182
Typha latifolia	84	28	134	246	62	+19	+30	14	0.83	264	161, 186, **187**
Ulex europaeus	56	26	336	418	75	+2	+6	15	0.93	422	146
Ulex gallii	21	18	57	96	53	-4	-5	19	0.80	98	145
Ulmus glabra	70	63	245	378	77	-4	-11	19	0.83	379	299

Species	G	L	R	Total	TF	RC	CF	90% conf. (CF)	P_2	N_2	Page(s)
Ulmus minor	31	14	25	70	60	+22	+25	25	0.64	87	299
Ulmus procera	40	48	118	206	74	-12	-18	16	0.81	195	299
Umbilicus rupestris	15	4	66	85	54	+5	+6	13	0.94	86	214
Urtica dioica	18	6	565	589	97	-2	-27	31	1.00	583	297
Urtica urens	54	43	83	180	56	0	+1	22	0.66	208	67, 234
Utricularia intermedia sens. lat.	7	3	6	16	26	+22	+23	46	0.67	20	198
Utricularia minor	9	4	11	24	31	+16	+17	36	0.73	27	198, 190
Vaccinium myrtillus	27	25	237	289	77	-6	-11	9	0.96	274	146, 217
Vaccinium oxycoccos	14	4	31	49	42	+14	+15	19	0.89	51	198
Vaccinium uliginosum	5	2	13	20	52	+8	+8	31	0.87	21	198, 201, 220
Vaccinium vitis-idaea	20	9	72	101	63	+4	+5	15	0.89	104	45, 148, 201
Valeriana dioica	10	15	30	55	33	-19	-21	21	0.83	48	161
Valeriana officinalis	46	38	222	306	64	-4	-7	13	0.89	302	164
Valerianella carinata	30	6	7	43	42	+56	+61	27	0.54	69	234
Valerianella locusta	30	24	11	65	31	+6	+8	36	0.31	131	214, 245
Verbascum nigrum	15	6	12	33	34	+25	+26	33	0.67	41	52
Verbascum thapsus	67	45	86	198	53	+7	+11	21	0.66	233	56
Verbena officinalis	22	3	15	40	33	+43	+45	22	0.83	44	214
Veronica agrestis	54	39	26	119	51	+11	+15	29	0.40	200	67, 234
Veronica anagallis-aquatica	27	24	21	72	38	-2	-2	29	0.48	101	158, 182
Veronica arvensis	117	58	285	460	86	+9	+33	24	0.83	484	78, 217
Veronica beccabunga	59	55	294	408	84	-5	-14	17	0.89	398	164, 186
Veronica catenata	21	22	25	68	42	-10	-12	28	0.59	77	158, 182
Veronica chamaedrys	48	17	487	552	97	+1	+8	25	0.97	554	297
Veronica filiformis	69	51	115	235	58	+2	+4	21	0.69	266	265
Veronica hederifolia	94	42	207	343	88	+11	+23	17	0.83	362	31, 67, 232
Veronica montana	55	38	104	197	55	+3	+5	19	0.73	217	31
Veronica officinalis	77	59	208	344	71	0	-1	19	0.78	365	122, 131
Veronica persica	76	34	275	385	88	+6	+15	16	0.89	394	265
Veronica polita	42	28	22	92	52	+14	+17	28	0.44	146	265
Veronica scutellata	52	36	45	133	47	+9	+12	24	0.56	175	168
Veronica serpyllifolia	106	48	361	515	92	+7	+36	27	0.88	529	81, **83**, 164
Viburnum lantana	16	17	48	81	52	-10	-11	19	0.82	78	28
Viburnum opulus	95	45	107	247	68	+18	+30	19	0.70	287	299
Vicia cracca	72	34	375	481	86	+3	+13	20	0.92	488	164
Vicia faba	38	2	1	41	54	+84	+89	23	0.33	117	298
Vicia hirsuta	76	51	119	246	66	+6	+10	20	0.70	279	95
Vicia lathyroides	3	8	5	16	25	-47	-48	41	0.73	11	135, 249
Vicia sativa	84	52	243	379	85	+4	+9	20	0.82	397	101
Vicia sepium	51	59	338	448	83	-8	-25	16	0.92	422	101
Vicia sylvatica	4	9	3	16	23	-50	-52	48	0.50	14	40, 212
Vicia tetrasperma	44	37	67	148	66	-2	-2	21	0.66	169	71, 90
Vinca major	93	12	42	147	56	+52	+64	14	0.78	174	285
Vinca minor	57	21	29	107	47	+34	+42	21	0.58	148	296
Viola arvensis	66	41	198	305	79	+3	+5	17	0.83	319	67
Viola canina	11	11	7	29	27	-9	-9	45	0.43	42	135, 145
Viola hirta	18	19	32	69	43	-10	-12	25	0.70	72	111
Viola lutea	3	18	13	34	46	-57	-59	16	0.97	17	124, **125**, 131, 220
Viola odorata	62	24	115	201	67	+14	+20	15	0.83	214	116
Viola palustris	30	36	211	277	76	-9	-16	10	0.94	256	171
Viola reichenbachiana	35	25	42	102	48	+5	+6	24	0.63	123	28
Viola riviniana	59	54	417	530	88	-4	-24	26	0.92	516	35, 120, 217
Viola tricolor	38	26	27	91	43	+10	+13	27	0.51	128	64, 135, 245
Viola x wittrockiana	27	2	1	30	41	+81	+85	26	0.33	84	285
Viscum album	21	5	13	39	28	+39	+41	27	0.72	47	234
Vulpia bromoides	58	24	44	126	42	+25	+32	20	0.65	158	54, **55**
Vulpia myuros	46	13	13	72	37	+48	+55	23	0.50	118	234
Wahlenbergia hederacea	9	3	11	23	52	+21	+22	33	0.79	26	156
X Cupressocyparis leylandii	14	0	1	15	45	+85	+85	19	1.00	15	300
X Festulolium loliaceum	6	9	1	16	17	-39	-42	59	0.16	43	
Zannichellia palustris	13	13	3	29	18	-9	-10	50	0.21	78	182
Zea mays	15	1	0	16	131	+85					298

Appendix 2

Methods for Measuring Change from the Repeat of Presence or Absence Plant Surveys and their application to BSBI Local Change

Authorship

Michael Braithwaite developed the concepts and methods presented in this appendix to the report. Peter Rothery reviewed the logic of the methods and suggested improvements to the mathematical presentation.

Section headings

A summary of this appendix is presented in Chapter 3 of the main report, together with an example application. This appendix is presented under the following main headings:

1. Introduction

Plant surveys at species level often consist of recording what plants are present in a survey unit without recording any measure of abundance. Usually such surveys cannot expect to be exhaustive in the sense of recording all the taxa present in a survey unit, so there are difficulties, when the surveys come to be repeated, in deriving a fair estimate of real change from the change recorded by the survey. This paper examines the several issues involved mathematically and derives methods of estimating relative change, real range and a weighted relative 'Change Factor' for use in the analysis of such surveys and applies them to BSBI Local Change (LC).

The main characteristics of the survey data to be taken into account in its analysis are as follows.

- There may be variation in recording skill and recording effort between recording units (these are tetrads in LC).

- There may be a systematic difference in thoroughness between the two surveys resulting in the relative over-recording of one survey against the other.

- Some taxa may be recorded much less efficiently than others.

These characteristics suggest that analysis proceeds in the following steps.

- Selecting those recording units where both surveys are considered to have been carried out sufficiently reliably for the results to be used for analysis.

- Adjusting the data to allow for over-recording of one survey against the other so that estimates of net change can be made taxon by taxon relative to a selected baseline.

- Estimating real ranges of the taxa from recorded ranges to allow for less than exhaustive coverage and the fact that some difficult or elusive taxa will have been recorded in a lower proportion of the recording units in which they are present than familiar taxa.

- Weighting the estimates of net change relative to the selected baseline by range to give a 'Change Factor' for each taxon suitable for comparing groups of taxa. On average change in widespread taxa is smaller in proportion to their range than that of scarcer taxa: a weighting is therefore required to make the change comparable.

The approach to these steps in the analysis is as follows.

- The selection of recording units to be considered as sufficiently reliable for analysis is made by the essentially empirical approach of carrying out a full analysis on different selections of the data and reviewing the results for consistency. The widest acceptable selection is chosen.

- The analysis is approached by first modelling the process of repeat recording from the standpoint of probability theory. This leads to a set of equations which have too many variables to be solved directly from the survey data. Assumptions, that are believed to be valid within certain limits, are then made to allow the equations to be solved and to allow estimates of relative net change and real range to be calculated with associated confidence limits.

- Finally an exponential transformation is developed to give a weighted relative 'Change Factor' (CF).

2. Methods for measuring change

2.1 Selection of recording units (tetrads) for analysis

While most of the sample recording units (tetrads) have been adequately recorded in both the Monitoring Scheme (MS) and LC it is apparent that some were poorly recorded, or not recorded at all, in at least one of the surveys.

The approach to selection is shown in the chart below:

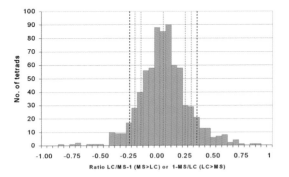

This chart seeks to compare the number of taxa recorded in a tetrad in MS and LC. Aliens and critical taxa have been excluded as the number of records made is much more recorder-biased than for the native taxa. To achieve some symmetry in the chart the ratio (LC-MS)/LC is plotted for those tetrads where LC exceeds MS and the ratio (LC-MS)/MS is plotted where MS exceeds LC. On average there is seen to be about 5.5% over-recording in LC relative to MS and the selection of tetrads is made about this median.

Median = 0.055			Total Tetrads = 755	
Range	Band	From	To	Tetrads
Narrow	± 0.20	-0.145	0.255	530
Middle	± 0.25	-0.195	0.305	585
Broad	± 0.30	-0.245	0.355	635

Broad, Middle and Narrow tetrad selections

Blue dots are Narrow, yellow come in for Middle and red for Broad. They are reasonably scattered, although there appear to be small clusters of red dots in Lincolnshire & Staffs/Derbyshire.

Three datasets were prepared by selecting 'Broad', 'Middle' and 'Narrow' bands about the mean. The full analysis described below was carried out on all three datasets before deciding how broad a band could be accepted without materially distorting the results. The statistics for the native taxa selected as having valid data show that the proportion of refinds rises as the selection is narrowed, as would be expected, however the ratio of gains to losses is 1.38 in Broad, 1.34 in Middle and 1.40 in

Narrow. This erratic trend is unexpected and suggests that the Middle selection is biased between over-recorded and under-recorded tetrads. The statistics are:

Broad	Gains	Re-finds	Losses	Total
Records	21,106	66,080	15,300	102,486
Proportion	0.206	0.645	0.149	
Middle	Gains	Re-finds	Losses	Total
Records	18,840	61,930	14,114	94,884
Proportion	0.199	0.653	0.149	
Narrow	Gains	Re-finds	Losses	Total
Records	17,149	56,804	12,269	86,222
Proportion	0.199	0.659	0.142	

The average over-recording in LC differs for the three datasets, which means that the adjustments made in the calculation of CF differ also. Bearing in mind the relatively wide confidence limits that are found to be the norm for individual taxa, the variation in CF for individual taxa is quite modest except for an insignificant number of taxa where by chance tetrads are brought into the dataset as it is widened with a group of extra gains, or losses as the case may be, for a particular taxon.

After balancing all the factors involved the Broad selection of tetrads has been adopted as the basis of analysis. This selection results in 635 of the 755 tetrads recorded for both MS and LC being included in the analysis (there are 811 tetrads in the sample but 56 were surveyed in only one or neither of the two surveys). All the individual statistics referred to below relate to this Broad dataset.

2.2 Probability model for repeat recording

Probability of recording a taxon

As the surveys are not exhaustive there is an element of chance as to whether a particular taxon will or will not be recorded in a particular survey in a survey unit in which it is present. The chance of finding a taxon during a given survey in a survey unit in which it is present is less than 1 (certainty) and has an average value that is characteristic of the species and may have some degree of stability in a particular survey, even though it is a function of many variables and will vary from survey unit to survey unit.

The model developed here is based on the assumption that this chance, or probability, that a particular taxon will be recorded in a survey unit in which it is present, (P), has an average value for a particular survey that is stable enough to be useful for analysis but may differ significantly from the probability that another taxon will be recorded.

The concepts of real and recorded range

Real range for a single survey

If the number of survey units in which a taxon is present is n_1 and the number in which it is absent is n_0, the range of the taxon is n_1 and the total number of survey units recorded in the survey is $n_1 + n_0$.

Real range for two surveys

Similarly for two surveys the survey units in which a taxon is present may be classified as:

		Survey 2	
		Present	Absent
Survey 1	Present	n_{11}	n_{10}
	Absent	n_{01}	n_{00}

The real ranges in the two surveys are $N_1 = n_{11} + n_{10}$ and $N_2 = n_1 + n_{01}$, respectively. The total number of survey units is $N = n_1 + n_{10} + n_{01} + n_{00}$.

Recorded range for two surveys

In the same way the recorded data for two surveys may be classified as:

		Survey 2	
		Recorded	Not recorded
Survey 1	Recorded	x_{11}	x_{10}
	Not recorded	x_{01}	x_{00}

The recorded range in the two surveys are $X_1 = x_{11} + x_{10}$ and $X_2 = x_{11} + x_{01}$.

Also, $N = x_{11} + x_{10} + x_{01} + x_{00}$.

In more familiar language note that x_{11} represents recorded 're-finds', x_{10} represents recorded losses, x_{01} represents recorded gains and x_{00} represents unrecorded plants that are 'missed' in both surveys plus survey units in which the taxon is absent.

If we denote the recording probabilities by P_1 and P_2 then the expected values (E) of the recorded frequencies are as follows.

$$E[x_{11}] = n_{11}P_1P_2 \tag{1}$$

$$E[x_{10}] = n_{11}P_1(1 - P_2) + n_{10}P_1 \tag{2}$$

$$E[x_{01}] = n_{11}(1 - P_1)P_2 + n_{01}P_2 \tag{3}$$

The equation for $E[x_{00}]$ is determined by $N = x_{11} + x_{10} + x_{01} + x_{00}$.

So, there are three independent equations but 5 unknowns, P_1, P_2, n_{11}, n_{10} and n_{01}.

When these equations are applied to the survey results the recorded values are taken as approximating to the expected values.

The first special case that can be considered is where there is no real change. If this is so $n_{10} = 0$, and $n_{01} = 0$. P_2 is determined from the ratio of equation (2) to equation (1); P_1 is determined from the ratio of equation (3) to equation (1) and the other unknowns follow. If a set of taxa were known to have suffered no real change N_1 and N_2 or P_1 and P_2 could be calculated for each of them and the ratio of N_1 to N_2 or P_1 to P_2 might be used a basis for estimating the over-recording of one survey against the other for all taxa, including those that had undergone real change.

The second special case to be considered is where some taxa suffer real losses but have no real gains and where other taxa have real gains but suffer no real losses.

Taking the taxa with real losses but no real gains first, then, where this is so, $n_{01} = 0$. Here P_1 is determined from the ratio of equation (3) to equation (1), the relationship $N_1P_1 = X_1$ gives N_1 but N_2 and P_2 are inter-related:

$$P_1 = x_{11}/X_2$$

$$N_1 = X_1 \, X_2/x_{11}$$

$$N_2 \, P_2 = X_2$$

Taking the taxa with real gains but no real losses next, then, where this is so, $n_{10} = 0$. Here P_2 is determined from the ratio of equation (2) to equation (1), the relationship $N_2 P_2 = X_2$ gives N_2 but N_1 and P_1 are inter-related:

$$P_2 = x_{11}/X_1$$

$$N_2 = X_1 \, X_2/x_{11}$$

$$N_1 P_1 = X_1$$

Conceptually it is easiest to think of the situation with real gains as a time reversal where the second survey is thought of as the first and vice versa. The real gains situation is then seen to be a mirror of the real losses situation. This underlying symmetry between gains and losses is something that it is necessary to preserve through the various steps of the analysis.

If the second special case can be accepted as a reasonable approximation it is only necessary to make one estimate to solve the equations, this being an adjustment for over-recording in one survey against the other. It is thus necessary to consider the consequences of the assumption that taxa which suffer real losses have no real gains and that taxa have which have real gains suffer no real losses.

The incidence of losses in increasing taxa and of gains in decreasing taxa

A taxon that is spreading overall may lose a proportion of its existing localities (especially those recent ones which have not become well established), though the losses are likely to be few in proportion to the gains. In this situation the consequence of the assumption is that the recording probabilities P_1 and P_2 are underestimated by treating real losses as missed in the second survey. The estimate of real range is based on these probabilities and will thus be overestimated, as will CF. Similar considerations apply to taxa that are declining

overall, but such taxa are less likely to colonise new localities, particularly if they are native taxa dependent on specialised habitats that are themselves in decline. There is thus some danger that gains may be overstated, albeit modestly, but less danger that losses may be overstated, particularly for native taxa.

For a taxon that is truly casual, being dependent on accidental introductions, there may be an extremely low proportion of refinds (though casuals do tend to recur in particular habitats, such as tips). In these circumstances the model tends to break down and the estimates of real range and CF may not be meaningful.

Planted taxa that do not become established are casuals, but with a longer lifespan than herbs and one that will often span the two surveys. Moreover some are planted in such quantity that extinction at tetrad scale is unlikely. Taxa that are often planted are not considered further here as planted vegetation was largely excluded from the MS survey and thus no valid earlier data is available with which to compare the LC survey of these taxa.

2.3 Adjusting for over/under-recording in one survey against the other

The raw survey data for LC shows a significant increase in range over MS for most taxa, typically around 8%. This is not in accordance with field experience and, as over-recording in LC relative to MS has been shown to be an issue, it is clear that an adjustment is required. To make an adjustment a baseline is required of what has not changed. No objective criteria have been found as a basis for the identification of taxa that have not changed their true range. While it may be fair to assume that the most widespread taxa have not changed their true range at tetrad scale, over-recording is found to be a function of range, with the scarce taxa being proportionately more over-recorded than widespread ones, so there is also a need to identify scarce taxa that have not changed and this is what has not proved possible. This is unfortunate as, if it was possible, the over-recording adjustment might be calibrated in a way that would allow real net change to be measured. As it is, a way has had to be sought to measure net change relative to an average for a group of taxa.

The *New Atlas* studies have shown that, as classes, alien taxa are increasing, archaeophyte taxa are decreasing and native taxa are more static. The adjustment for over-recording has thus been based on a selection that consists of the native taxa as defined in *PLANTATT*, excluding all trees and shrubs as many are increasingly planted in areas where they are not present as natives and excluding also those other taxa with a high proportion of alien *New Atlas* records, such as the halophytes that have colonised inland roadsides. Taxa are also excluded where the results are thought to be affected by identification issues: these critical taxa include most subspecies and hybrids.

It is disappointing to have to use such a wide set of native taxa as a baseline as there is reason to suspect from other studies that at least the scarcer native taxa are in decline as a class.

The basic approach to the over-recording adjustment is to calculate an adjusted value for proportional net change, Relative Change, such that the average of the adjusted values over all the selected taxa is zero. This adjusted value is the residual from the relationship derived for the selected taxa for which it is assumed that the net change is zero.

The relationship is found by taking the selection of native species least affected by recording bias, as detailed above, and plotting proportional net change (net change divided by recorded range) against recorded range, where recorded range is the recorded range in MS for losses and the recorded range in LC for gains (to preserve symmetry between gains and losses). A linear regression line is found to give an adequate fit and the equation defining the regression line is used as the basis for the over-recording adjustment not only for the selected native species but for all taxa.

Thus for taxa with net losses:

Proportional net change = $(X_2 - X_1)/X_1$
(this will be a negative figure)

Relative Change = $(X_2 - X_1)/X_1 - (a + bX_1)$

And for taxa with net gains:

Proportional net change = $(X_2 - X_1)/X_2$
(this will be a positive figure)

Relative Change = $(X_2 - X_1)/X_2 - (a + bX_2)$

As some taxa with small net gains have a small relative net loss after the adjustment it at first appears that the calculation for these should be:

Relative Change = $(X_2 - X_1)/X_1 - (a + bX_1)$

But all taxa with net gains are plotted by X_2, so this would not be correct, though the difference would not be material.

Relative Change as defined above falls between 0 and 1 for gains and 0 and -1 for losses. It can equally be presented as a percentage change and it is in this format that it is used as a statistic in the main report. Note that very widespread taxa have few recording units left to expand their range into and can thus only have gains that are a small proportion of their range. This situation leads to some non-linearity in Relative Change as a measure of change, but, as it is only significant for very large gains and losses, it is not in practice material for repeat surveys such as LC where most change is modest.

This adjustment for the LC data is shown as:

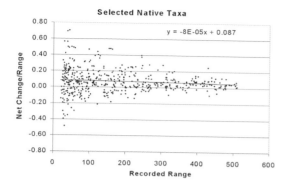

This chart shows the unadjusted data. The relative over-recording is apparent from the regression line. The equation shown on the chart is abbreviated – the version used is y = -0.0000751x + 0.087035.

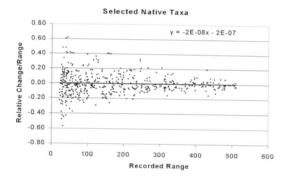

This chart shows the adjusted data, the regression line is now very close to the x axis.

It is ironic to use recorded range as a basis for the over-recording adjustment, even though the actual adjustment made is only very weakly related to range. It would be more logical to make the adjustment in a way that was related to the recording probability, P. This method is not available because a circular argument arises where the calculation of the probability of finding a species is dependent on knowing the relative recording effectiveness of the two surveys and vice versa.

2.4 Estimating recording probabilities and real range size

This over-recording adjustment can be interpreted in a way that enables the basic probability equations to be solved and estimates obtained for P_1, P_2, N_1 and N_2.

Now:

$$N_1 P_1 = X_1$$

$$N_2 P_2 = X_2$$

Therefore:

$$(N_2 - N_1)/N_1 = (X_2 P_1/P_2 - X_1)/X_1$$
$$= (X_2 - X_1)/X_1 - (1 - P_1/P_2)X_2/X_1$$

This can be interpreted as being the same as the equation for the adjustment for over-recording of taxa with net losses, so

$$a + bX_1 = (1 - P_1/P_2)X_2/X_1$$

Using this relationship the over-recording adjustment for each taxon is used to estimate P_1/P_2 for each taxon.

For taxa with net losses P_1 and N_1 are already estimated, so P_2 and N_2 can now be estimated also.

Also

$$(N_2 - N_1)/N_2 = (X_2 - X_1 P_2/P_1)/X_2$$
$$= (X_2 - X_1)/X_2 - (1 - P_2/P_1)X_1/X_2$$

This is the same as the equation for the adjustment for over-recording of taxa with net gains, so

$$a + bX_2 = (1 - P_2/P_1)X_1/X_2$$

For taxa with net gains P_2 and N_2 are already estimated, so P_1 and N_1 can now be estimated also.

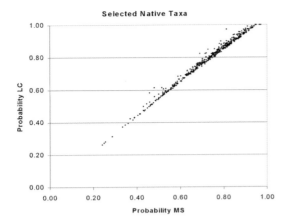

Selected Native Taxa

Probability LC vs *Probability MS*

The probability of recording a taxon is consistently higher in LC than MS, though the degree of consistency is related to the over-recording adjustment. For a very few taxa the estimate of P_2 exceeded 1 and has been normalised to 1.

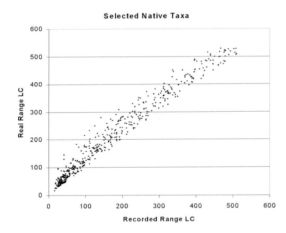

Selected Native Taxa

Real Range LC vs *Recorded Range LC*

The estimate of real range is always equal to or greater than the recorded range as all taxa are under-recorded to a degree.

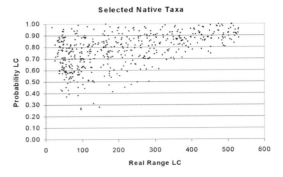

Selected Native Taxa

Probability LC vs *Real Range LC*

Widespread taxa are all well-recorded, scarce taxa vary greatly in how well they are recorded.

2.5 Change Factor – a weighted measure of change

The chart of Relative Change against range demonstrates that, on average, scarce taxa change more than widespread taxa. At its simplest this is because a scarce taxon is present in a recording unit as a single highly localised population while a widespread taxon is present in a recording unit in a number of diffuse populations. This reflects the strong correlation between the frequency and abundance of a taxon. When the countryside is affected by a variety of forces of change over the years it is more likely that a single population will be lost than several diffuse populations. In mathematical terms these local extinctions can be shown to follow an exponential trend related to the number of populations in a recording unit.

If a taxon is present in a recording unit in z populations and the chance of any one population being lost in a given time period is C, the probability of it becoming extinct is C^z. It follows that the taxon will decline on an exponential curve over time.

In practice a taxon is not equally abundant over the whole of its range. Typically its distribution is clustered: the taxon is plentiful in its heartland and scarce at the fringes of its distribution. It follows that even a very widespread taxon may suffer losses at tetrad scale, but that the losses can be expected to occur near the limits of its distribution.

In this situation a weighting is required before the estimates of Relative Change can be compared fairly over groups of taxa.

It is more convenient mathematically to discuss 'Relative Survival' rather than Relative Loss. As noted above, Relative Loss is scaled between 0 where there is no change and 1 where a taxon has become extinct in the survey area. Relative Survival is simply 1 minus the Relative Loss so it is scaled between 1 for no change and 0 for extinction.

A hypothetical taxon present in every recording unit would be expected to have a survival of close to 1. For the purposes of the weighting model such a taxon is taken as having a survival of 1. Now an exponential curve can be defined by just two points so, in a chart of survival against range in the first survey, it is possible to fit such a curve between the point defined by a survival of 1 at maximum range, N, and the point defined by the estimates of real range, F_n, and Relative Survival, S_n, for a chosen taxon. The model postulates that all taxa whose data fits a point on this curve have changed by the same amount in the sense required for the weighting adjustment.

To set a standard value of change for a particular exponential curve, the curve is extended and the value at a range of 1 recording unit is taken as the standard. This value can therefore be thought of as measuring the chance of a hypothetical taxon with this characteristic surviving from the time of the first survey to the time of the second survey in a single recording unit in which it had been present as a single population. This survival value is then converted back into a measure of loss by subtracting from 1 to give the 'Change Factor' (CF).

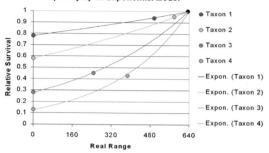

Comparing Survival of Taxa with Different Frequency by an Exponential Model

- Taxon 1
- Taxon 2
- Taxon 3
- Taxon 4
- Expon. (Taxon 1)
- Expon. (Taxon 2)
- Expon. (Taxon 3)
- Expon. (Taxon 4)

Examples of the exponential weighting for four hypothetical taxa with a variety of values for real range and Relative Survival

The equation of the exponential function which passes through the points (F_n, S_n) and $(N, 1)$ is:

$$y = \exp\left[(N - x)\ln S_n / (N - F_n)\right]$$

this can also be written in the form:

$$y = S_n^{[(N - x)/(N - Fn)]}$$

For taxa with a Relative Loss this equation converts under the classification used above, where $F_n = N_1$ and $S_n = N_2/N_1$, to:

$$y = \exp\left[(N - x)\ln (N_2/N_1)/(N - N_1)\right]$$

The value at $x = 1$, is then

$$y_A = \exp\left[(N - 1)\ln (N_2/N_1)/(N - N_1)\right]$$

and

$$CF = -1 + y_A = -1 + \exp\left[(N - 1)\ln (N_2/N_1)/(N - N_1)\right]$$

The discussion of Relative Survival has been about taxa with net losses. As before taxa with net gains may be thought of as having time-reversed losses and the method is then applied in a similar way but using the real range at the time of the second survey.

For taxa with a Relative Gain, where $F_n = N_2$ and $S_n = N_1/N_2$:

$$y = \exp\left[(N - x)\ln (N_1/N_2)/(N - N_2)\right]$$

$$CF = 1 - \exp\left[(N - 1)\ln (N_1/N_2)/(N - N_2)\right]$$

The weighting can be related to log transformed ranges. For the Relative Loss situation, note that:

$$\ln y_A = [(N-1)\ln (N_2/N_1)/(N-N_1)]$$

or

$$\ln y_A = [(N-1)/(N-N_1)][\ln N_2 - \ln N_1]$$

In other words, on a log scale the index is the difference in log transformed ranges weighted in proportion to $1/(N-N_1)$, relatively more weight is being given to those species with a larger range in the first survey

This discussion suggests that that CF may be thought of as the degree of loss suffered in recording units at the edge of a taxon's range where it was present at the time of the first survey as a single highly localised population. It is emphatically not the degree of loss suffered over the taxon's range as a whole and still less is it the degree of loss in a taxon's population size as that, while unknown, may be expected to be concentrated in the recording units in the heartland of its distribution which may or may not have suffered change.

The degree of weighting involved in the CF calculations is modest for scarce taxa but large for very widespread taxa. It is not unexpected that there comes a point for very widespread taxa with small gains and losses where the results are unacceptable, as imperfections in the data (such as the failure to record a common taxon where it is present) are a higher proportion of the change recorded by the surveys where the change is small and are multiplied up by the weighting to distort the result. Thus a valid CF cannot be calculated for very widespread taxa, how widespread is an exercise in judgement for a particular survey. For LC no CF is presented for taxa recorded in more than 534 tetrads in total in MS and LC, out of the 635 tetrads selected for analysis. A similar problem in relation to a further small group of widespread species is discussed in the 'Limitations in Methodology' appendix.

There is an obvious problem with very scarce taxa with little survey data. No CF is presented for taxa recorded in less than 15 tetrads in total in MS and LC.

The Change Factor for a particular taxon uses two values derived from the survey data, its Relative Change and its real range. The estimate of real range is calculated using the probability equations and will always exceed the recorded range. This implies a further weighting for taxa with low recording probability, P.

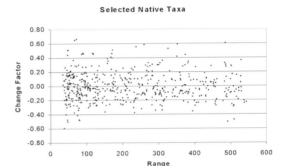

Selected Native Taxa

Unlike the chart for Relative Change, this chart of the Change Factor has a similar degree of scatter over all range sizes included.

2.6 Confidence limits

A major benefit of the probability model is that it allows confidence limits to be estimated at taxon level, albeit somewhat crudely, for the estimates of Relative Change and the Change Factor.

Relative Change

The standard deviation (SD) based on the binomial distribution of the difference between the recorded ranges $X_2 - X_1$, assuming independence of recording in different units and successive surveys, derived from the refinds/gains/losses data for a taxon is calculated as:

$$SD\,[X_2 - X_1] = \surd(P_1(1-P_1)N_1 + P_2(1-P_2)N_2)$$

This allows the significance, the number of SDs, to be calculated for Relative Change as (Relative Change)N_1/SD for taxa with relative net losses and (Relative Change)N_2/SD for taxa with relative net gains.

The 90% confidence limits for Relative Change are calculated as 1.645(Relative Change)/Significance.

Change Factor

For the Change Factor the SD is based on the difference in estimated actual range, $N_2 - N_1$. For known P_1 and P_2 this difference is estimated as

$$X_2/P_2 - X_1/P_1$$

with SD given by

$$SD\ [X_2/P_2 - X_1/P_1] = \sqrt{[(1 - P_1)N_1/P_1 + (1 - P_2)N_2/P_2]}$$

This allows the significance, the number of SDs, to be calculated for the Change Factor as $(N_2 - N_1)/SD$.

The 90% confidence limits for CF are calculated as 1.645(CF)/Significance.

Limitations of calculated confidence limits

The calculation of confidence limits assumes that all taxa have been over-recorded in LC relative to MS to a similar degree for a given recorded range. Where this assumption does not hold the confidence limits will be either too narrow or too broad. Taxa may have a very regional distribution and it is found in some of these cases that regional variances affect the reliability of the results in a way that these binomial confidence limits cannot measure. Other special cases are discussed in the 'Limitations in Methodology' appendix.

3. Comparison with the *New Atlas* Change Index

The *New Atlas* used a Change Index (CI) to measure relative change between the two Atlas surveys.

- CI uses a logit function with a respected pedigree which is applied to the recorded range of a taxon in each of the two surveys. The values calculated are on a logit scale and are symmetrical across the whole spectrum from presence in one recording unit to presence in all recording units, though it becomes unstable for very low and very large recorded ranges. Over-recording between surveys is allowed for by calculating relative change as the

residuals from a linear regression line of a graph of the logit function values for one survey against the other. If the data demands it a further weighting adjustment can be applied to normalise the values.

- CI does not provide for the estimation of confidence limits at taxon level.

- CI uses a logit scale which, while mathematically sound, has no fixed upper and lower limits making the significance of the values difficult to visualise. In contrast CF uses a scale from -1 to 1, or may be presented as percentage change by multiplying by 100, so its significance can be readily visualised, as long as the effect of the weighting adjustment is considered.

- CI and CF have much in common. A comparison between the logit and exponential weightings is shown below:

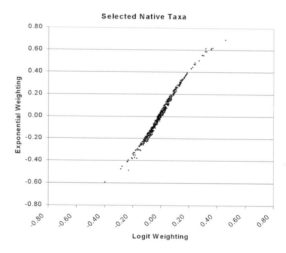

There is a close correlation between the two weighting methods, here applied to the real range calculated by the probability model.

Table 1. Summary of definitions, terms and equations

N - total number of units in each survey

N_1 and N_2 - number of units with species recorded in surveys 1 and 2

P_1 and P_2 - recording probabilities for species present in a unit for surveys 1 and 2

x_{11} - number of units with species recorded in both surveys (refinds).

Term (Definition)	Net loss	Net gain
Actual presence:		
Actual range	N_1	N_2
Actual proportionate change	$(N_2 - N_1)/N_1$	$(N_2 - N_1)/N_2$
Weighted relative change (exponential model)	$\exp[(N - 1)\ln(N_2/N_1)/(N - N_1)]$	$\exp[(N - 1)\ln(N_1/N_2)/(N - N_2)]$
Change factor (CF)	$\exp[(N-1)\ln(N_2/N_1)/(N - N_1)] - 1$	$1 - \exp[(N-1)\ln(N_1/N_2)/(N - N_2)]$
Recorded presence:		
Recorded range	X_1	X_2
Recorded proportionate change	$(X_2 - X_1)/X_1$	$(X_2 - X_1)/X_2$
Adjustment to recorded change (regression of change on range)	$a + bX_1$	$a + bX_2$
Relative change (residual from regression of change on range)	$(X_2 - X_1)/X_1 - (a + bX_1)$	$(X_2 - X_1)/X_2 - (a + bX_2)$
Equations for estimating:		
P_2/P_1	$a + bX_1 = (1 - P_1/P_2)\, X_2/X_1$	$a + bX_2 = (1 - P_2/P_1)\, X_1/X_2$
P_1	$P_1 = x_{11}/X_2$	$P_1 = x_{11}/[\,X_1 - X_2(a + bX_2)]$
P_2	$P_2 = x_{11}/[X_2 - X_1(a + bX_1)]$	$P_2 = x_{11}/X_1$
N_1	$N_1 = X_1 X_2/x_{11}$	$N_1 = X_1[X_1 - X_2(a + bX_2)]/x_{11}$
N_2	$N_2 = X_2[X_2 - X_1(a + bX_1)]/x_{11}$	$N_2 = X_1 X_2/x_{11}$

In this section we review the limitations of the methodology used in the Local Change surveys and its analysis and the usefulness or otherwise of some procedures.

Limitations of the Change Factor as a measure of change for arable weeds, aquatic plants, planted species (including crops) and true casuals

The Change Factor is derived using a model based on the concept that there is an average Probability of a species being recorded in a tetrad in which it is present in a particular survey. Two special cases are considered: the case where a species is increasing and where apparent losses point to under-recording in the second survey and the case where a species is declining and apparent gains point to under-recording in the first survey. While this model works adequately for many species in the British flora as they have low mobility it breaks down if there are both real gains and real losses to any significant extent. This situation applies particularly to arable weeds, aquatic plants, planted species (including crops) and true casuals that do not survive the winter. These are discussed in turn.

Arable weeds are sporadic in their appearance principally because they appear from a long-lived seed bank only when cropping allows. Some occurrences do relate to the transport of soil to new areas whether in bulk or in small quantity as mud on vehicles, boots or animals but these may be ignored as a first approximation except for strongly increasing species. With this proviso the Probability model gives a valid estimate of range but it is the range over which a species is present in the seed bank, not the tetrads in which it may be observed in any one year. Similarly the estimate of Probability relates as much to how often the species appears from the seed bank as to the chance of it being recorded when it has done so.

Some aquatic plants appear to be good examples of species which are sporadic in their appearance because they die out of some sites and colonise others. A simple example is a cycle of ditch cleaning which leaves open water to be colonised that sooner or later becomes choked with emergent vegetation, but other examples involve new sites as when some ponds are drained and others dug. For aquatic species that exploit such habitats the estimates of Probability may be much too low and the estimates of real range much too high. The Change Factor itself is only modestly distorted as it is derived from the change in range and the ratio of Probabilities, not the absolute values. However the estimates of confidence limits are not valid as they do depend on the absolute values and become much too broad.

Planted species (such as specimen trees) and crops (particularly those that are only grown when special subsidies are available) also show real gains in some tetrads and real losses in others though the time cycle varies from species to species. True casuals may be even more sporadic. Inconsistencies of recording between the two surveys preclude the measurement of change in planted species and most casuals are too scarce to come within the species available for analysis. For the casuals that do qualify for analysis the estimate of

Relative Change is the best estimate of change available.

Problems in the recording of trees and shrubs

It was realised that it was unfortunate that the Monitoring Scheme had excluded planted specimens, mainly because the impracticality or impossibility of assessing status on a tree by tree basis in the field had led to inconsistent practice between recorders, and that there was thus no alternative but to change the procedures for Local Change. Nevertheless it was not appreciated quite what a wide range of species are planted and for which the records made would be invalid as a basis for the measurement of change. It is disappointing indeed that we have had to exclude most trees and shrubs from our assessment of change in woodland species.

The incidence of plantings is such that Dutch naturalists are reluctant to recognise any tree as native rather than naturalised in Holland (*pers. comm.* Ruud van der Meijden), and we are not far from that position in much of Britain where even in nature reserves so many trees have been planted at one time or another or are self-seeded from planted stock nearby that the native stock is no longer pure. The inability to measure change in trees and shrubs on this occasion is particularly ironic when so much effort has recently been put into tree planting and has brought about something of a transformation in the appearance of the countryside at landscape scale.

Such issues will remain for a further repeat survey in the future. The boundary between 'the wild' and town and garden is as opaque as ever and there is, in consequence, still much recorder variation in just which trees and shrubs it is considered permissible to record. For example municipal plantings tend to be viewed as outwith a recorder's scope as do garden hedges whereas the same species planted by a farmer in a similar hedge a little down the lane are viewed as 'fair game'. Meanwhile the range of species available to a farmer from non-specialist tree nurseries has increased out of all recognition and as a result many recorders are flummoxed by the range of *Alnus* species, say, that they encounter.

In some senses the inability to measure change in trees and shrubs is not the disaster it may appear. We have increased our knowledge of the distribution of such species, particularly those neophyte species that were unevenly recorded for the *New Atlas*, and that is valuable not least to assist other naturalists who study organisms, such as fungi and insects, dependent on these species as hosts. The detail of the extent of the spread in planted species may not be particularly interesting: the general trend is apparent from distribution maps and the detail, if it were available, would tell us little or nothing about natural processes such as the extent of bird-sown spread in *Cotoneaster* or the effects of eutrophication and climate change, as all would be masked by the pattern of plantings.

Problems in the recording of grassland species affected by introductions

Anecdotal evidence from recorders suggests that the deliberate or accidental introduction of native species is more of a factor in changes in their distributions than may have been realised. Seed mixes of at least nominally native wildflowers are now widely used when reseeding amenity areas as grassland and other species may arrive as contaminants in seed mixes or be brought in accidentally by vehicles. Such introductions are perhaps to be expected as part of the dynamics of plant species in a developed country and, if so, can be viewed neutrally but their incidence does raise problems in interpreting change in relation to other driving forces such as eutrophication and climate change.

The 39 most widespread species

We have left 39 very widespread species out of the Local Change analysis on the grounds that their Change Factor cannot be calculated validly. It is interesting to look at these species to see what we can learn about our recording practice.

Most of the 39 species show a Relative Gain that is probably not real because the over-recording adjustment is excessive, but one or two species show a possible real net loss. A few species show surprisingly large gains, most of these are fairly clearly related to under-recording in the first survey (the two extreme ones are *Agrostis stolonifera* and *A. capillaris*), but there could be a few real gains as well.

Specific findings are that *Anthoxanthum odoratum* is not ubiquitous in eastern England and may have real losses there while *Prunella vulgaris* and *Veronica chamaedrys* may have real gains. These are species that might be spreading into upland areas along forestry tracks and the like.

The main problem with the data is not at the Relative Change stage, where the variation from what one might expect is not excessive, but at the Change Factor stage: the weighting applied is too extreme in relation to the accuracy of the results. This is a reflection on the limitations of the tetrad recording method for the most widespread species. A survey of small plots rather than tetrads is required to observe change. Such data is already available for these 39 species from the Countryside Survey, but has not been imported into the analysis of Local Change as it is not directly comparable.

Problems with other widespread species

The fact that the over-recording adjustment ignores Probability has a downside. It turns out that for a handful of species which are widespread and exceptionally well recorded (high *P*) the over-recording adjustment leads to a misleading CF. Typically the Mapped Change is close to 0 but RC becomes about -7% and CF about -14%. The indications are that the over-recording adjustment should be about 3% not 7% for these species.

The species most affected by this problem are *Calluna vulgaris*, *Capsella bursa-pastoris*, *Cirsium palustre*, *Cynosurus cristatus*, *Galium aparine*, *Hedera helix*, *Mercurialis perennis*, *Rubus fructicosus* agg. and *Viola riviniana*.

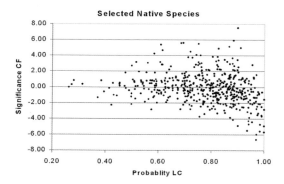

The asymmetry in this chart relating to the apparently high significance of the losses in a small group of species with Probability LC between 0.9 and 1 is due to this problem.

The species accounts in the Broad Habitat section refer to this problem where applicable. It is also referred to in the accounts of the Bog and Dwarf shrub heath habitats, which are those most affected.

The usefulness of 6 and 8 figure grid references

Much effort was directed at seeking to record notable species with accurate localities, often by GPS. There was an understanding that practice would vary between recorders as to what was notable and this has proved to be the case. It is therefore instructive to consider what benefit has been gained from the effort made. The benefit would seem to be twofold.

Firstly, and perhaps most importantly, there is the gain to general botanical recording at a vice-county level: it is absurd to carry out a substantial recording programme without at the same time gathering as much data as practical to enhance the general VC dataset. BSBI Local Change has been very successful in introducing GPS recording as the norm for scarce plant recording and this can but lead to long-term benefits in better quality data.

Secondly the accurate localities will be of benefit in future repeat surveys: where the Monitoring Scheme data available to Local Change recorders did include routes walked and 6 figure grid references they gave an extra sense of purpose to the survey and assisted the refinding of plant populations. It has not been practical to measure the extra success this has led to, or to any bias that it may have introduced, but the success of Local Change as a survey to measure change has, as might have been expected, been shown to depend critically on the extent to which species have been relocated where present and any procedures that assist relocation must be valuable.

The usefulness of logging time spent recording

Surveyors were asked to log time spent recording and were given a rough target of ten hours a tetrad. This log was never intended to be more than background data of possible interest. It is perhaps most likely to prove useful in future repeat surveys to give an understanding of the constraints or otherwise with which a particular tetrad list was compiled.

The usefulness of recording plant status

It has not been possible to use the information collected on plant status: that is to say whether a species is present as a native or is an established alien (whether archaeophyte or neophyte), planted or casual. This is partly because the information was not consistently transferred from the field cards to MapMate but mainly because no way of actually using the information was apparent as it became evident that an exercise to separate records of species as planted from records as native or established would not be sufficiently accurate and would be unduly time consuming. The information is nevertheless of some value at VC level as a contribution to the VC dataset.

BSBI Local Change
Summary of Key Features

- Part of a three year project with Plantlife funded by the Heritage Lottery Fund

- Survey in 2003 and 2004 of the A, J and W tetrads of one-in-nine hectads – the same as those previously surveyed in 1987-88 for the BSBI Monitoring Scheme

- Ireland not included at present

- Alien taxa to be recorded are those recorded for the New Atlas plus planted field-crops

- Species that are planted or casuals to be recorded as such, but the distinction between natives and established aliens only to be recorded when it is notable

- Use of 'MapMate' to enable records to be entered on computers locally and centralised electronically using its distinctive 'synchronisation' facility

- Emphasis on recording in pairs to provide opportunities for less experienced recorders to go out into the field with more experienced recorders

- Use of 1:25,000 maps to record routes

- Target of ten hours total time for field recording per tetrad, except in uplands

- Emphasis on recording notable species with 6 or 8 fig grid references, using a GPS where possible

- Limited grants currently available for the purchase of GPS

- Supplementing the records made with a local assessment of the gains and losses that the lead recorder for each tetrad considers to be real

- Emphasis on the need for permission for access to private land

- Guidance on safety

BSBI Local Change
Instructions for Recorders

Preface

All BSBI members and other botanists in Britain are invited to take part in the survey 'BSBI Local Change' 2003-04. This booklet explains how to do field recording for the survey.

Objectives

BSBI Local Change is a survey of pre-selected sample tetrads (2 × 2 km national grid squares) to be completed in the two field seasons 2003 and 2004.

The sample tetrads are those that were surveyed during the BSBI Monitoring Scheme 1987-88. BSBI Local Change is thus a second survey of these tetrads. The aim is to record as many as possible of the taxa – species, subspecies and hybrids – that are present in the tetrad. One cannot expect to find all the taxa present in a reasonable amount of recording time but one can expect to record a truly representative list. As BSBI Local Change is a repeat survey there will be an emphasis on refinding those taxa recorded in the 1987-88 survey.

Background

The New Atlas of the British and Irish Flora, 2002, has provided distribution maps for our flora that are far more comprehensive than the 1962 Atlas. These maps at hectad (10 x 10 km square) scale have demonstrated major change for many of our scarcer species.

Working at a much finer scale the Government's Countryside Survey, a survey which, unlike the New Atlas, was designed specifically to measure change, has provided evidence of change in the flora by the repeat recording of the vegetation in carefully located small plots within a large set of selected 1 km squares.

Meanwhile tetrad recording, especially in England, has been the choice for many of the recent local recording projects. This suggests a need to demonstrate the degree to which repeat recording at tetrad level can also measure change. Many quite widespread native species are perceived by botanists to be losing ground. These remain so widespread that little change is evident at the hectad level of the New Atlas, while at the plot level of the Countryside Survey they become so rare the change at individual species level is not measurable. A suite of such species, including many of the wetland species that show confusing trends in the New Atlas due to under-recording in the 1962 Atlas, can be expected to show local change in the sense of statistically significant changes in their tetrad distribution over time.

It is now fifteen years since the BSBI Monitoring Scheme 1987-88. That scheme had two elements. The first was a comparison of data collected at hectad level, on a one-in nine basis, to the 1962 Atlas. This element is now superseded by the New Atlas. The second element was the collection of data at tetrad level for future monitoring, using the A, J and W tetrads of the one-in-nine hectads as a sample. The time has now come to test the value of the tetrad data by repeating the survey. There has been much debate about the effect of the inevitable variation in coverage obtained by any recording scheme on the results. It is indeed inevitable that not all the real gains and losses at tetrad level will be detectable by a repeat survey. Nevertheless the experience of other recording schemes, and the New Atlas in particular, has been that much of interest is detected.

BSBI Local Change is part of a joint three-year project with Plantlife, 'Making it Count for People and Plants', funded by the Heritage Lottery Fund.

Geographical Scope

The survey covers England, Scotland, Wales, the Isle of Man and the Channel Islands. Northern Ireland and the Republic of Ireland are not to be covered at present. Recording will be limited to the pre-selected sample tetrads. Recorders will be invited to record in specific tetrads mutually agreed between themselves and the local organiser.

Taxonomic Scope and the Treatment of Alien Plant Status

As for the New Atlas the standard flora to be used for the project will be the 'New Flora of the British Isles' by C.A. Stace (second edition, 1997, Cambridge University Press). All Recorders are strongly urged to obtain a copy of this or the companion 'Field Flora of the British Isles'. The aim is to collect records of all the native species, subspecies and hybrids recorded by Stace, and of all alien plants which are individually numbered and described in the text (as opposed to those aliens that are only mentioned in the introductions to families or genera).

In these instructions we mostly use the word species, even though taxon or taxa would often be more correct.

Fashions in the recording of alien species continue to change. The Monitoring Scheme instructions requested that plants obviously cultivated or planted should be excluded. The instructions for the New Atlas reflected the concept introduced by Stace of recording everything that occurs in a 'wild' situation. In particular planted trees in the countryside were recorded as they may be a major feature in the landscape with an influence on the wildlife found there. The recording for the New Atlas also sought to classify records of aliens as to whether they were established/naturalised, surviving, casual or planted.

BSBI Local Change introduces a revised concept of recording all plants that occur in the 'wild' whether they are planted or not. This means that any plant outside a garden may be recorded including planted trees and field-crops. Field-crops are included as there are usually few species involved and their presence or absence indicates something of the nature of the countryside and contributes to defining the weed flora present in the fields in which they are cultivated.

There can be no hard and fast definition of where gardens end and the 'wild' begins. Public parks and the parks and woodlands of larger houses are often important refugia for our native plants. They usually also contain a great variety of planted species. A sense of perspective must be sought when recording in such places. It is helpful to record a representative selection of the major plantings, particularly if they are of native species, but it is unrealistic to expect to record a complete inventory of all the species that occur in Stace. Similarly there is no intention that the survey should imply a complete inventory of street trees. Within gardens it remains permissible to record true weeds but not deliberately introduced plants that happen to have self-seeded or spread vegetatively. Further it is accepted that it is wholly impracticable to seek to record gardens systematically for their weeds.

As we are to record planted species it is of importance to distinguish them from natives and established aliens. They are therefore to be recorded as **P** for planted. It is equally important to record casuals as such, as by definition they are not expected to remain at the site where they have been found until a future survey. These casuals, together with more or less isolated individuals of self-seeded woody plants that may survive longer, are to be recorded as **C** for casual. The category 'surviving', as used for the New Atlas project, will thus not be used as such for BSBI Local Change. Normally it is not necessary to clarify whether an established population is considered to be native or alien as that will either be obvious from the species recorded or will be difficult, or even impossible, to determine in the field. Exceptionally it may be clear that a population is alien when it could be expected to be native, or vice versa. In such cases the plants should be recorded as notable species as explained below.

Full definitions of plant status categories will be found at the end of this booklet.

The numerous critical microspecies of the genera *Hieracium*, *Rubus* and *Taraxacum* are outside the scope of BSBI Local Change and should be recorded as the aggregate only.

Difficult Taxa

It is crucial that only taxa that have been certainly identified are recorded. In the event of identification problems recorders should seek such help as is available locally and leave out what they have been unable to identify. In particular this may mean ignoring some species and recording a member of a difficult pair of species as an aggregate where an aggregate name is available. Voucher specimens should be retained, if conservation considerations allow, for records that are of importance in a wider context for submission to BSBI Referees, as explained in the BSBI Year Book.

In the limited time available in any tetrad, it is far more important to aim to cover the area as methodically as possible than to spend excess time on difficult taxa with which you are not familiar.

Project Organisation

BSBI have appointed Pete Selby as BSBI Volunteers

Officer to carry through BSBI Local Change. He is setting up a network so that the records made in the survey can be entered on computers locally using the computer programme 'MapMate' and centralised electronically using its distinctive 'synchronisation' facility. VC Recorders will receive further instructions on project organisation and on MapMate.

At local level, recording will normally be organised by the BSBI Vice County Recorder or designate. In some areas there will be nationally organised field meetings. Those of you who are able to participate should first contact the VC Recorder in the areas in which you could help in the field, after studying the map of the 10 km squares covered by the project. In addition to your local area there may be other areas not far away where you could record and more distant areas, where your assistance might be especially welcome, where you could record when on holiday. Please try to be as flexible as possible.

If you are relatively new to recording we will endeavour to pair you up with people who have more experience so that you can hope to learn as much as possible. These opportunities for learning are very much a key part of the project so please do not feel inhibited from volunteering because your experience is limited.

Field Recording

The computer programme MapMate used for the project has the facility to generate lists of the species recorded during the 1987-88 survey of the tetrad with a marker to indicate whether or not the species has already been refound during any earlier visits during BSBI Local Change. Our aim is to make such lists available to as many of you as possible. In the field you will then have the option of doing your recording straight onto these printouts or, if they are unavailable or your find them cumbersome in the field, of using the standard recording cards used for the New Atlas. The advantage of using the computer printouts is that you are more likely to refind a species if you know that it was recorded there previously and this will be especially so towards the end of the survey of each tetrad when there will be only a relatively short list of species not refound.

The MapMate printouts not only list the species previously found but also give 6 figure grid references for the rarer ones where they are known from the 1987-88 survey.

Allocation of Tetrads and Recording in Pairs

As a general rule we envisage that one recorder will be given primary responsibility for each of the tetrads to be recorded with a view to being out on most of the recording visits made there. This designated recorder will be responsible for planning the recording after guidance on local priorities from the VC Recorder.

A major objective of the project is to provide opportunities for less experienced recorders to go out into the field with more experienced recorders. Please therefore try to work with your local organiser to help this to happen. Many of us are used to recording when we have a gap between other commitments so it will

take some thought and patience if we are to achieve this objective as far as practicable.

Planning Visits and Use of Separate Cards and Maps

For typical lowland tetrads the target total time for field recording is ten hours, typically divided into three or four visits at different times of the year of two or three hours each. This target will not be practicable or, indeed, necessary in many upland tetrads where one comprehensive visit at a suitable time in the summer may be all that is appropriate.

The target time is not intended to be prescriptive. For example, if you are able to take extra time to train the less experienced and find that this has slowed you up, you should adjust your target as appropriate.

In many areas the Monitoring Scheme recording in 1987-88 included marking maps with the route taken or making notes of the detailed localities visited. These maps or notes will be made available to you as far as possible. Before recording in a tetrad you should buy a copy of the 1:25,000 map and study both this and the records of previous routes walked. If practicable, a drive around in the car, stopping at suitable vantage points, can be very helpful not only to get a feel of the lie of the land but also as an opportunity to look out for physical changes.

You should then come up with a plan as to how you feel the target time should be spent and how it should be divided between different visits. The routes walked in the 1987-88 survey should be re-walked if that is at all practicable. You will then have to consider what access is needed to private land and obtain permission to visit. You may have to modify your plans if access to certain areas is denied. This need not necessarily be a problem as you are only aiming to visit a representative selection of habitats, and indeed you cannot expect to cover the whole tetrad in detail in the time available.

In planning visits it can be a mistake to use up almost all the time in recording in good botanical habitats and not to leave enough time for the small fragments of habitat which may contain additional species. These include not only ponds and quarries but old walls, farm tips and small areas where recent construction work has disturbed the ground. In upland areas new access roads may be a place to look for weedy species.

A particular effort should be made to re-visit the localities where notable plants were recorded in 1987-88 with 6 figure grid references.

It is fundamental that a new recording sheet or card is used for each visit. There is an option as to whether an individual visit should be further divided and some thought is needed about this before recording begins. This is an area where the designated tetrad recorder should be mindful of guidance on local priorities from the VC Recorder. In some tetrads you might choose to record each of the four 1 km squares separately. In another tetrad there might be two or three botanical interesting areas which you feel should be recorded separately from the rest of the tetrad, such as an ancient wood, a wetland and an area of herb-rich grassland. Our advice must be not to make life too complicated for yourself and to rely instead on the detailed recording of notable species, which is explained below.

Whatever option is used you will need photocopies of the 1:25,000 map on which to mark the actual route walked for each recording sheet or card submitted. The limited photocopying of your personal maps for non-commercial scientific research is not regarded as a material breach of copyright. Please do not abuse this concession by passing around copies in such a way that recorders do not purchase maps for themselves.

How to Mark Up the Recording Sheet or Card

Please also refer to the example of a completed card printed in this booklet

Recorder(s)

The Recorder, or Recorders if you are working in pairs, must be entered. If there are more than three of you it will usually be better if you split up and record separately, as long as less experienced recorders are not left without support.

Grid Reference

This may just be the grid reference of the tetrad in the form 'NT64A', but, if you intend to record only a 1 km square or a single site, a 4 or 6 figure grid reference may be appropriate. Remember that a grid reference in the form 'NT6040' means a 1 km square and not a tetrad.

The diagram shows the nomenclature of tetrads in a 10 km square. The three tetrads pre-selected for the survey are A, J and W.

E 08	J 28	P 48	U 68	Z 88
D 06	I 26	N 46	T 66	Y 86
C 04	H 24	M 44	S 64	X 84
B 02	G 22	L 42	R 62	W 82
A 00	F 20	K 40	Q 60	V 80

To find tetrad **J (28)** in 10 km square NT 64 look along the 'eastings', the numbers along the bottom of the map, and find <u>6</u>2. Then look along the 'northings', at the side of the map, and find 4<u>8</u>. The bottom left hand corner of tetrad **J** is where the lines 62 and 48 meet. Tetrad **J** consists of the four 1 km squares 28, 29, 38, 39.

Locality

This should be a name taken from the Ordnance Survey map that suitably describes the area visited, even if

it is just the tetrad as a whole. Remember that it acts as a check should there be any problem with the grid reference.

Date

This should be the actual date of the visit. As already explained each separate visit should be recorded on a separate sheet or card.

Recording Time

Enter the time spent recording in hours to one decimal place, e.g. 2.2 hours means about 2 hours and 15 minutes. You can of course use minutes if you like and leave the person summarising the data to make the conversion.

Route Taken and Map

The route taken should be marked on a copy of the 1:25,000 map. It is sometimes possible to cut out the relevant part of the map and stick it onto the sheet or card at the end of the day, but if there is not room on the sheet or card it is better stapled to it.

Main List of Species Found

As usual in recording, the main exercise consists of striking through the species name for each plant recorded, being careful not to obscure the BRC number which is used for imputing the data. If you record a species in error please correct this by placing a cross at each end of your strikeout line. If you then genuinely find this species enter it separately as if it was a notable species (see below).

It has been explained above in the section on taxonomic scope and the treatment of alien plant status how BSBI Local Change approaches the recording of whether an alien plant is planted, casual/surviving or established/naturalised. The symbol **P** or **C** is to be written alongside the species name for planted or casual.

A species may be present with more than one status. For example, an alien tree species may be present as planted trees that have self-seeded seedlings or saplings associated with them. In principle these could be recorded separately as two records one with **P**, one with **C**. In practice this will seldom be appropriate. It will usually be best to keep things simple and record the planted status only and ignore the self-seeded plants as incidental. If the self-seeding has really come away and the wood is regenerating as a whole with the self-seeded alien as a component it is established and should be crossed of in the normal way. If the self-seeding is considered notable it can be recorded separately under notable species (see below).

If you are using MapMate generated sheets you will find that some species have an **L** (lost) or **G** (gain) against them. L means that the plant was recorded in 1987-88 but has not yet been recorded in 2003-04. G means that the plant was not recorded in 1987-88 but has already been recorded in 2003-04. A species with neither an L or a G against it is a species that was recorded in 1987-88 and has already been refound in 2003-04. If you are using these MapMate generated lists you need not record again those species already found in 2003-04 unless you want to, or unless you consider that the record is notable in itself, when you should add it to the list of notable species.

Notable Species

BSBI Local Change is emphasising the recording of 6 or 8 figure grid references for notable species found. If the survey is repeated at future dates the fate of these species will become a key element in the assessment of change between successive surveys. Many BSBI members now routinely carry a GPS (Geographical Position System) with them when recording, so that they can accurately determine 8 fig grid references for notable species that they find. If you are not familiar with GPS, please ask your VC Recorder to explain it to you. A limited number of grants of £90 each are currently available towards the purchase of a GPS, which costs about £120, for recording work.

It is very much up to you to decide what is notable in the tetrad that you are visiting. In principle any species which is present only in a small quantity in the tetrad is notable, even though it may be widespread in the Vice County as a whole. Clearly one will not always know on first coming across a species on a visit whether it will be found again or not and it may well be that, when one comes to the end of a day, one may decide, with the benefit of hindsight, that a particular species should be added to the notable species list after all. This is fine as long as one can remember where the plant was in fact found. In choosing notable species one may wish to exclude some planted trees as relatively unimportant. Clearly the number of notable species per sheet or card will vary considerably but something between six and twelve might be typical.

It will also be necessary to include in the notable species section

• Species not printed on the sheet or card
• Species crossed off in error in the lists of species but genuinely found later

• Species for which you wish to record a comment on plant status as natives or established aliens on the grounds that they are present as established populations with an unexpected status. The status is recorded as **N**, native, or **E**, established/naturalised, with a comment to explain the circumstances.

• Other species for which you wish to record a comment. A comment might relate to the quantity of a species present and its habitat. The habitat descriptions are not prescribed, so you can use the words that seem most helpful

• Species for which specimens have been collected for identification. These are included so that the record can easily be corrected or annotated when a determination has been made.

For MapMate generated sheets it will equally be necessary to list all taxa found that are not already on the list. However these will almost certainly include species that are in no way notable but were just not recorded during the 1987-88 survey.

Tip – If you come to a small site with many species of interest, such as a pond, you may find it best to record this site on a separate card with a 6 fig grid reference. This avoids having to decide which of the species to list as notables as all of them will have the grid reference of the small site against them.

Summary of Information Required for Notable Species

• Species Name – in full or abbreviated
• Grid Reference – 6 or 8 fig
• Locality Name – from OS map
• Alien status as **E** (only if notable), **P** or **C**
• Comments – may include quantity present and habitat. Please keep these comments short so that they can be easily entered on a computer

Examples of the recording of notable species from the 2002 pilot tetrad NT64A, Berwicks.

Species and Status	6/8 Fig Grid Ref	Locality	Comments
Moehr tri	NT 60794149	East Morriston, nr	Patch. shelter belt
Sagin ape erecta	NT 60704143	East Morriston, nr	Few, by old road
Echinop exaltat	NT 609419	East Morriston, nr	In flower, road bank
Populus tremula **P**	NT 604416	East Morriston, nr	Two by new pond
Leontodon saxatilis **E**	NT 601410	West Morriston	Naturalised on lawn, prob intro with grass seed

Local Assessment of Change

The main analysis of the survey results will be done centrally and will look at the broad picture on a regional scale. At this scale the inevitable variation in recording coverage from tetrad to tetrad is expected to even out enabling interesting trends to be distinguished. Nevertheless it is accepted that recorders on the ground will be aware of reasons for gains and losses of species that are not self-evident from the records. A new feature of BSBI Local Change is that your assessment of the real changes in each tetrad will be collected.

When the recording in a tetrad is complete a final list of gains and losses will be printed off from MapMate. The Recorder who has done most of the recording in a tetrad, with or without the help of the VC Recorder, will then go over this list of gains and losses and mark against each species their considered opinion of whether the change is real. It is expected that much the most common reason will be 'missed'. By 'missed' is meant gains that are not considered real because it is believed that the species was probably overlooked by the 1987-88 survey and losses that are not considered real because it is believed that the species was probably overlooked during the current survey. A further important reason is 'invalid'. A comparison between the two surveys will be 'invalid' where it is suspected that an identification error was made in the previous survey or where there is a mismatch as would be the case if an aggregate was recorded in one survey and a segregate in the other.

We ask that gains that are considered real be divided between deliberate introductions and the rest. The rest will include accidental introductions and natural colonisation. Deliberate introductions by planting, sowing and dumping are expected to account for a majority of the gains observed and we consider it essential to try to separate these from gains from other causes.

Remember that only deliberate introductions since 1987-88 can be real gains, earlier deliberate introductions that were not recorded in 1987-88 are 'missed'.

This concept of separating deliberate introductions from the rest is not applicable to losses.

We have decided, with some regret, that a more detailed analysis of the reasons for gains and losses may not be practicable centrally. Nevertheless we ask you to record your assessment of the reasons for the gains and losses as a local record and a worked example is given below. We would like this detail to be included in your submission as it will help us to understand how you have approached the exercise and thus contribute to our interpretation of it.

When this exercise is complete the annotated list may be submitted as it is by post or in spreadsheet form by e-mail.

Examples of the local assessment of change from the 2002 pilot survey in NT64A, Berwickshire

Change	Species	Standard Reason	Comment
Gain	Aesculus hippocastanum	Missed	Planted species not recorded 1987
Gain	Cerastium semidecandrum	Missed	Chance find 2002
Gain	Juncus bufonius s. s.	Invalid	Aggregate recorded 1987
Gain	Verbascum thapsus	Real	Roadside casual 2002
Gain	Populus tremula	Deliberate introduction	Planted by new pond since 1987
Gain	Spergularia marina	Real	Salted road verge colonist
Gain	Potamogeton natans	Real	Arrived after new pond created, probably not planted
Gain	Rumex longifolius	Real	This has been spreading in the Scottish Borders
Loss	Trifolium medium	Missed	Could be a genuine loss, due to eutrophication of road verge, but uncertain
Loss	Juncus bufonius agg.	Invalid	Segregate recorded 2002
Loss	Vulpia bromoides	Real	Roadside casual 1987
Loss	Lamium amplexicaule	Real	Crops not suitable 2002
Loss	Ranunculus hederaceus	Real	Field corner drained
Loss	Mecanopsis cambrica	Real	On wall in wood 1987, not there 2002

Consent to the Release of Records

All records are accepted on the understanding that the information provided by you as their Recorder will be entered into a computerised database, will be used in the production of reports for BSBI Local Change and subsequently for nature conservation, research and education and will be available for public information. Records remain the intellectual property of the Recorder at all times.

Notice

WARNING: BSBI will not accept any responsibility or liability for any injury, damage or loss to persons or their property while involved with this survey. You are urged to read carefully the notes relating to safety in the field. Remember also that you MUST obtain the permission of the landowner before venturing onto any private land.

Appendices
Plant Status Definitions

Native

A native species is one which arrived in the study area without intervention by man, whether intentional or unintentional, having come from an area in which it is native; or one that has arisen *de novo* in the study area.

Alien

An alien, or introduced, species is one that was brought to the study area by man, intentionally or unintentionally, even if native in the source area; or one which has come into the area without man's intervention, but from an area in which it is an alien.

Alien species are further divided between
Established

An established species is one that has been present in the 'wild' for at least five years and is spreading vegetatively or reproducing by seed.

Planted

A planted species is one that has been planted deliberately in a 'wild' situation but is not established.

Casual

A casual species is one that is present briefly or intermittently. If present for more than five years then neither spreading vegetatively nor reproducing by seed.

Name and Address for Correspondence
Pete Selby,
BSBI Volunteers Officer,
12 Sedgwick Road,
Bishopstoke,
Eastleigh,
Hampshire,
SO50 6FH

Safety in the field (with thanks to TCG Rich).

Reprinted, with a few amendments, from the Atlas 2000 Instruction Booklet

The guidelines below are intended to minimise the risk of an accident in the field and, in the event of an accident, to minimise further risk and subsequently to help others help you. Simple precautions need not interfere with recording; most are common sense, and may help save your life or that of someone else. Be aware of these points and adapt them to your local conditions.

1. **It is always safer to go in pairs or groups than alone.**

2. **Footwear and clothing** should be suitable for the season and general environment, especially in wilder areas:

   a) Waterproofs – Jackets, hoods, leggings. Bright colours make you conspicuous but some, especially yellow, attract flying insects.

   b) Warm clothing, including hats and gloves.

   c) Suitable footwear in good condition with a good tread (e.g. stout walking boots or shoes or Wellington boots). Spare laces may be useful.

3. **Equipment**: maps, compass, food and water, watch etc. are standard requirements. For more remote areas, a safety kit containing spare clothing (in waterproof bags), spare food (especially high energy biscuits, chocolate, sweets, etc.), whistle, torch with spare batteries, first aid and a survival bag are highly recommended. Suntan lotion, insect repellent and bite treatment may also be useful as would a GPS unit if available.

A basic first aid kit should contain:

   2 triangular bandages
   1 large pre-packed sterile dressing
   1 6.25 cm wide crepe bandage
   1 25 g packet sterilised cotton wool
   12 adhesive wound dressings, assorted sizes
   6 safety pins
   1 tube antiseptic cream
   1 tube antihistamine cream
   pencil and paper

4. **Inoculation** against tetanus is strongly recommended for anyone engaged in field work with a booster every 5 years. If you receive special medical treatment or have a medical condition it is advisable to carry details of your requirements and. where applicable, additional medicine.

5. **Weather** conditions should be checked in advance, particularly in coastal or mountain regions.

6. **Itinerary** details, estimated time of return and, if applicable, car registration number should be left back at 'base'. Include details of who should be informed and at what time in the event of non-return. If you change your plans through the day, inform your contact.

7. **Hazardous sites and conditions** such as mine workings, recently sprayed crops, heavy machinery, shooting parties and aggressive animals should be avoided. Take extra precautions when-visiting:

   a) Rivers, streams and lakes. Be wary of unstable banks and flash floods. Check water depth, bottom condition and other hazards if wading. Avoid water in spate.

   b) Bogs, swamps and soft sand. Be wary of saturated peat and of floating mats of vegetation which can close over a victim if breached. Cross a bog on the tussocks. Watch for uneven surfaces that can caused ankle injuries. If you find yourself sinking:

i) lie flat on your back to spread weight and remove rucksack straps

ii) use rucksack or survival bag for support
iii) get your legs into a horizontal position if possible
iv) turn onto your front and move back to firm ground using tussocks for support, pulling rucksack along by strap

8. **Roads and motorways**: a permit from the Department of Transport is needed for surveying motorways. The DoT safety instructions should be followed. On other roads wear high-visibility, reflective clothing. Do not work on roadsides in poor visibility. Park in a safe place off the road. Be wary of bends, hill crests, junctions, road works and narrow cuttings. Work in pairs – one recorder, one look-out.

9. **Railways** should not be surveyed without permission from British Rail. Their safety instructions should be followed exactly.

10. **Ministry of Defence** land should not be surveyed without MOD permission. Their safety instructions should be followed.

11. **Coastal**: tide tables are essential, and should be understood and adjusted for BST, GMT and local conditions.

Be wary of fast changing weather conditions (an onshore wind can accelerate the time and height of high tide), quicksand/mud (use a wading pole if necessary and cross soft mud with short rapid steps), and fast tides on flat terrain.

Make sure escape routes are clear – tidal creeks can fill very quickly even at the top of marshes. If working on an exposed rocky coast when a swell is prevalent, one member of the party should be checking for unusually large waves. Take particular care climbing down to beaches on steeply backed shores. Beware of the danger of falling rocks from cliffs. Be wary of unexploded mines and bombs, etc. Do not touch but mark their position and tell the coastguard or military. A life jacket may be prudent.

12. **Cliffs and crags** should be studied under the guidance of an experienced rock climber or mountaineer with appropriate equipment. Training is essential. Beware of falling or loose rocks, avoid cliffs in anything but fair weather.

13. **Upland areas**: take suitable clothing and safety kit (as above). Watch out for changing weather conditions and for symptoms of hypothermia (feeling cold, tired, listless, irritable, uncontrollable shivering, unreasonable behaviour, slowing of mental and physical response, stumbling/falling, dizziness, slurring speech, difficulty of vision, physical resistance to help, collapse, stupor or unconsciousness). Temperatures fall by about 1° for every 150 m of elevation.

Dehydration contributes to exhaustion and exposure; maintain calorie and fluid intake and minimise heat loss. Set off early to avoid being benighted. To lessen the danger from lightning, if caught in a storm, AVOID caves and rock crevices and stay in the open. Look for a broken rock scree in a safe situation away from the crest of a hill, and sit on a dry rucksack or rope with your knees up and hands in your lap. Do not support yourself on your hands or by leaning back – keep your points of contact with the ground as close and dry as possible.

14. **Inner cities**: be aware that in densely populated areas, a botanist with eyes on the ground is easy prey.

15. **Procedures in an emergency**

a) GETTING LOST Try to reconstruct your route. Study the map for landmarks and then hold your course with the compass until you reach an identifiable feature to locate yourself. Don't take short cuts or ford rivers.

b) INTERNATIONAL DISTRESS CALLS The Alpine distress call is 6 long, rapidly repeated whistle blasts/torch flashes repeated at one minute intervals until answered. An SOS call (··· — ···) is also likely to be understood.

c) INJURIES First aid as available. Pay particular attention to staunching blood flow and preventing hypothermia. Try to keep warm and dry and summon help immediately. If alone use the distress calls; if with colleagues send for help making sure the victim can be relocated.

d) MISSING PERSONS If a colleague is missing at time of rendezvous, commence a search of the itinerary route. Leave your own note to say you have started search. If no trace is found after an agreed period, inform police.

16. **Diseases**. For the interests of field recorders, here is some information on two diseases known to be contracted in the countryside.

WEIL'S DISEASE

Infective bacteria causing this disease are carried in the urine of rats and voles. The chance of contracting Weil's Disease is very low but it can be fatal. The following points should be noted:

1. Risks are greatest after periods of high water or flooding when rat runs are flushed out.

2. Holes in river banks suggest rat/vole activity – operate upstream of them.

3. Greater care should be taken in stagnant or slow moving water (cases have been associated with the rivers Lee, Chelmer, Stort and Taff).

4. Abrasions should be covered with waterproof plasters.

5. Wear Wellingtons in water to protect feet.

6. Prevent water contact with thin mucous membranes (e.g. eyes, nose, mouth).

7. Wash after contact with river water and before touching food.

If you have been at risk and develop flu-like symptoms (high temperature, chill feeling, pains in joints – especially calf muscles), tell you doctor immediately and mention Weil's Disease. An ELISA blood test can be carried out quickly at The Leptospirosis Reference Unit, Public Health Laboratory, County Hospital, Hereford HR1 2ER.

LYME DISEASE

This is a bacterial infection transmitted by infected ticks which attach to the skin and suck blood. The adult ticks live on sheep and deer and mice are thought to be the major reservoir of the bacteria. In 50–75% of cases the first symptom is a red rash around the tick bite, which expands and clears in the centre. When the rash fades, flu-like and meningitis-like symptoms occur, followed by more serious complaints of the disease affecting the heart and nervous system. Months or years later arthritis can affect the patient. Many long-term symptoms are similar to those of syphilis. The following points should be noted:

1. Prevent tick bites by tucking trousers into socks or by wearing boots.

2. After exposure to suspect habitats, examine yourself for ticks and remove any immediately, either with tweezers or by wiping with alcohol to loosen their grip and then brushing off. Carry alcohol or tweezers in your first aid kit.

If after a tick bite you develop a rash, flu-like symptoms or enlarged glands, tell your doctor and mention Lyme disease. A serological test can detect the disease, which can be treated with antibiotics.

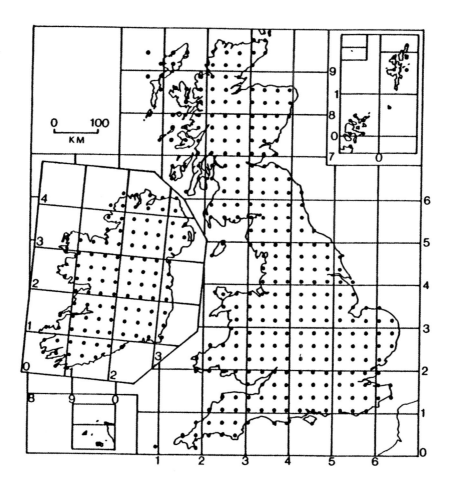

Map showing the 10 km squares selected for BSBI Local Change, within which the A, J, W tetrads only will be reworked

<table>
<tr><th colspan="2">GRID REFERENCE</th><th colspan="2">LOCALITY</th></tr>
</table>

GRID REFERENCE					LOCALITY
N	T	6	1	4 1	Fans

TETRAD		A

VICE-COUNTY		HABITAT Old railway – now farm
BERW	0 8 1	track + bankings + quarry + wood + arable adjacent

DATE						RECORDER(S) NAMES
1 1	0 7	2 0 0 2				ME Braithwaite

ROUTE AND TIME TAKEN RECORDING

45 mins.

—— : route

RARE, NOTABLE, CRITICAL, AND OTHER SPECIES, AND INFRASPECIFIC TA...

SPECIES	LOCALITY	6-FIG GRID	DATE	OTHER DETAILS
Aphanes inexp				(error corrected)
Solan tuber P — Potato				
Horde disti P — Barley				
Tritic aest P — wheat				
Rumex longit		6137 4162		colony
Rumex obt x long		6137 4162		grassland, with both parents
Mentha fon varias		6153 4174		damp hollow, small colony
Lychnis chalcedon C		6158 4173		dumped soil in quarry, three flowering stems
Spergul rubra		6159 4170		sandy quarry edge, c. 12 plants
Poa pratensis		617 419 (best guess)		(now noticed not recorded 1987, definitely this as not P. humilis)

NOMENCLATURE FOLLOWS KENT (1992) <u>LIST OF VASCULAR PLANTS OF THE BRITISH ISLES</u> AND STACE (1991) <u>NEW FLORA OF THE BRITISH ISLES</u>

BSBI FIELD CARD   N. ENGLAND   RP 24
BIOLOGICAL RECORDS CENTRE 1994

PLEASE CROSS THROUGH SPECIES NAMES ONLY   UNDERLINE = SUBSPECIES, ½AGG = INCLUDES OTHER TAXA, X = HYBRID

N. ENGLAND   RP 24

Appendix 5
Participants

We list below the individuals and organisations participating in the survey. The individuals are the botanists who contributed field records in their own name. Others contributed as members of the organisations listed or on BSBI field meetings.

Individuals

Abbott P P, Abdulla M, Abraham F, Acton P, Adams J, Adams K, Adkins M, Aisbitt R, Aitchison C, Aldridge H E, Allan D, Amphlett A, Angel J, ap Rheinallt T, Armstrong D, Ash H J, Aslett J, Aston A E C, Atkins J, Atkinson A, Atkinson M, Aungier F, Averis A, Averis B, Bailey J A, Bailey S, Baker R D, Balkow K, Ball S, Ballantyne G H, Ballinger B R, Ballinger C B, Bamforth A, Banthorpe A, Banthorpe M, Barber R, Barnett K, Barron M, Bateman C, Batty B D, Batty P, Beckett G, Beckett K A, Bell D, Bennallick I J, Benoit P M, Beven D, Bishop E, Black M, Bland R, Boatman D, Bolton A, Bonner I R, Bonner P, Boon C R, Boothby B, Borradaille L, Bowie K, Braithwaite M E, Braithwaite P F, Brookman D, Brown D, Brown L, Bruxner C J, Buckingham S, Budd P, Bull A L, Bullard E R, Bulleid J, Bungard S J, Burfoot G, Bursnall G, Burston P, Burton R M, Butler J K, Butler S I, Button M R, Cadbury C J, Campbell A, Canaway M, Carruthers J, Carter E, Cavanagh K, Cavanagh P, Chappell M, Chater A O, Cheffings C, Chicken E, Church A R, Clark J M, Clark S, Clarke J, Clarkson M, Clayfield J, Clement E J, Cleverly P, Clough B E, Cockerill M, Coker A, Coker S, Coleman C, Coles G, Collar J, Colston A, Compton S, Cook D S, Cook P J, Cooper A, Cooper N, Cooper S, Copping A, Corbet G B, Corner R W M, Cottingham K, Cox S, Craig J, Craster M, Crawley M J, Crewe J D, Cross A, Crossley J E, Crossman N, Crow E, Cullen D, Cullen N, Cunningham K, Cutler H, Daffern J, Dale V, Daly A P, Daly F, Davies M, Davis T, Dawes A P, Dawes R A, Day J J, De Saumarez N, Dean E, Dean H, Denholm I, Dickson W, Dingle T J, Diserens J, Diserens N, Dixon C, Dobson R, Doig E, Dolan L, Doncaster T, Donncha M, Donovan P M, Douglass J, Dowell J, Doyle U, Drewett D, Dunster C, Dupree D, Durkin J L, Duthie K, Dyson C, Eades R, Earl D P, Earl J, Easy G M S, Edgington J, Edwards B, Ellis R W, Elloway R, Elston D, Erskine S E, Ettlinger S, Evans A E, Evans D, Evans I M, Evans P A, Evans S, Evans T G, Everiss E, Eycott A, Eyres B, Farrell L, Faulds A, Faulkner A, Fenton J, Field G D, Fielding J L, Fiormaggia H, FitzGerald R, Folkerd R O, Follett P, Foote B, Ford J, Ford M, Forrest N, Forster S, Foster S, Foulds A, Fraser J W, Fraser M, French C N, French W F, Gaffney J E, Gale B, Gallacher C, Gallacher J, Galley J, Gamble P H, Garner P G, Gaskell L W, Gee D R, Gent G, Gerry P, Ghullam M, Gibbons N, Giddens C, Goater B, Goater J, Godfrey A, Godfrey D J, Godfrey M, Goodchild R F, Gordon V, Gosnell J, Gosnell R, Goulder R, Graiff D, Grant D W, Grant M L, Green G H, Green I P, Green J A, Green P G, Green P R, Greenway C, Greenwood E F, Gregory M, Groom Q, Groom R E, Groome G, Gudge A, Gudge J, Haes E C M, Hall J, Hall L, Hall M, Hall T, Halliday G, Halls J, Hammler E, Hannah A, Hardy D, Hardy T H, Harkas J, Harmes P A, Harold D, Harris E J, Harris Z, Harrison K K, Harrison P, Harrison R, Hart D, Hart K, Harvey H, Harvey P, Hathway R, Hawell J R, Hawes P T J, Hawker D, Hawker H, Hawkins R D, Hawksford J E, Hay W, Heath J, Heath K, Hedley B, Helm S, Helyar W G, Herd E, Hesbeth R, Higginbottom C, Higgins M, Hind S H, Hirons G, Hoare A G, Hoare M G, Hodge J B S, Hodgson D, Hodgson R M, Hogarth B G, Hold A, Holt C M, Holt M, Holwill A, Hopkins I J, Hopkinson V, Houldsworth M, Hounsome G, Houston L, Hubble D, Hubble H C V, Hudd J, Hudson J, Hughes C, Hughes D, Humphreys D, Hunt S, Hunter R E, Hurford C, Huston K, Hutchinson G, Hyde J, Hyde P A, Idle A, Iliff J, Iliff M, Imlach J, Ing J, Irvine C M, Ison J, Jack S, Jackson E H, Jackson-Houlston C M, James C, James T J, Jarvis J, Jeeves M B, Jenkins B, Jenner B M, Jepson P, Jermy A C, Johnson G, Johnson N, Johnson W L, Johnston P, Jones J, Jones V, Joyce C, Kanefsky C, Karn W, Kay G M, Kay Q

381

O N, Keen R, Kelly M, Kendrew J, Kightley S, Killick H J, Killick J, Kingsbury S, Kirby J N J, Kirby P, Kitchen C, Kitchen M A R, Kitchener G D, Kitching I J, Knapp A G, Knight L, Knight D, Knight T D, Lakey D, Lambert A, Lambert M, Lambley P W, Lammiman F R, Lamming N, Lancaster J, Lang D C, Last B, Last W G, Lavery E, Law N, Lawson P, Leadbetter D C, Leak A, Leaney R M, Lear A, Lees R, Leonard M, Leslie A C, Leslie J F, Lewis A, Lewis R, Lewis V, Lindsay E K, Lindsay E L S, Lines G, Lipscombe C, Lister F, Livingstone B N, Locksley A, Lockton A J, Longrigg S, Love J, Lowell J, Lush M J, Lynch R, Mabey R, MacCance R, Macdonald E, MacFarlane M G, Mack B, Mackie P, Macpherson A C, Macpherson J, Macpherson P, Maier P, Manning M, Marchant P G, Margetts L, Marsh A, Martin L, Mashanova A, Masheder R, Maskew R, Mathias D, Matthew H W, Maurice P, Mawer D, Maxwell S, Maybury N K, Maycock R, McCallum I, McCance R, McCarthy W N, McCosh D J, McDonnell E J, McIntosh J, McKean D R, McKee A, McLauchlin J, McNaught A, Meek E R, Meiklejohn J W, Mellor S D, Mercer J, Middlehurst J, Middleton R, Miles C, Millar C, Millar N, Millman P, Mills E, Millward D J, Mitchell R, Mitchell W, Moon J R, Mott J B, Mundell A R G, Murdoch F, Murphy R J, Murray J, Murray S, Muscott J, Mutch A, Myles S, Nalder M, Negal J, Nelson W, Newbould J, Newlands C, Newton A, Newton J, Newton P, Nicholson R A, Nisbet G, Nobbs P, Norde R, Norman E, Norton J A, O'Donnell S, Ogilvie M, Oliver J, Oliver M, O'Reilly J, Orledge G M, Oswald P H, Page K W, Palmes P, Pankhurst R J, Pankhurst T, Parker J, Parker S J, Parry D, Parry J, Parslow R E, Partridge J W, Paul A, Payne A G, Payne R M, Pearman A V, Pearman D A, Pearson T, Perkins D W, Perry I, Phillips B W, Phillips J, Phillips P, Pickard M, Pickett D, Pilkington S, Pinches A C E, Pink M, Pink V, Pinkney K, Plant D, Plant E, Poingdestre J, Pollock R, Ponting M, Pool M, Pope C R, Pope J, Porter M S, Poulton M W, Powling A, Pratt E A, Presland J, Preston C D, Preston-Mafham K, Price P, Priest S, Proctor G, Proctor H, Proctor L, Pryce R D, Pugh M, Pullen P, Ralphs I L, Rand C, Rand M W, Raymond W D, Read G, Reay P, Redshaw E J, Reid A W, Reiser C, Reynolds J M, Ribbands B, Rich E J, Rich T C G, Richards A J, Richards K, Richmond R M, Ridgway, Roberts, Roberts F J, Robinson J, Robinson L, Robinson M C, Robson C, Rogers E V, Roper C, Ross A, Rothero G P, Saag M, Salisbury G, Salter M, Samuels E, Sanderson N, Sankey P A, Schumann F, Scott P, Scott R, Scott S, Scott V M, Sears E, Seed L, Selby P J, Sergeant, Sharman J L, Sharp C, Shaw M M, Sherlock R, Showler A J, Showler J M, Silverside A J, Simkin J, Simkin S M, Simpson B, Slade H, Slocombe K E, Small C, Smethurst, Smith A, Smith C, Smith C J, Smith G, Smith M, Smith P A, Smith P H, Smith R E N, Smith S, Smith T, Spence L, Spence S, Spencer S, Spiers A, Spowart T, Squires S, Stapleton P G, Stead M O, Steeden C F, Steeden N J, Steel, E, Stenger E, Stephens M L, Stephenson E M, Stern R C, Stevenson A, Stevenson C R, Stewart A, Stewart E, Stewart J, Stewart N F, Stewart R J, Stille S E, Stokes M, Stokes R M, Storey C, Storey M W, Strachan I M, Stribley M J, Stroud D, Sturt E, Sturt N J H, Summers A, Sumner B, Sutcliffe M, Sutton M, Swale J, Swan G A, Swettenham P, Swindells S, Tarpey T, Taylor J, Taylor M, Taylor N W, Taylor S, Tebble M, Teearu T, Teesdale I, Tero C, Terry P, Thomas E, Thomas P, Thomas S, Thompson H, Thompson W A, Thomson S, Thorne A K, Thorne K, Tibbot J, Tolfree M P G, Tolfree P, Toogood S, Toone G, Toone S P, Townsend E, Tregear R, Trotter S, Trueman I C, Tucker W H, Tupholme A, Turner C, Tyszka M, Upton A, Urquhart U H, Usher M B, Vass P A, Veall R M, Velander K A, Vickery R, W McCarthy, Waddell J, Wagstaff E, Wagstaff J, Wainwright M, Wake A J, Walker K J, Wall J, Wallace I, Wallington L, Walls J, Walls R M, Walton M, Walton W, Waterhouse, G, Watson K, Watson S, Watt A, Webb C, Webb J, Webb M, Webb T, Welch D, Wells T C E, Welsh J, Westall C B, Westgarth A, Westley P, Weston I, Wheeldon G, Whild S J, White A, Whiteway J, Whitfield L, Wilcox M, Wild C E, Wilkin V, Williams D, Williamson H, Williamson J, Willmot A, Wilmore G T D, Wilson J A, Wilson R, Wilson T, Winfield R, Wolfe S, Wood D C, Wood J, Wood M, Woodall A, Woodhams B, Woodhead F, Woodliff J, Woodman J P, Woodruffe P, Woods A, Woods M, Woodward S F, Wortham P, Wynne G, Young A, Young D M, Young E, Young G, Young M E, Youngman R, Zagni P

Organisations

Bradford Botany Group, Carymoor Environmental Centre, Cheshire Recording Group, Devonshire Association Botany Section, Exmoor Natural History Society, Hampshire Flora Group, Hull Natural History Society Field Group, Inverness Botany Group, Isle of Wight Natural History and Archaeological Society, Leeds Naturalists' Club, Liverpool Botanical Society, Loughborough Naturalists, Manchester Field Club, Norfolk Flora Group, Northamptonshire Flora Group, Orkney Field Club, Perthshire Natural History Society, Somerset Rare Plants Group, Surrey Botanical Society, Sussex Botanical Recording Society, Upper Wharfedale Field Society Botany Group, Yorkshire Naturalists Union